THE PRIVATE LIFE OF BIRDS

THE
PRIVATE LIFE
OF BIRDS

MICHAEL BRIGHT

BANTAM PRESS

LONDON · NEW YORK · TORONTO · SYDNEY · AUCKLAND

TRANSWORLD PUBLISHERS LTD
61–63 Uxbridge Road, London W5 5SA

TRANSWORLD PUBLISHERS (AUSTRALIA) PTY LTD
15–25 Helles Avenue, Moorebank, NSW 2170

TRANSWORLD PUBLISHERS (NZ) LTD
3 William Pickering Drive, Albany, Auckland

Published 1993 by Bantam Press
a division of Transworld Publishers Ltd
Copyright © 1993 by Michael Bright

All the photographs have kindly been provided by the following
photographers from Bruce Coleman Ltd: Jen & Des Bartlett; N.G. Blake;
John Cancalosi: R. Carr; Gerald Cubitt; Jack Dermid; Francisco Erize;
M.P.L. Fogden; Jeff Foott; C.B. & D.W. Frith; J.L.G. Grande;
Carol Hughes; Jan Van De Kam; Stephen J. Krasemann; Gordon Langsbury;
Wayne Lankinen; Frans Lanting; Charlie Ott; W.S. Paton; Dr Eckart Pott;
Norbert Rosing; Leonard Lee Rue; Konrad Wothe; Gunter Ziesler; Christian Zuber.

Line drawings © Robin Prytherch

A catalogue record for this book is available from the British Library
ISBN 0593 022319

Typeset in 11/13pt Times by
County Typesetters, Margate, Kent.

Printed in Great Britain by
Mackays of Chatham Plc, Chatham, Kent.

To Susanne

ACKNOWLEDGEMENTS

Compiling a collection of bird stories is not something one can do alone and so I would like to thank an enthusiastic band of writers, researchers, ethologists, ornithologists and bird-watchers who have helped me in this endeavour. I would especially like to thank Kate Hubert, Conor Jameson and Scott Jones for their help in researching and pulling together the stories that made up 'A Bird's Eye View', 'Bringing Up Baby', 'Hunters, Gatherers and Pirates' and 'Living With People'. Thank you to Robin Baker for comments and criticisms on 'Across the World'. In addition, I would like to thank: Clive Catchpole, John Krebs, Peter Marler and Peter Slater for the initial help in compiling *Animal Language* upon which 'Sound Sense' and 'Solos, Duets and Choruses' is based; and other researchers and writers who have contributed, directly or indirectly, stories, suggestions and comments, including, in alphabetical order: Thomas Alerstam, David Attenborough, Brian Bertram, Jeffrey

Boswall, Mark Brazil, John F. Burton, Phil Chapman, John Croxall, Euan Dunn, Tom Eisner, Peter G. Evans, Peter R. Evans, Bruce Falls, Ian Fergusson, Jim Flegg, Peter Grieg-Smith, James Gulledge, Eliot Haimoff, Peter Harrison, David Helton, David Hosking, David Houston, Janet Kear, Roz Kidman-Cox, Donald Kroodsma, Chris Mead, Eugene Morton, Fernando Nottebohm, Ian Newton, Mike Ounsted, Robert Payne, Robin Prytherch, James Serpell, Tony Soper, Stuart Strahl, Lance Tickell, Nigel Tucker, Haven Wiley and the late Gerald Wood. Without their dedicated and painstaking observations, and the research of scientists and authors from all over the world, many of whom are included in the reference list, I would have little to write about.

I would like to thank Jim Cochrane of Bantam Press for his support throughout the project, and his skill not only at recovering meaningful sections of the English language but also ensuring that what started off in the singular did not increase in value by the end of the sentence! Thanks also to Robin Prytherch for the pen-and-ink sketches that have helped bring the words to life. And finally, a big thank you to my wife and to the younger members of Family Bright who have been deprived of a father for the duration, one of whom, arriving at the start of a holiday designed to get away from it all, remarked casually, 'Where are you putting your word-processor, Daddy?'

CONTENTS

PREFACE

BIRDS ARE REMARKABLE CREATURES. THEY LIVE ALL OVER THE WORLD and in all conditions. There are those that are found in the bitter cold wastes of the Antarctic and others capable of surviving in the hottest of deserts. They are found roosting and nesting in the darkest caves, swimming in the depths of the sea and flying over the highest mountains.

Birds can be found in the most extraordinary and inhospitable places. Imagine a bird that feeds in the sea yet heads many miles inland to the centre of a hot desert to feed a chick which waits patiently in the incredible heat. Just such a bird – a gull – lives in Chile. In Hawaii there is a duck with an equally bizarre lifestyle. It sweeps across sulphurous volcanic streams, gobbling up the flies that it disturbs from the algae matts growing in the hot acidic water. And on Lake Natran in East Africa, flamingos nest in the centre of a vast alkaline lake bed, the like of which has claimed many a human life.

Torrent ducks survive in the white waters of the most powerful rapids, and swifts nest on the rocks behind thundering waterfalls. Above the Himalayan peaks, migrating birds have been seen flying alongside aircraft, and elsewhere geese have collided with high-flying jumbo-jets. Under the North Sea the crew of a deep-sea submersible examining seabed oil installations were startled to come face to face with a swimming cormorant.

Birds have exploited every available ecological niche and in doing so have adopted every imaginable strategy to obtain food. There are generalists, like the laughing gull, which can adapt to any conditions and are found all over the world, while other species, such as the kakapo and the takahe, are so specialized that they are highly localized in their distribution and therefore vulnerable to change. Among birds there are hunters, foragers, scavengers, meat-eaters and vegetarians. There are birds that like fruit or flowers, and others that eat seeds or leaves. There are scratchers, diggers, hoarders and pursuers. There are high-speed aerial acrobats, waddlers, walkers and runners. Some birds can swim and dive, others soar and glide. There are parasites, murderers, robbers and blood-licking vampires.

Birds come in all shapes and sizes and in all forms and guises. At the jumbo end of the scale there is the enormous African ostrich, standing 2.4 metres tall and weighing up to 127 kilograms, while at the other end is the diminutive bee hummingbird of Cuba, just 57 millimetres in length and weighing 1.6 grams. There is the spectacularly feathered peacock – an example, perhaps, of evolution gone haywire – and the functionally drab sparrow – the ultimate 'little brown job'.

But whatever their size, shape, colour or behaviour, the nine thousand or so species of living birds, of all the animal kingdom, have received the most scientific attention and have been the most studied group on our planet. Even today we are finding and recording new species hidden away in remote parts of the world and revealing new and intriguing aspects of bird behaviour. Birds have been the first creatures to warn us of the way we are mistreating the planet: egg-shell thinning in raptors drew attention to the dangers of the indiscriminate use of pesticides, and large numbers of emaciated puffins and auks warned of overfishing in the North Atlantic.

Since the time of Aristotle the study of birds has been a legitimate field of endeavour, and gradually, over the centuries, professional scientists and amateur naturalists have been able to reveal a wealth of avian secrets. Today birdwatching is a popular pastime. Birds, after all, are relatively easy to see. Most people have at one time or another fed the birds in the garden, stopped to watch the spectacle of a large flock of starlings or lapwings, been excited by a kestrel hovering beside the motorway, or watched gulls scavenging and fighting along the seashore. On television, birds from all over the world are brought right into our living rooms for us to watch and enjoy. Who can fail to be struck by the breathtaking beauty of colourful feathers and iridescent plumage and to be humbled by the sheer spectacle of birds in enormous flocks?

But what do we know of the everyday, private life of birds, or those intimate moments – the times when the binoculars are put away, the film camera stops whirring, or the curtains are closed on the window overlooking the bird table in the garden? We may have had tantalizing glimpses of bird behaviour – a flurry of feathers, a bobbing of the head, a sudden flash of colour or an exchange of food. But what do these events mean; what is their significance?

The Private Life of Birds takes a look at some of the many puzzling questions about birds and the way they live, and in doing so reveals some of their amazing stories.

Are birds intelligent? Can they make tools? Can they count? How does a long-distance migrant find its way from one end of the world to the other and return unerringly to the same area each summer? And why do migrating birds fly such incredible distances anyway? How does a vulture, soaring high in the sky, locate a carcass? How does a blackbird find a worm in the ground? Why do starlings gather in flocks? Why is there a dawn chorus? Why do some birds have just one partner throughout life while others chop and change? Why does a bird like the reed warbler accept a cuckoo's egg in its nest? Why do some birds live in burrows or underground while others make nests at the tops of trees? How do night-flying birds and cave-dwellers find their way in the dark? How can it be that the feather is, weight for weight, one of the strongest but lightest structures in nature?

The questions are endless and the stories they give rise to provide a fascinating insight into a group of animals that have been on the planet for over 150 million years. *The Private Life of Birds* offers a personal selection of stories about bird behaviour from all over the world that reflect our current knowledge. Our story starts, quite naturally, at the beginning, when birds first arrived on the earth.

1

LEGACY OF THE DINOSAURS

IT WAS JUST AN AVERAGE SORT OF A DAY ON THE SHORES OF AN ANCIENT sea, about 150 million years ago. Europe as we know it today had not formed. Much of what is now Bavaria was then on the floor of a shallow salty lagoon separated from the Tethys Sea to the south by coral reefs and bordered on its northern edge by a landmass that is now central Germany. This was the Jurassic period in the Mesozoic era. It was a time of plenty. The dinosaurs and their relatives were reaching the peak of their development, and included in their numbers were some of the most powerful animals on the earth. The climate was tropical, the sea warm. Coral reefs fringed the shallow water, creating atolls and lagoons. Marine life teemed in the Tethys Sea, but the lagoons were devoid of oxygen and too salty and therefore barren in comparison. Out to sea, dolphin-like ichthyosaurs and long-necked plesiosaurs chased fish and squid. In the air, the clack of dragonfly wings broke the still silence and bat-like flying reptiles dominated the skies. On land, fleet-footed dinosaurs chased small primitive mammals the size of rats or mice.

On a low, small barrier island at the edge of the sea a strange, large-eyed, dinosaur-like creature with a long tail glided down from a tree fern. On long hind legs this crow-sized character scrambled upright amongst scrubby vegetation of ferns and cycads, scavenging for carrion that had washed ashore. Occasionally, it snatched at fish in the shallow water, spiking them on the small, sharp, pointed teeth set in its long narrow jaws. It was not like the other small predatory dinosaurs that scampered about in and around the undergrowth. Its body, arms and tail were covered by feathers, not scales. It could fly, albeit a short distance, to the safety of a cycad, landing on the trunk and hauling itself up the scaly bough by the claws on its wings. The creature's impact on life along that ancient shoreline was probably minimal, but 150 million years later its impact on the scientific community was considerable.

In the mid-nineteenth century Darwin had launched his revolutionary theory of evolution. The fittest survive, he contended, and the process of cumulative change in the characteristics of plants and animals, generation after generation, accounts for the origins of all living things. In short, he felt that the fishes gave rise to amphibians, amphibians to reptiles, and reptiles evolved into birds and mammals. What Darwin needed to substantiate his views was evidence; he needed 'missing links', creatures with characteristics that were, say, part reptile and part bird. Not long after Darwin had offered his theory, the fossilized remains of such a creature were discovered; it was the very creature that had scoured that ancient Jurassic shore all those many millions of years ago. It was one of the most important fossil finds of all time, and it was given the name *Archaeopteryx*, meaning 'ancient wing'. Its significance to science lay in the fact that it was part dinosaur, but more importantly, part bird; in fact, it was considered the earliest known bird.

THE DINOSAUR CONNECTION

The first specimens of *Archaeopteryx* were discovered in the mid-nineteenth century. The place was the Solnhofen quarries, in the Altmuhl Valley between Munich and Nuremberg, to the west of Eichstatt. The quarries had been worked since Roman times for the marble-like, yellow-grey limestone which splits conveniently into thin slabs. This rock was deposited over 150 million years ago. Calcium-rich mud was washed into clear, shallow lagoons cut off from an ancient Jurassic sea by coral reefs. The dead bodies of animals, which had dropped into the lagoons or had been washed over the coral reefs from the sea or down rivers from the land, rested gently on the ooze and were smothered by the fine sediments. The salty, oxygen-depleted water meant that their carcases were not broken down by micro-organisms but were entombed intact. So today, hidden between the leaves of limestone are the fossilized skeletons of those ancient creatures that had been enveloped in the Jurassic mud. So fine was the preservation that the membranes of jellyfish and the hairs of primitive insects could be seen in the rock.

The first bird specimen was a 6-centimetres-long feather. It came as quite a shock to the naturalists of the day because they believed that birds had not appeared on the earth during this geological period. It was thought that pterosaurs ruled the skies and that birds were unlikely to have made it into the air before the demise of these 'flying dragons' along with the dinosaurs and their other relatives about 90 million years later.

At first the fossil feather was considered a hoax, but a month after a description of it was published the scientific community was rocked again – not just with a feather but with a headless fossilized skeleton which also showed impressions of feathers on the wings. It looked like both a dinosaur and a bird.

Darwin's followers seized on *Archaeopteryx*. Thomas Henry Huxley, who had so ably taken on Bishop Samuel Wilberforce in the famous debate on evolution at the British Association for the Advancement of Science in Oxford in June 1860, used the specimen to support his notion that birds and reptiles were closely related. In a paper published in 1867, Huxley drew attention to more than a dozen anatomical features that were shared by birds and reptiles but which do not occur in mammals. He even went so far as to propose that the two Classes were, in fact, one and introduced the term 'Sauropsida' to encompass the new grouping. More importantly, Huxley thought that birds were the surviving remnants of the dinosaurs and that the missing link on the reptilian side was a small, fleet-footed dinosaur. A certain Herr Oberndorfer had found such a beast in rocks in Bavaria in the late 1850s, and in 1859 Johann Wagner named it *Compsognathus*, meaning 'pretty jaw'. Huxley felt that while *Archaeopteryx* was a crow-sized bird resembling a dinosaur, *Compsognathus* was a chicken-sized dinosaur resembling a bird.

Compsognathus was a small theropod dinosaur, and although it closely resembled *Archaeopteryx* it could not be its ground-based predecessor, for the two animals were contemporaries. Theropods, however, are thought to be the key group that gave rise to the *Archaeopteryx*-like early birds, and one group of theropods – the dromaeosaurids or 'running lizards' – are thought to have the closest affiliations with *Archaeopteryx*.

The theropods were predatory dinosaurs. They had a bird-like body plan and were bipedal; they had sharp teeth or horny beaks,

An artist's impression of Archaeopteryx *(top) closely resembles, in shape and size, that of a small theropod dinosaur* Compsognathus *(bottom).*

and some are thought to have had feathers. They were fast runners and had long stiff tails which gave them greater manoeuvrability, the mass of the tail helping to stabilize the body when negotiating a tight turn. They sprinted after lizards and small, primitive mammals on the small dry islands where they lived. One fossil specimen was even found with a lizard in its stomach. It would have chased its prey at high speed and snatched it with its clawed hands or thrust out its long neck and grabbed it in its lethal jaws.

Many of the theropod dinosaurs had bird-like features. Some are depicted with feathered crowns like hoatzins or crests like casso-waries, and others are shown with feathers on the arms and back, thought to be for insulation. Some biologists believe that the dinosaurs, or at least some of them, were warm-blooded. Certainly, the temperature control systems of birds like the fast-running ostrich, with a body temperature of 39.2°C, might serve as a model for the fast-moving predatory theropods. There is strong evidence to suggest that they, at least, were warm-blooded. Feathers, which are nothing more than modified reptile scales, may have helped to maintain body temperature.

Dinosaurs were also egg-layers. Just like the egg of a bird, the dinosaur egg contained a growing embryo surrounded by liquid food and protected by a shell. And some dinosaurs, like the duck-billed ones, laid their eggs in nests over which the parents were thought to have stood guard.

Behaviour is difficult to determine from a pile of bones, but some

Some bird-like dinosaurs, such as dromaeosaurids (running lizards), were fast, fierce predators. These 2-metre-long, two-legged flesheaters had a 'switchblade' claw which could be flicked forward for attack. It is not difficult to imagine male dromaeosaurids squaring up to each other in the manner of fighting cocks, and contesting the right to be top dinosaur.

bird-like dinosaurs have skeletal features whose function can be guessed. Specimens of predatory 'running lizards' have a long, sharp, sickle-shaped claw on each hind foot. Would it be too exaggerated to imagine them engaging in clawing contests, like duelling fighting cocks?

Speculation aside, all the small predatory theropod dinosaurs have one extraordinary thing in common – they really do resemble birds. And today some scientists go so far as to consider that birds are living dinosaurs, the legacy of an ancient line which disappeared so dramatically at the 'time of great dying'. Modern birds still have dinosaur-like toes and ankles, and scales on the legs and feet, but at some point in the remote past – most likely some 150 million years ago – feathers replaced scales, beaks lost their teeth, and the birds took to the air. How, though, did they get up there? Did they jump from a tree or flap off the ground?

ANCIENT WINGS

Archaeopteryx had reptile-like features: solid not hollow bones, a long bony tail, three long, clawed fingers at the end of the forelimb, and dinosaur-like ribs and vertebrae. Its long legs had stiff ankle joints and the feet had four long, clawed toes. It could have walked, or perhaps climbed, like the 'running lizards', with the second toe raised.

It had a thin flexible neck, long slim jaws and sharp little teeth. Curiously, modern birds still have the propensity to have teeth. In an experiment, tissue from the inner jaw of an unhatched chick was grafted onto another part of its body. The transplant grew and produced tooth-buds. Although reptile-like teeth have been absent from birds for millions of years, their blueprint is still locked up in the genes of modern birds.

Archaeopteryx had feathers much like those of modern birds. It possessed wings and a small wishbone or 'merrythought' (furcula), a feature at first thought unique to birds but now found in some dinosaurs. In modern birds the wishbone is an important attachment for flight muscles, so it is likely that *Archaeopteryx* had at least some of its pectoral muscles attached to the wishbone and therefore available for limited flight.

Most modern birds have a large breastbone for the attachment of their powerful flight muscles which also protects the internal organs during flight. In *Archaeopteryx* the breastbone was absent. Instead, *Archaeopteryx*, like many of the dinosaurs and like some crocodiles and lizards today, had abdominal ribs (gastral ribs) which acted as a fish-bone-like brace along the creature's underside. The ribs were not fixed to the rest of the skeleton but helped to protect the internal organs.

Modern birds fly with the help of air-sacs, extensions of the lungs which enter the bones and which help deliver oxygen to where it is needed when a bird is flying. There are small openings at the top of the upper-arm bones, for example, through which the air-sacs run. There is no skeletal evidence to suggest that *Archaeopteryx* had this system.

The fingers of a bird are fused together. The manus, as the fused fingers are called, lends support to the wing. *Archaeopteryx* finger bones were separate. Also, bird feathers are anchored to the bone by ligaments whereas those of *Archaeopteryx* were free from the skeleton.

From these features it is suggested that *Archaeopteryx* could run, climb, leap, glide and flap, but what with poorly developed flight muscles, a reptilian lung-system and unanchored feathers, it was probably a second-rate flyer. The pelvis and hind legs show that it was a good runner. The long, stiff tail counterbalanced its body, preventing it from toppling over. The rigid rods of the more distal vertebrae, seen in many of the theropod dinosaurs, kept the tail stiff and helped it to manoeuvre at speed. The foot was also adapted to running, with metatarsal bones partially fused, a pattern halfway between the reptiles (with no fused bones in the foot) and birds (with fused bones).

The most interesting aspect of *Archaeopteryx*'s anatomy, though, is that despite the limitations it actually did have the wherewithal for flight. But there are two views about why and how *Archaeopteryx* took to the air. One view considers that early birds ascended into the skies while the other favours the idea of a descent.

The small predatory theropod dinosaurs were probably fast runners. Their tracks have been preserved as fossilized footprints, and by studying the pattern of the footfalls it is possible to calculate the speed at which the animals were running. In Arizona, footprints in Jurassic rocks have revealed that theropod dinosaurs no bigger than small dogs were able to sprint as fast as horses can gallop.

Might the proto-birds amongst these small dinosaurs have

developed feathers on the forelimbs that acted as aerofoils to increase running speed? The flightless rhea of South America uses this trick. The notion is an interesting one, for *Archaeopteryx*'s foot is not a climbing or branch-grasping foot but more of a running foot. Theropod ancestors may have leaped progressively higher, assisted by flapping the feather-covered arms, in order to catch flying insects. If they did so, this would eventually have led to flight. Proponents of the theory further suggest that the feathered arms could sweep up prey, much in the way that small, insectivorous bats use their membranous wings to gather prey into the mouth.

The alternative and more conventional view follows the way of the flying squirrel. *Archaeopteryx*'s 200-million-year-old theropod predecessors first climbed trees, so it is suggested, and then they launched off into the air and glided to the ground. Landing on the ground parachute style was an easier way to end a flight successfully than landing on a tree. *Archaeopteryx* would then scramble up the next tree and launch off into the air again. A flapping flight would have helped it stay on course and enable it to go a bit further. The next logical step would have been to go from tree to tree.

Recently, a scientist closely examined the pattern of the feathers of an *Archaeopteryx* specimen and found that they were arranged in the same way as those on the wings of modern birds capable of powered flight. The feathers on the leading edge of the wing were smaller than those on the trailing edge. Air pressure is greater at the front of a wing, so this part must be narrower and stronger than the trailing part. *Archaeopteryx* was unlikely to have been an elegant flyer but the feather configuration suggests that it could have done a little more than just glide.

This possibility is also supported by the shape of the feathers themselves. They too were asymmetrical. The central spine or shaft of the feather had a narrow set of leading vanes and a wide set of trailing ones. If the feather were sectioned it would show an aerofoil shape. In modern birds, the more pronounced the asymmetry the faster the flyer. Flightless birds, significantly, have symmetrically shaped feathers. The asymmetry of *Archaeopteryx*'s feathers shows that it was capable of powered flight.

The proto-bird, though, was limited by the absence of the pulley-like system that modern birds possess to bring the wings above the body. *Archaeopteryx* could only manage a half-stroke when flapping its wings.

The claws on each wing would have helped it climb trees, so the inadequate climbing foot would not have precluded it from shinning up the nearest cycad. The wing claws are narrow, curved and fine-tipped and look much like the claws of tree-climbing birds and mammals, such as woodpeckers and squirrels. They might also have been used in preening.

Perhaps the most intriguing piece of evidence for the climb-and-glide version is that of the hind claw on each foot. If the proto-bird was confined mainly to the ground, the claws would have been worn down like those of a pheasant or grouse. But *Archaeopteryx*'s hind limb claws were very sharp. This also gives rise to further speculation: sharp claws on the feet are characteristic of fish-grabbing birds. Might *Archaeopteryx* have been mainly a fish-eater rather than a shore-based scavenger? The sharp claws on *Archaeopteryx*'s feet would have been ideal for snatching a slippery, wriggling squid or fish from the surface.

Alternatively, might *Archaeopteryx* have chased its prey beneath the waves? Some seabirds, like the auk family, swim underwater using their wings, as do the chicks of the primitive-looking hoatzin of South America. The hoatzin chick has its finger bones unfused, much like those of *Archaeopteryx*, and it has two claws on each wing, and it just might give us some idea of what *Archaeopteryx* was capable of doing. The chick is able to clamber about in the undergrowth using its wing-claws to haul itself up on twigs and small branches. But the more significant piece of behaviour is the way in which it escapes predators. The chick leaps into the water below the nest and swims to the bank. When the coast is clear it can use its claws to haul itself back to the nest. So, might *Archaeopteryx* have been able to do the same? Could this ancient bird not only have walked, climbed, glided and flapped, but also swum?

A swimming-and-fishing hypothesis is further supported by the structure of *Archaeopteryx*'s teeth. Those ancient water dragons, the fish-eating dolphin-like ichthyosaurs and the blunt-nosed crocodile-like mososaurs, had sharp teeth too, but they had characteristic thick, rounded roots. The teeth of *Archaeopteryx* were the same shape, further evidence to support the notion that this proto-bird was, indeed, a fish-eater.

Not all palaeontologists, however, are convinced that *Archaeopteryx* was on the direct line to modern birds. Fossils of sparrow- and crow-sized early birds found in Spain, China and Texas hint that birds were already airborne and bird-like at or not long after the time *Archaeopteryx* was living. They also showed the capability of powered flight and were specimens that might relegate *Archae-opteryx* to an evolutionary sideline.

Other work suggests that *Archaeopteryx* was a small, fast-moving dinosaur that needed feathers to keep warm. And another hypothesis proposes that it was a youngster whose bones were not fused and whose cartilages were not ossified. Could it be that *Archaeopteryx* was a feathered juvenile, with an insulating layer of feathers when small which grew up into a larger featherless theropod when adult?

Whatever the truth, one thing is clear: during the last 150 million years birds have explored and exploited every ecological niche and, as with all animal groups, there was a tendency to gigantism. There were toothed, 1.2-metres-long, flightless divers, 2.1-metres-tall rails, and huge flightless birds that became the planet's dominant predators – the avian equivalents of tyrannosaurids on land and plesiosaurs in the sea. 'Terror birds', 3 metres tall, tore at the flesh of polar-bear-sized ground sloths, and albatross-like pseudodontorns – ancient birds with wingspans up to 5.5 metres across – soared in the skies.

The title of largest flying bird, however, goes to a teratorn, one of a group of giant condor-like vultures that flew over Argentina in the Miocene between five and eight million years ago. It was discovered in 1980 and was given the name *Argentavis magnificens*. And magnificent it must have been. It stood 1.5 metres tall and had a wingspan of 7.5 metres. The wing measured 1.2 metres front to back. The body must have been about 3.4 metres long from beak-tip to tail, and it weighed upwards of 120 kilograms.

Teratorns were predatory birds. Each specimen unearthed to date has had a narrow hooked beak and a jaw mechanism that indicates a bird which grabbed small animals such as mice, frogs, lizards, nestling birds and, perhaps, fish. It swallowed them whole. *Argentavis* had a large, 55-centimetres-long skull and its jaws had a gape sufficient in size to swallow a creature over 15 centimetres in diameter. The fossilized skeletons of small armadillos and hare-like rodents are found in the same rocks that contained *Argentavis* and they may well have been part of the bird's diet. *Argentavis* is thought to have been an early relative of the stork and New World vulture, and the remarkable thing is that this gigantic bird actually flew.

Some scientists question whether such an enormous bird could do so, but those who have examined the skeleton have identified the correct-sized wing bones. There are also the impressions of feathers, such as secondaries, and the marks on a wing bone of where the feathers were attached. The largest flight feathers are estimated to have been 1.5 metres long and 18 centimetres wide. If it had the wings and feathers for flight, say the researchers, then it must have flown.

FLIGHT

Powered flight is not an easy thing to achieve and it is costly in energy terms. Many groups of animals, including squid, frogs, snakes, squirrels, lizards and flying fish, have tried flying at one time or another but true powered flight has only evolved in insects, pterosaurs, birds and mammals (bats). The birds were not the first. By the time an ancient proto-bird launched itself unsteadily into the air, insects had been flying for many millions of years.

Some insects, like the dragonflies, grew to a tremendous size. *Meganeura monyi* weighed about 454 grams, had a 70-centimetre wingspan, and terrorized the Carboniferous swamps of western and central Europe about 280 million years ago.

The pterosaurs reached their zenith with a real Texan giant, the skeleton of which has been found in rocks of the Late Cretaceous in North America. It was handicapped by modern science with the tongue-twisting Aztec name *Quetzalcoatlus*, the 'feathered serpent', *Quetzalcoatlus northropi* had a wingspan of up to 15 metres – the size of a small aircraft – and was the largest living thing ever to have flown.

The birds, if *Archaeopteryx* was an early one, took to the air about 150 million years ago and shared the skies with insects and pterosaurs. Whether they climbed up and jumped from a tree like a flying squirrel or ran along the ground until they had sufficient ground speed to 'rotate' like a modern aircraft is still a matter for speculation. Mathematicians and experts in aerodynamics, armed with slide-rules, video-cameras, batteries of computers and complex formulae have proved that both routes to the sky are possible. At present it is difficult to decide with any certainty which way was the right one. Suffice it to say that naturalists tend to favour the trees-down hypothesis. After all, that's the way many other flyers, such as frogs, snakes and squirrels, got into the air. But whichever way they got there, they had to come to terms with that great leveller – gravity.

Put simply, flying is a balance between thrust and drag, and lift and weight. Weight is dealt with by making the body as light as possible: modern birds have skeletons made of lightweight, hollow bones strengthened by an internal honeycomb of cross-struts. The skull is lightweight and teeth have been replaced by a beak. Heavy liquid urine is not stored in a bladder; instead uric acid, as any car-owner will know, is discharged with the faeces. Ovaries are kept to a minimum size until needed in the breeding season. All these are adaptations to reduce body weight.

Thrust is provided by strong flight muscles attached to the enlarged keel in the body and the thickened pectoral crest on the

(upper picture) During the upward recovering stroke, a bird's wing is partly folded and the feathers closed to reduce air resistance. The tendon attached to the upper part of the breast muscles is looped over the shoulder bone (scapula) to form a rope-and-pulley mechanism which raises the wing.

(lower picture) During the downward stroke, the wing bones are extended and the feathers spread to increase air resistance and provide lift. The bulk of the breast muscles, pulling the wing down, provide the power for flight.

28

humerus of the wing. As can be seen when carving the turkey, there are two major packages of flight muscle. The outer muscle is the pectoralis which pulls the wing down, providing the power stroke. The underlying muscle is attached to a tendon which passes over the top of the shoulder, like a pulley, and pulls the wing up. A bird's flight muscles make up a considerable part of its body weight, up to a third in powerful flyers.

The balance between the other forces of lift and drag is achieved in part by the shape of the wing. A bird's wing is not flat, but slightly curved. A bird flies because its forward movement generates enough lift along the curved wings to overcome its weight and the resistance of its body passing through the air. In cross section, the wing is an aerofoil shape with a blunt leading edge and a tapering trailing edge. As the air hits the blunt leading edge it divides into two streams that flow above and below the wing. The air passing over the top speeds up over the curve and the pressure there drops. On the underside the reverse happens – the air slows down and the air pressure rises. The wing is thus both 'sucked' upwards and 'pushed' upwards. The more curved the aerofoil of the wing, the greater the lift.

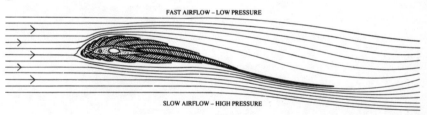

The cross-section of a bird's wing resembles that of an aeroplane. Air passing over and under such an aerofoil shape provides the lift necessary for flight. As air moves across the wing, the air pressure on top decreases and the pressure below increases, causing the wing to lift. As long as the lift is greater than the weight of the bird and any drag caused by the bird's resistance in the air, the bird will remain airborne.

Unfortunately, however, it is not as simple as that, for extra drag is introduced as air passes over the wing. The high-pressure air below tries to get to the low-pressure air above. It does this along the thin trailing edge of the wing and manifests itself as a spiralling vortex at the wingtip. The most efficient wings are those that minimize these vortices and therefore the drag.

One of the most efficient wing shapes for the elimination of vortex-linked drag is the crescent wing of swallows, martins and swifts. The backwardly curved wing is more efficient than a flat, untwisted, elliptical wing shape. Seabirds also show the trend, not with the entire wing, but at the wing tips. They have long, heavy wings with highly tapered, aft-swept tips. The birds share crescent shapes with fast and long-distance swimmers. In the sea, tuna, mako sharks and fin whales have crescent-shaped caudal fins or flukes to reduce drag.

The angle that the wing makes through the air is also significant. If it is angled upwards slightly the lift increases, but if it is angled too high the bird will stall and fall out of the sky.

The ratio of the length of wing to its breadth is also important. It is called the 'aspect ratio'. A short, wide wing is said to have a low aspect ratio. A bird with this configuration can flap fast, but is not a good glider. Pheasants have low-aspect-ratio wings. A long, narrow wing has a high aspect ratio and is typical of gliding birds, such as the albatross, which flap their wings only occasionally.

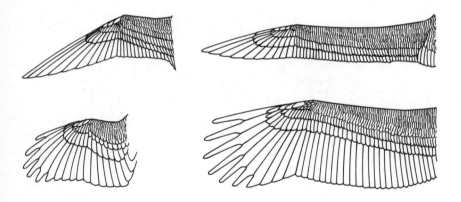

Four basic wing shapes: Top, left: *long-distance migrant wader;* right: *albatross;* bottom, left: *resident or short-distance migrant passerine;* right: *condor/vulture. The shape of the wing matches a bird's lifestyle. Waders travelling long distances have long, pointed wings which create lift with little drag for highly efficient flight. The elliptical, slotted wings of passerines are adapted for slow flight in forests or shrubby habitats. A long, thin wing enables the albatross to glide at high speed above the sea surface with little effort. The condor's wide, ragged-tipped, slotted wing is for soaring at high altitudes and low speeds.*

Another factor to take into account is that a bird's wing is not only the device that keeps it aloft but is also the propulsive mechanism that makes it go along. In effect the wing is like an oar and it has to be twisted so that it exposes the largest possible surface area on the active stroke and the least resistance during the recovery stroke, while still retaining sufficient lift to keep the bird in the air. The joint, therefore, between the first wing bone, the humerus, and the shoulder girdle is a universal one, allowing the wing to move in any direction and therefore capable of making all the complicated movements required of powered, flapping flight.

The most significant adaptation for bird flight, however, is the use of feathers (see below). In the wing of modern adult birds the flight feathers are attached to the wing bones. These have been modified to form a strong, firm platform. The long primaries are attached to the fused bones of the wrist and hand, while the secondaries attach to the ulna of the lower forelimb. The entire wing structure provides the bird with two large and strong aerodynamic surfaces with the minimum of weight.

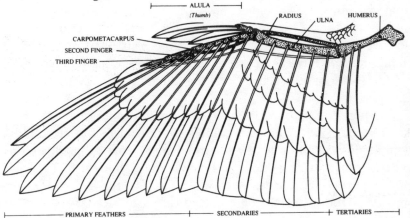

The primary feathers in a bird's wing are attached directly to the hand bones and the number can vary from nine to twelve. The secondaries are joined to the forearm (ulna) and can number as few as six in hummingbirds and as many as thirty-seven in albatrosses. A few tertiaries may be attached to the upper arm (humerus). Primaries, secondaries and tertiaries are the main flight feathers. Groups of smaller contour feathers (coverts) cover the quill bases of the longer feathers in order to make the upper and lower wing surfaces aerodynamic. Attached to the thumb are a group of three to four short-vaned feathers which together make a small separate spurious wing (alula) and which help short-winged, mainly ground-dwelling birds, to fly at slow flight speeds.

Using its elaborately designed wings a bird is able to glide or flap. The glide is relatively simple. A bird need only balance lift and drag to fly a relatively shallow glide path. In this way a gliding bird is able to travel the maximum distance with the minimum of effort. This makes the 'trees-down' hypothesis for *Archaeopteryx* and the origin of bird flight an attractive proposition. Climbing up a tree and gliding down to the next is an efficient way of foraging. Some modern birds follow the pattern, even those with powered flight. They alternate bursts of upward flapping flight with periods of downward gliding, thus producing an undulating flight pattern that is 10–20 per cent cheaper in energy terms than straight, horizontal flight.

The speeds at which birds fly are still unclear. Birds have been timed flying from A to B, plotted on radar, compared to moving aircraft and cars or just 'guestimated', yet we still cannot agree on which is the fastest and which the slowest. The spine-tailed swift was claimed at one time as the fastest flyer but the way it was timed has been called into question. The stopwatch was started as the swifts passed a house in Assam and then stopped when they disappeared behind a hill some two miles away. The claim was a staggering 199 mph but it seems highly unlikely that a living thing could possibly achieve such a speed. So, by general consensus, the fastest powered flight seems to have been exhibited by an eider duck that clocked up a more reasonable record-breaking 47 mph. Birds *can* go faster, though.

The peregrine stoops to catch its prey and plummets at tremendous speeds. In theory it could reach 230 mph but it would be completely out of control and would be unable to catch its prey, probably a fast-flying duck. So it is generally thought that a power-diving peregrine reaches somewhere in the region of 112 mph, making it the fastest living creature on earth. Radar tracking has confirmed this; although a pilot in an aircraft diving at 174 mph towards some ducks reported being overtaken by a peregrine!

What fuel, then, does a bird in flight use and what power can it summon? How does it exploit the power to make the wings drive it through the air? And how does it dissipate the considerable amounts of 'waste heat' that are generated by a bird's 'engine' during a long flight? These are key questions which until recently have been very difficult to answer, that is, until scientists began to train birds to fly in controlled conditions in wind tunnels.

In some German experiments, a hybrid pigeon was bred that was half English Tippler and half high-flying Russian Grivuni. They called it, not unexpectedly, the Grippler, and it turned out to be an ideal test flyer. Gripplers not only took to wind tunnels but also wore tiny face masks from which respiratory gases could be collected. The birds happily flew in the tunnel for an hour, and in some cases up to three hours, flying the equivalent of a long-distance sortie of about 110 miles.

The results of the fuel tests were intriguing. The pigeons were found to start out by burning carbohydrate fuel (glycogen sugar), but after an hour they switched to fat fuel, which they used for the remainder of the flight. This made sense. Sugars represent instant energy. They can be burned up without oxygen and release enough energy to enable a bird to get going quickly. 'White muscle' is used for this type of instant action. But by burning fat with oxygen a bird releases twice as much energy per unit of fuel as if it burned carbohydrates, so it can fly further with less fuel on board. This kind of cruising flight is achieved with 'dark muscle' which is criss-crossed by tiny blood vessels carrying red oxygen-rich blood.

It was also found that pigeons have a minimum metabolic performance at a flight speed of about 11–12 metres per second. If the bird speeds up, its metabolic rate understandably rises too. What came as a surprise, however, was that the metabolic rate also goes up at slower speeds. So, a pigeon flying at this optimal speed for fuel efficiency (no faster and no slower) could remain the longest time in the air for a given supply of fuel.

The pigeon tests also examined wing strokes. The main lift and forward propulsion forces, they confirmed, are on the downstroke. The lift maximum is in the middle of the stroke but the propulsive maximum lay near the end of the downstroke.

The next interest was waste heat. Flying generates enormous amounts of heat and there were thought to be two main ways in which it was lost: convective cooling via the surface of the skin to the slipstream by spreading the feathers slightly or dangling the legs; and evaporative cooling via the respiratory system.

It was found that in general the birds first exploited convective cooling methods. At low air temperatures the legs and feet are carried in the feathers. At 10–15°C the hind limbs are carried on the surface of the feathers. At 20°C the legs hang down slightly and at 25°C they dangle in the slipstream. The feet, it seems, with their efficient circulation, act as effective radiators and help cool the body.

Meanwhile, inside the bird, when the body temperature reaches that of the ambient air temperature – just as it would for a migrating bird crossing a hot desert (see chapter 3) – an evaporation method of cooling must come into play. Just a small amount of exhaled water dissipates a large amount of heat, but what if the bird is on a long journey? How much water can it afford to lose?

Birds are apparently more tolerant of water loss than we are. A loss of just 3 per cent of body water can be serious for a human being but birds can suffer losses of 5 per cent without problems, and some birds on migration tolerate up to 10 per cent water loss. However, even birds cannot go on for ever without water and so a barrier to long-distance flying can be water availability and not fuel consumption. In low air temperatures, when convection is working, a bird can fly further than one in higher temperatures which is using up water for cooling purposes, even though both may have the same amount of fuel on board. A Grippler pigeon, for instance, can travel 558 miles non-stop in twenty hours at its optimal flight speed, using its own energy supplies, as long as the air temperature does not exceed 5°C. At 25°C the same pigeon with the same fuel supply could only remain in the air for a couple of hours and might only cover a distance of 56 miles, by which time it has used up about 5 per cent of its body water and must land to drink. Both water and fuel, it seems, limit a bird's flying time.

Wind tunnel tests in the USA have revealed some of the other secrets of bird flight. A key structure in powered bird flight turns out to be the wishbone or furcula. It is, perhaps, significant that the presence of a wishbone has been noted in all the early proto-bird fossils. Recent work has shown why it is important.

High-speed X-ray photographs of a starling flying in a wind tunnel have revealed that the wishbone is a flexible structure which acts like a spring during flight. With each beat of the wings the two ends of the U-shaped bone bend apart. By the end of the downstroke, the wishbone is bent to one-and-a-half times its resting width. On the upstroke it recoils. This is unique to birds. In most bone-and-muscle systems the bones act as levers and the muscles as motors. The bones are usually rigid, rarely do they bend or flex. The wishbone stores energy when it is bent apart and this is released when the wing recovers on the upstroke. The released energy contributes to the wingbeat motion.

The movement of the wishbone, it is thought, also helps a bird to breathe when in flight. The X-ray pictures revealed that a European starling breathes three times every second, while its wings beat twelve to sixteen times per second. As well as lungs a bird has a system of air sacs throughout its body, which help cool it and make it lighter for its size, but there is more to it than that. A larger clavicular air sac is found between the branches of the wishbone, and others are found at the posterior part of the sternum. Movements of the wishbone and sternum during flight change the size of these sacs.

As the wing is depressed during the downstroke, the wishbone spreads to inflate the clavicular air sac and the sternum rises to compress the posterior air sacs. During the upstroke the wishbone collapses, squashing the clavicular sac, and the sternum descends, inflating the posterior sacs. If this is happening more often than the bird is actually breathing, it is suggested that it might be a mechanism by which air is pumped back and forth between air sacs and lungs in an effort to meet the increased metabolic demands of flight.

It is likely that movement of the wishbone also assists in flight, by increasing the spread of the wings in the downstroke and by enhancing the recovery of the wing during the upstroke, but this has yet to be proved. The furcula does not necessarily function in the same way for all birds. Different birds with different styles of flying have different-shaped wishbones – hawks have a short, stout furcula, parrots a more delicate structure. As for the origins of this mechanism, *Archaeopteryx* had a stout, boomerang-shaped wishbone with the thickest part aligned transversely and it is unlikely that it could bend. The wishbone probably started out as a strengthening strut, and only later, when birds developed a greater propensity for powered flight, did it begin to be a part of the flight mechanism itself.

FEATHERS

Somebody once carried out the undeniably tedious task of counting all the contour (main) feathers on a bird's body. The aim was to find out which bird has the most. The winner was a whistling swan and it had 25,216 contour feathers, 80 per cent of which were on the bird's head and neck. This, perhaps, gives us a clue as to the original function of feathers – insulation. They evolved, most likely, from reptile scales.

A reptile species with scales that had a tendency to fray at the edges may have gained an advantage over those species that did not have this characteristic. Frayed scales would have trapped warm air against the creature's body, and so those species with frayed scales would have had some advantage in temperature control. They would either have survived in cold conditions which killed off the other species or were quicker off the mark every morning before the sun came up and won the competition for food.

There is, indeed, some speculation that feathers evolved before the birds arrived and that many of the small, predatory theropod dinosaurs were feathered. It was only a short evolutionary leap from feathered arms to feathered wings, and subsequently feathers became an important instrument on the road to flight.

Ruby-throated hummingbirds have only 940 contour feathers, the smallest being on the eyelids. The tiny bee hummingbird of Cuba has eyelid feathers just 0.4 millimetres long. The longest feathers are, perhaps, the 1.5-metre upper tail feathers of the peacock and the 1.2-metre middle tail feathers of the great argus pheasant.

Feathers are made of keratin, the same material that makes fingernails and horns. They come in all shapes and sizes – the large quills for flight, fanlike feathers in the tail, downy feathers for the body, tiny hairy filoplumes, whose function has been a mystery until recently, and, for the more extravagant, a spiky feathered panache on the head which figures in display.

A contour feather consists of a central shaft or rachis which is hollow at its base and solid at the top. On either side of the shaft are the blades or veins which consist of side barbs attached to the shaft at an angle. Each barb bears rows of yet smaller branches. The sub-branches on the side nearer the tip, known as the barbicels, have a row of downward-pointing hooks. There might be a million or more hooks on each feather. On the other sub-branch or barbule are small ridges on which the hooks of the adjacent branch can fix. The parallel rows of side-branches are zipped up like a zip fastener, providing a strong lattice of interlocking filaments that give the wing vein strength yet still keep weight to a minimum. If the feather is damaged and the filaments are pulled apart all the bird need do is zip them up again when preening. That is something that was denied the leathery-winged pterosaurs: if their wings were badly ripped they fell out of the sky.

The veins on the flight feathers are asymmetrical. The narrower vein is at the leading edge of the feather and the wider vein on the trailing edge. Feathers on the bodies of flying birds or the wings of flightless birds are symmetrical. The contour or body feathers also

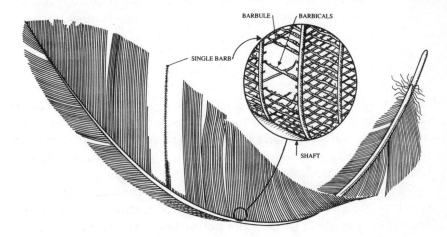

Combining lightness with strength and flexibility, birds' feathers are remarkable structures. The vaned feather illustrated consists of a central shaft to which are attached hundreds of barbs. Each barb interlocks with its neighbour with hooks. The hooks give the vein strength and, if damaged, can be zipped up again easily during preening.

have a slightly different structure. The top part is zipped up like the flight feathers, but towards the bottom of the shaft it becomes fluffy, loose-textured filaments which do not interlock and resemble downy hair.

Night-flying owls have the opposite feather construction. The ends and leading edges of their flight feathers are without zips, giving the feather a ragged but soft edge to reduce noise. Day-flying owls have normal feathers.

Baby birds have feathers that are without hooks and are hair-like from top to bottom. The central shaft is short and the filaments form a thick mass of fine insulating down. Many water birds have downy feathers below their outer plumage. Air trapped under the down helps to maintain body temperature in the cold water. The air can sometimes be seen escaping when a waterbird dives. The trapped air can make the bird too buoyant and so as it dives it flattens its plumage to expel the air.

The largest feathers in flying birds tend to be the flight feathers or remiges. The outer part of the wing is clothed in the primaries or pinions. These are attached to the second and third fingers and the wrist bone or carpometacarpus. The primaries at the wing tips can be controlled and twisted individually. As the wing is moved back they might turn almost perpendicular to the wing, much like a Venetian blind, so that the air can pass through and drag is reduced. There are generally eleven of them.

The secondaries, which are attached to the ulna in the forearm, vary in number depending on the lifestyle of the bird and the shape of its wing. Fast-flapping hummingbirds have few secondaries, maybe no more than six, whereas soaring albatrosses have as many as forty. The secondaries are less important for normal flight than the primaries. If a bird's secondaries are cut in half the bird can still fly, but only the tips of the primaries need be removed to ground it.

Other wing feathers include the tertiaries on the humerus of the upper arm and the coverts on the leading edge. There is also a small group of flight feathers that grow from the bone that was once the thumb, and which form a mini wing-like structure known as the alula or 'bastard wing'. The alula comes into its own at slow speed and resembles the 'slots' in an aircraft wing. The feathers are raised as a bird attempts to land or is hovering in an updraft. They control the stream of air over the wing surface, making the airflow smooth and free of turbulence and therefore providing sufficient lift at low flying speeds to keep the bird airborne.

The other important flying feature is the tail. When slowing down or landing a bird like a duck or booby is able to fan out its tail feathers and direct them downwards. Used in conjunction with the feet, they act as an airbrake. Some birds, such as kestrels, are able to fan out the tail feathers widely, which helps them to hover.

The most intriguing feather type is the filoplume, whose function has until recently been something of a mystery. A filoplume consists of a single hair-like shaft tipped with a small tuft of barbs. It never stands alone but always close to a contour feather. Filoplumes are the tiny feathers often left on the skin when a pigeon is plucked and it was always thought that they had something to do with sensing when a bird's plumage is dishevelled. Research in Germany has shown that this is exactly what they do.

The work demonstrated that filoplumes are associated with sensory receptors in the skin. These are able to detect mechanical movements and respond to ruffled feathers. When the associated contour feather is disturbed the receptors burst into action. A signal is passed back from the receptor along nerves directly to the central nervous system. Thus the bird knows exactly where the disturbance has occurred and can take the necessary action. This is important, for displaced feathers can be responsible for heat loss or inefficient flying, which suggests another function for filoplumes. Being sensitive to movement, filoplumes might also have a function in flying. The sensors could be activated by air currents around the plumage and therefore provide the bird with a comprehensive series of inflight checks.

Most birds have feathers covering the entire body bar the feet. But two bird families contain species in which feathers are absent from the head and neck too – they are the Old and New World vultures. The two families are unrelated but they have similar characteristics, a case of convergent evolution. Both have bald heads and often naked necks, an adaptation, no doubt, to their feeding habits. Vultures spend many of their mealtimes with their heads in bloody and greasy carcasses. The blood and grime would play havoc with feathers. So, rather than have the inconvenience of keeping them clean, they do without altogether.

MOULTING

Just as reptiles slough their scales periodically, birds moult their feathers. Whether moulting is a throwback to the habits of some dinosaur ancestor is hard to say, but for birds it is a vital function under the control of the bird's internal body clock and triggered by the release of hormones.

During a bird's life, feathers are damaged or lost. Individual ones are replaced immediately, but each year all the feathers are renewed. The process varies from species to species. European garden birds moult several times a year, shedding key flight feathers from the right side and left in such a way that they are not lopsided. An imbalance of feathers would prevent a bird from taking off and would leave it vulnerable to predators. By losing feathers gradually, temperate garden birds ensure that they can forage, escape danger, and keep warm, albeit at a reduced level of efficiency. Large birds of prey may take a couple of years to renew their plumage, moulting feathers continually in order to stay airborne and able to hunt. Birds in tropical places, free from seasonal demands, may also moult slowly. Parrots, for example, take up to nine months to renew their feathers.

The female hornbill, incarcerated in her nest hole in the trunk of a tree (see pages 280–1), takes advantage of the situation and moults all her feathers at the same time. She sits there naked until the time approaches to be let out, before which she grows her new set of feathers. Many waterbirds also moult their feathers all at once, making them vulnerable to predation. Often, they will congregate in one remote and relatively safe place while their new plumage grows. Over 100,000 shelduck, for example, representing almost the entire population of north-west Europe (save for three or four thousand Irish birds that meet up at Bridgewater Bay in the West of England), congregate in the Grosser Knechtsand area of the Waddenzee to moult. British birds wait for fine evenings with little cloud cover and a following wind before making the journey there. If the weather is bad or the wind is in the wrong direction the birds don't go.

Immature birds begin to arrive at the moulting site in June and the adults follow in July. A few late arrivals from eastern Europe may pitch up in September. The moult over, British, Dutch and Irish birds return to their breeding sites in October. Birds from Scandinavia, the Baltic States and Poland overwinter along southern North Sea coasts, and many stay on the moulting site, dispersing to their breeding sites the following March.

Similarly, in the southern hemisphere, at the beach and amongst the dunes of Punta Tombo on Argentina's Patagonian coast, non-breeding Magellanic penguins begin to arrive in October. Juveniles born the previous year turn up from November onwards. Previously they had been following fish and squid north, but come the southern spring they head back south and to Punta Tombo to moult. By December the beaches are filled with lethargic non-breeding adults and juveniles, together with hard-working parents tramping up and down the beach as they bring food to their chicks and then return to the ocean to feed. By February the penguin population is so large that the birds stand shoulder to shoulder right up to the water's edge and the moult begins. Living in such a harsh environment, penguins cannot lose all their feathers. The resulting loss of heat would be fatal. Therefore they grow their new feathers in between the old ones. The old ones are stripped away during preening, but the process does leave the birds looking rather ragged and unkempt. For two or three weeks the birds do not feed, but by the end of March most will have completed the moult and returned to sea and their migration north.

The moult is demanding in energy terms. Captive birds show an increase in metabolic rate of about 30 per cent, but in the wild some of this additional energy requirement would be offset by reduced flying and foraging. The nature of nutrients needed is also significant, for keratin contains a higher proportion of the amino acid cystine than is found in other animal and plant proteins. Moulting birds therefore require large amounts of cystine in order to grow new feathers and some get this from an extraordinary source – the flight muscles. Canada geese, for example, are flightless for several weeks after the moult as their wing muscles atrophy, that is, some of the muscle tissue breaks down temporarily in order to provide the amino acids that build the proteins that are to become feathers. The muscles are brought back up to scratch by a bout of intense feeding.

FEATHER CARE

Servicing is important for any flying machine and birds are no exception. Feather care is a daily chore and a good part of a bird's day is devoted to maintaining its plumage and keeping it in tiptop condition.

Where water is available, birds first take a bath. Sparrows some- times splash about at the edge of a pond or puddle in a behaviour known as 'stand-out' bathing. Robins ruffle their feathers, flick their wings, spread their tails, and dip their heads in and out of the water in order to splash water onto the body, an indulgence known as 'stand-in' bathing. Babblers jump in and out, time after time, in a kind of 'in-out' bathing, whereas swifts, swallows and frigate birds exhibit 'flight-bathing' – they take a quick dip whilst skimming the water surface.

Kingfishers 'plunge-bathe' by diving repeatedly from a perch into the water, and some hummingbirds actually fly through waterfalls. Tropical parrots shower in a rainstorm – 'rain-bathing' – while hornbills obtain their bath-water from wet vegetation, a form of 'foliage bathing'. Some birds do the same with dew.

A combination of bathing methods is also common. Vireos will plunge-bathe for a while and end up in the water as stand-in bathers. A nervous wren will test the water with a few plunges before stand-in bathing. Birds are vulnerable at this time and must be alert for predators.

Birds, such as seabirds and waterbirds, that spend much of their time on or in the water, predictably 'swim-bathe'. This may occur on the surface or underwater. A surface-bathing grebe dips its head and neck underwater and thrashes its wings, submerging the front part of the body and soaking its ruffled feathers. The head is then rubbed against its flanks. It might finish with a session of 'barge-swimming', that is, with its rear end underwater and wings open below the surface. A grebe might also dive down with feathers ruffled and wings open, each time returning to the surface where it sits low and wallows in the water.

Penguins have their own kind of bathing in which they lean to one side in the water and thrash the body with the flipper on the upper side. They thrash one side and then the other and, whilst doing so, have a tendency to go round in circles. Gulls also have a sideways rolling action during bathing.

In most cases bathing does not involve the total soaking of the feathers. Rather it is a wetting procedure that precedes more careful grooming. After a good shake and a wing flap (and a rapid vibration of tail and wing tips in passerines) to remove surplus water, a bird is ready to get down to the serious business of oiling and preening.

Oil is obtained from a preening gland under the tail, either by squeezing it with the beak or rubbing the head against it. The fatty secretion is daubed or rubbed on the plumage. A bird might use the bill to anoint its feathers or roll its head back and forth. Passerines have trouble getting oil on the head and so have adopted a novel approach. They squeeze the oil onto the beak, transfer it to a foot and then scratch it into the feathers of the head.

Oiling was once thought to impart some kind of waterproofing to the plumage, but nowadays it is felt that there is more to it than that. The oil has antibacterial properties and also acts as a fungicide. However, an interesting observation on the waterproofing aspect was recently conveyed in a letter to the learned journal *Nature*. A researcher at the Hospital for Tropical Diseases in London noted, with some angst no doubt, that birds had deposited their visiting cards on the roof of his car. Overnight there was a heavy downpour, and in the morning he noticed that although the car roof was covered with rain droplets, an area of about 23 centimetres around each dropping was clear. His suggestion, then, is that 'birds have in their bodies a substance with powerful water repellent properties and that some of this is excreted in their faeces.' Might this be represented in their preening oils?

Some birds have powder-down patches consisting of specialized feathers that disintegrate to produce a fine powder. The powder supplements preening oil or replaces it in birds without a preen gland, such as pigeons. The use of powder down is seen most obviously in birds, such as herons and bitterns, that feed on slimy or fishy foods, such as freshwater eels. Inevitably the wriggling creature will touch the bird's plumage and the slime clogs the feathers. The bird's answer is to rub the offending part against a powder-down patch, much like applying a dab of shampoo, and then scrape off the amalgam of powder and slime using a specialized comb-like scraper on the side of the middle toe. With the slime thus removed the bird can oil and preen in the usual way.

Preening involves either nibbling or passive stroking. The more precise feather care is provided by the careful nibbling away at the feathers with the tip of the beak. The feathers are put in order, any parted barbs are zipped up again, preening oil is worked in, and dirt or parasites are removed. Stroking is less precise and is used to dry feathers, smooth them down and work in oil.

Birds with restricted access to water, such as those in deserts, steppes and savannahs – ostriches, seriemas, rheas, bustards, sandgrouse – rely on 'dust-bathing'. They might scrape out a dust wallow, toss dust over the plumage, let it fall over and between the feathers and then shake it off, often using movements normally associated with bathing in water. But regular dust-bathing is an important aid to preening for many birds. It helps a bird rid itself of excess preening oil and other fats, together with dried skin, feather debris and any clinging parasites. Sparrows and wrens flick dust with their wings, while partridges and quails flick up dust with their feet. The hoopoe squats on the ground and rakes dust around its breast and then tosses up the particles into the plumage using its feet.

One noisy band of sparrows was once seen to dust-bathe in a sugar bowl at a works canteen. It was the only 'dust' they had available.

SUNNING: MAINTENANCE OR WARMTH?

Birds, like people, like to be in the sun and they will often go sunbathing. For some it might just mean loafing about in a sunny spot, while for others it might mean a set piece of sunning behaviour.

House sparrows are content to find a perch on an outermost branch or on a flat or sloping roof out of the wind and simply squat or preen in the sunshine. Dunnocks run about drying themselves on grass stems after a water bath and then sit on the ground in the sun. Bee-eaters may ruffle their feathers and sit in a hunched position with their backs to the sun. The feathers are raised so that the skin is exposed. Turkey vultures show the same behaviour in the morning. Individuals have been seen to sit for 15–30 minutes with their backs to the weak morning sun, feathers raised and naked skin exposed. These are relatively simple sunning attitudes and one of five identifiable postures that naturalists have recognized.

A second posture adopted by sunning birds is the 'wings-down' position. They sit on the ground, or on a roof, or a post, and simply let the folded wings drop, often with the side of the body or back facing the sun. Many waders adopt this sunning posture. The greater roadrunner goes one better. It drops its wings, holding them away from the body slightly, and raises the feathers on its back.

In the lateral posture, a bird half-squats with its body side-on to the sun. The neck is often extended, the feathers ruffled, the feet hidden and the beak open. The eye on the sun side is kept open as if the bird is staring at the sun, and the body is sometimes tilted in order that the maximum surface area is exposed to the sun. Sometimes the sun-side wing is folded, while at other times the wing is opened and held beside the body. The tail is fanned and brought alongside the extended wing, so that the maximum surface area of plumage is exposed. The bird turns from time to time so that both sides benefit from the sun's rays. Jays, blackbirds and other thrushes are frequently seen in this sunning position.

Some birds, such as dunnocks, treecreepers, and swallows, raise their wings, albeit briefly, to expose the undersides. They may perform the exercise several times during sunning. They also turn the body and ruffle in order to maximize exposure. Parrots seem to take this to an extreme. They lie on one side and raise a wing in the air. Domestic pigeons are the best-known wing-lifters, raising the wing nearest the sun almost vertically and fully opening it. They do the same thing when rain-bathing.

The serious avian sunbathers adopt the full spread-eagle position. The entire dorsal surface is exposed when the bird lies flat on the ground and spreads out its wings and tail feathers. Storks and other long-legged birds do their spread-eagle sunning standing up, with wings spread out fully and angled towards the sun.

Vultures adopt the 'full-spread frontal posture', with their wings aligned at right-angles to the sun, primaries fully spread and neck ruff erect. A row of vultures in this position is often depicted as omens of doom, but they are simply sunbathing.

Why, though, should birds sunbathe? What benefits do they gain? Are they simply warming up, a process described by avian-toilet expert Kenneth Simmons as 'sun-basking' – or does the sun have some remedial significance, perhaps for feather and skin maintenance, which Simmons terms 'sun-exposure'? The sun delivers ultraviolet light, visible light and infra-red radiation or heat. So, which aspect of the sun's rays is the bird utilizing – is it heat or is it light that is important?

Although birds are warm-blooded, they are susceptible to cold. They must maintain an active body temperature of around 40°C (slightly less at night or during periods of inactivity) and this is mostly sustained by burning food to release energy. This works fine as long as the ambient air temperature is above a certain minimum. That minimum is different for birds living under different climatic conditions. Passerines living in temperate regions have their minimum at 18°C. Cold-adapted birds, such as willow grouse and ptarmigan, can tolerate lower temperatures, down to 9°C, whereas hot-adapted birds, such as vultures, have a minimum at 30°C and must work hard to keep warm if the temperature falls below that for any length of time.

The energy cost of relying on an internal supply of heat, though, is high. Birds have various ways in which to conserve energy. They fluff up their feathers to trap a layer of warm air next to the skin, and also tuck in the beak and feet to reduce heat loss. But what if they could get some of their energy for free, from the sun? Clearly, temperature control is a possible function of sunbathing – another legacy, perhaps, from their dim and distant dinosaurial past.

The curious thing, however, is that some birds sunbathe when the ambient air temperature is above their *maximum* tolerance, usually between 30°C and 38°C, depending on species and circumstance. These birds are seen to pant and generally seem to be uncomfortable to the point of being in a state of considerable heat stress. It is unlikely that they are interested in saving energy, they have too much. What then could they be achieving by sunbathing?

One suggestion is that the ultraviolet light has some beneficial effect on the condition of the plumage. Sunlight, perhaps, transforms fractions of the preening oil into Vitamin D. The bird takes in the extra vitamins when nibbling away during preening. Oil from the preen gland is known to contain precursors that, in the presence of sunlight, can be transformed into the vitamin. We can do the same, only the precursor is in our skin. Interestingly, the birds which would benefit most from added vitamins are those that mainly eat plant material, and it could be significant that birds on a wholly insectivorous diet, like the swifts and nightjars, are the ones with the least-developed preen glands.

There are also mechanical benefits to be gained from sunbathing. Studies in the field by the British vulture specialist David Houston have shown that these soaring birds bend their longest flight feathers out of shape while aloft. Back on the ground, the feathers take two to three hours to straighten if a bird remains in the shade. In the sun, it takes no more than two to three minutes.

Another suggestion is that any parasites clinging to the feathers or skin are liable to become more active when exposed to the sun and therefore more easily removed during preening. Most sunbathers preen after their bout in the sun. In one study in North America it was noticed that birds sun themselves more often just after the moult, a time when they also show 'anting' and 'smoke-bathing' (see below), the three kinds of behaviour possibly related to a lessening of skin irritation by parasites. When new feathers are growing, the skin is supplied with more blood than at other times of the year, a perfect food supply for blood-sucking ectoparasites and a source of constant irritation for the bird. Anything the bird can do to alleviate the itch has got to be good news.

ANTING: FEATHER CARE OR FOOD?

Birds sometimes do the most curious things. A crow will drop down to the ground close to an ants' nest, lie spread-eagled amongst the ants, and make movements as if it had started to preen. Why should it engage in such strange behaviour? Does it receive some kind of auto-erotic stimulus from the ants? Is it a means of removing parasites? The search for an explanation for anting has been controversial, and it is still, to some extent, a mystery. Nevertheless, a lot of birds do it.

At one time or another nearly 250 species have been seen to engage in this unusual form of behaviour, known quite simply as 'anting'. It occurs in two ways – either the bird seizes an ant in the bill and applies it liberally to its plumage, a process known as 'active anting', or it appears to bathe in ants, when it is known as 'passive anting'.

Starlings are active anters. They spread their wing and tail feathers, presenting them to one side, and apply the ant by stroking it along the ventral tips of the primary feathers and the underside of the tail near to the vent. The choice of ants is not random. Starlings seek out individuals of the ant family Formicinae in which the sting has been converted into a spray. When under attack or disturbed by a vigorously anting bird, the ant sprays formic acid from the tip of the abdomen. Droplets of acid can be seen on the bird's plumage. Sometimes the ants are used singly; at other times they are gathered in a wad in the bill. Often, actively anting birds will go into a frenzy, grabbing one ant after another until some kind of state of ecstasy is reached. After use, the ants are discarded or swallowed.

European jays are passive anters. They squat on the ground, open their wings, thrust them forward, and allow the ants to crawl up the feathers. They then quiver their wings, encouraging the ants to discharge their defensive acid spray.

Of other birds observed, babblers, tanagers and weavers are active anters, while crows and waxbills are passive. Blackbirds, redwings and thrushes are sometimes active and sometimes passive. The grey thrush of Japan is a passive anter which goes through the motions of active anting but without any ants in its bill.

As for an explanation, the traditional view has been that anting is part of a bird's regular flight maintenance. The head and wing movements are stereotyped – the birds deliberately shake and stretch just as they would during normal preening. It is thought that the formic acid kills any tiny ticks, mites or lice that might be clinging to the skin or feathers, but there is no evidence that there is any reduction in parasites after anting. It is likely that tiny creatures, such as lice, would be repelled and dislodged by the acid spray but again there is no evidence that this is what the bird is intending to do. Another view is that the acid helps to remove a build-up of dried skin, stale preening oil or dirt. And a further suggestion has it that moulting birds use the acids to soothe the skin when the new feathers are growing.

In North America and northern Europe, observers have noted that anting occurs mainly after a bird has completed breeding, at a time when both adults and juveniles moult. This, however, might be simple coincidence for this is also the time of the year when humid, thundery weather stimulates ants to swarm in huge numbers.

For a more recent explanation, we must turn to chemical ecology, the study of the ways in which plants and animals interact at a chemical level, the way chemicals, for instance, are used for defence and communication. The study was conducted by Tom Eisner at Cornell University in New York State.

Eisner worked with Florida blue jays. He noticed that the birds immediately, almost automatically, began to show anting behaviour as soon as ants were presented to them. And they always ate the ants after anting. Eisner wondered whether they were, indeed, simply discharging the noxious substances before making a meal of the ants or whether the behaviour was for some other reason. Blue jays, after all, are voracious insectivores and ants are by far the most numerous insects readily available to them. Eisner and his team decided to test the birds.

From one batch of ants they removed by microdissection the glands that produce the formic acid. Other than that, the ants looked quite normal to the birds. Interestingly, when ants without the acid were presented to the jays, the birds stopped anting and simply ate the ants. When given normal ants with acid, the birds returned to anting behaviour.

In blue jays, at least, anting behaviour seems to be strongly linked to preparing the food for later consumption. This does not, however, rule out its role in removing parasites. The two pieces of behaviour need not be mutually exclusive. But which is the primary reason for anting – anting for comfort or anting for food? Did an ancestral blue jay develop anting behaviour primarily to utilize the ant's defence system for itself, or was it a means of overcoming the system in order to eat it?

In further studies, Eisner presented the blue jays with another insect which produces a defensive spray – the bombardier beetle. This tiny beetle sprays predators with a boiling blast of noxious chemicals which leaves the beetle's abdomen with an audible puff. When offered the beetles the birds behaved in the same way as with the ants. They seized the beetles in the bill, and performed their anting behaviour before swallowing their prize. This time, though, the researchers could hear the beetle each time it sprayed, and, knowing the capacity of the gland and rate of discharge, were able to work out the exact moment when the gland was empty. Only at this point did the birds eat the beetles. Here was an even stronger link between anting and feeding.

So, why choose anting as a way of preparing food in the first place? It does seem a roundabout way of ridding the insect of its distasteful chemicals. A simpler way would be to rub the creature on the ground but, says Eisner, this would present the bird with a fundamental problem – it would not be able to see approaching predators who might be interested in eating it; its head would be too close to the ground. It would be far better to grasp the insect, stand on a favourite perch with a clear line of sight, and discharge the chemicals in relative safety, say, on a twig or on its plumage, where it would receive the additional value of dislodging parasites.

In flat desert areas, where a bird is able to see for some distance, even at ground level, a bird would not need to take its food to a look-out perch. It could just as well discharge the defence chemicals directly on the ground. Eisner went in search of desert birds that like ants and watched how they behaved. The birds, right on cue, wiped their insects, not on their plumage but on the ground. Here was further evidence that, for blue jays at least, feeding is a fundamental reason for anting behaviour.

This still does not, however, explain why anting birds appear to be in some kind of ecstasy when anting, with eyes closed, wings spread and in such a state that they have been known to fall over. It also does not explain the occasional observation of birds apparently anting with moth balls or apple peel.

PHOENIX FROM THE FLAMES

And, if anting seems a bizarre thing to do, what about 'smoke-bathing? Birds such as rooks are seen to stand on smoking chimney stacks and hold open their wings in the same position as if anting. Others have taken smoking cigarette ends and brandished them about their plumage in the same way that anting birds spray themselves with ant acid. Fires have even been started by birds taking smouldering cigarettes back to their nests: tops of trees have gone up in flames as well as entire buildings in which the birds were nesting. The behaviour, alas, remains a mystery.

GROUNDED: FLIGHTLESS BIRDS

Not all birds fly. Where there is no need to flee from ground-based predators, such as on isolated islands where the hunters are absent,

49

birds stay with their feet firmly on the ground. And where there is no competition or predation, there has been a tendency to grow big . . . very big.

In Australia, at the beginning of the Miocene about twenty million years ago, the large mihirungs, a family of large emu-like birds with great, strong beaks, began to roam an island continent that was much wetter than today. The green centre then *was* green with southern beech forests and numerous lakes. The mihirungs shared the wetlands with ancient ducks and pelicans, and even flamingos. The shape of the jaws indicates that these giants were plant eaters, although their powerful nature does not suggest what food that might have been. The largest mihirung, *Dromornis stirtoni*, is known only from leg bones, but is thought to have stood 3 metres tall and weighed in excess of 500 kilograms – the heaviest known bird.

In New Zealand another giant race of flightless birds arose. They were the moas. Moas were more lightly built than the mihirungs. They had powerful legs, broad pelvic girdles and long flexible necks capable of reaching the uppermost branches of trees containing berries and other fruits. Over the millennia they simply got bigger and bigger until they eventually became the tallest known birds in the world. Their discovery, in 1936, was all due to a dead horse. New Zealand farmer Joseph Hogden and his son Rob were digging a hole in which to bury the unfortunate beast when they chanced upon the moa bones. The place was Pyramid Valley in North Canterbury and it was thought to be the site of an old swamp in which the birds had become trapped. Those skeletons found well down in the swamp deposits were intact, but many of those close to the top were headless. This has led some commentators to speculate that eagles swooped down and removed the heads and necks as the swamp victims sank deeper and deeper into the morass.

Skeletons of moas have been found in New Zealand from birds about the size of a swan to those, like *Diornis maximus*, up to 3.7 metres tall. Being flightless they had no use for a keel and their wings were absent altogether.

On Madagascar the 3-metres-tall elephant birds, *Aepyornis*, weighed a staggering 450 kilograms and laid eggs with a liquid capacity of 7.5 litres, the biggest eggs of any known bird. The largest were about 84 centimetres long and 72 centimetres in circumference. They were at the limit of egg size; any larger and the shells would have had to be so thick to keep in the liquid that the giant chick inside would have been unable to break out.

In the Mediterranean, islands such as Malta were home to giant swans. Despite a 2.7-metre wingspan, the birds were thought to have been flightless. They had a relatively small breastbone which would have provided little attachment for flight muscles. Their flightlessness reflected the fact that few large predators reached the islands after the Mediterranean refilled about five million years ago. Remains of the giants have been found alongside dwarf elephants just a metre high.

Today, two main groups of birds are flightless – the surviving ratites, which live on the ground, and the penguins, which forsook flying for swimming. And there are an assortment of rails, parrots, ducks and cormorants which have also given up flying.

The largest living flightless birds are the ostriches. Along with their native ratite relatives, emus, rheas, cassawaries and kiwis, they share a flat sternum. With no flight muscles, the birds have done away with the need for an enlarged and elongated keel. Instead, many have shifted their powerbase to the legs.

All living ratites, bar the kiwi, have long legs and short toes. The forest-dwelling, sedentary cassawary of New Guinea and northern Australia is renowned for its powerful belly-tearing kick. The grassland-living, nomadic emu of Australia and the plains-living rhea of South America are fast runners, an ability taken to its extreme in the African ostrich. This enormous bird is the avian equivalent of the antelope and it has been clocked at speeds up to 60 mph. But it is not only the speed that is remarkable, it is the stamina too. Ostriches have been seen to travel at 28 mph for twenty minutes or so without signs of being tired. They can outrun lions and other predators, but if cornered can deliver a kick with such an impact that it can stave in a skull or tear open a stomach.

Among the ratites wings have not disappeared altogether. The ostrich still has large wing areas covered with a scruffy assemblage of long fluffy feathers without zipper-like barbules that are used for display, balance and shielding the young from the sun. The rhea, from South America, uses an outstretched wing to help it turn at speed. The kiwi's wings have almost completely disappeared, reduced to two small buds hidden beneath the fluffy plumage.

The three species of kiwi live in New Zealand and are, perhaps, the most peculiar of the flightless birds. They seem to have bucked evolution. The evolutionary development of our modern-day avifauna is, after all, as much dependent on the presence of competitors as the absence, and not all species have found themselves isolated in an untouched landscape in relatively recent geological times. The kiwi in New Zealand, which was devoid of mammals until people came along, is one species that bears all the hallmarks of a creature that has grown up in exceptional circumstances. In the absence of mammalian competitors to vie with it for the niche it occupies it has turned out to be one of the most extraordinary of birds.

The kiwi is flightless, nocturnal, and possessed of immense olfactory powers, making it unique amongst present-day birds. Its nostrils are located at the tip of its long thin beak, enabling it to sniff out its prey even in total darkness. It is an evolutionary throwback to the days when birds were at an intermediate stage in their development, and reminds us that apparently anachronistic species can survive if their circumstances remain reasonably constant. It is only when change occurs at a faster rate than adaptation that birds run into difficulties, and as long as all else remains equal, the world's bird population can progress together on a level ecological playing-field.

The kiwi's mammalian equivalent is the European hedgehog, both bird and mammal sharing a long probing snout and the habit of snuffling about on the ground for worms and insects. Indeed, the kiwi's fur-like feathers, reliance on a sense of smell rather than sight, and nocturnal habit are more reminiscent of a mammal than a bird. The kiwi is often referred to as an 'honorary' mammal, having filled the ecological niche normally occupied by a mammal: the hedgehog is not represented in New Zealand and the kiwi takes its place.

On islands, where ground-dwelling birds have been able to evolve and thrive unmolested by predatory mammals, flightlessness is common. Aldabara, a coral island in the Indian Ocean, has its flightless rail. It is a curious little bird which is so tame it may trip up an unwary scientist and even steal his breakfast. Lord Howe Island, off eastern Australia, has a very rare woodhen (a flightless rail) which is equally fearless of people, a trait that makes its survival questionable. Similarly, the large San Cristobal mountain rail in the Solomon Islands is threatened by widespread logging.

New Caledonia has its kagu, a slate-grey pigeon-like bird which is flightless but can glide short distances. It is threatened by logging, mining, collectors, cats, dogs, pigs, and rats, and there is some concern that its particularly splendid pre-dawn calls will be lost for ever.

New Zealand has several other surviving flightless birds, including the green-coloured, ground-living parrot – the kakapo – and the curious broad-beaked takahe.

Unfortunately, the smaller flightless birds have become so specialized during their isolation that they are highly vulnerable when circumstances change; and change they did when people sailed to the islands bringing rats, cats, goats and all manner of vermin that quickly destroyed the birds. One particularly horrifying tale is, perhaps, the case of the world's only flightless passerine, the Stephen Island wren. The entire population was eliminated by a lighthouse keeper's cat. One bird, though, has got its own back. The weka, a 53-centimetres-long rail, has an appetite for rats and mice and is thriving on the new invaders.

On water, flightlessness for the Magellanic steamer duck of South America and the Falkland flightless steamer duck has resulted in a very unusual form of locomotion. These large ducks scoot across the water moving their wings in the manner of a paddle-steamer. They upend in shallow water and dive down in deeper water to forage for mussels. One bird has been found with over 450 mussel shells in its crop and stomach. Falklands birds have been seen to dive down 9 metres in dives that may last for a half a minute or more.

Diving has been taken that little bit further by the flightless cormorant of the Galapagos Islands, some distance off the coast of Ecuador. This bird uses its degenerate wings for steering underwater whilst propelling itself along with paddle-like feet. The feathers on the wings of all cormorants, flying and flightless alike, are loose-fitting so they are thoroughly soaked by the end of a fishing trip. Flying species must dry them before they are able to take off. They stand with wings spread out in the sun. Flightless cormorants still behave in the same way, even though their wings are comparatively tiny. The flightless cormorant, like the land-living ratites, has lost the large keel to which the flight muscles would have been attached.

But a bird need not be flightless to be a diver. Swimming using the wings, like the common guillemot, or with webbed feet, like the great northern diver, flying birds frequently dive deeper than 50 metres. One razorbill was reported to have dived down to 137 metres.

Diving and swimming in pursuit of a meal is not necessarily a recent evolutionary move on the part of birds. Speculation that *Archaeopteryx* plunged like a baby hoatzin takes swimming right back to the origin of birds. Indeed, some of the early birds were clearly swimmers. In chalk deposits dating from the Late Cretaceous in Kansas, the fossil remains of 'birds with teeth' were found in the nineteenth century by Otheniel Charles Marsh of Yale University. These were more modern-looking birds than *Archaeopteryx* and they were toothy waterbirds – fisheaters. The fossils came from rocks laid down on the floor of a shallow sea that bisected North America about 100 million years ago.

There was a large, 1.2-metres-long, flightless diving bird *Hesperornis* ('western bird') with only the remnants of wing-bones retained, but with a backbone and hind legs like a modern diving bird. With its legs set well back on the body, it most likely swam like a modern diver (loon), paddling with webbed feet to propel it underwater in pursuit of fish, cephalopods and crustaceans. The neck was relatively long and flexible, and the jaws were lined with sharp, curved teeth which had thick roots in the manner of other fisheaters, like the ancient mososaurs and modern crocodiles. The teeth sat in grooves along the jaw rather than individual tooth sockets.

Another toothed and flightless diver was *Baptornis* ('diving bird'), as was *Enaliornis*, found in Early Cretaceous rocks in Britain. Much later in the Eocene, after the dinosaurs and their relatives had been eliminated, ecological niches became vacant and the birds were first to fill them. In the water, penguins, found as fossils in New Zealand, developed into streamlined, underwater swimmers. Some were enormous, standing as high as a man, 1.5 metres tall and weighing 120 kilograms. Today, penguins are still the champion divers.

The deepest divers tend to be the largest penguins – the emperors of the Antarctic. Birds with depth recording devices attached to their back have been found to dive down to 265 metres, making the emperor penguin the deepest diving bird. To reach that depth a bird must be underwater for about eighteen minutes. Emperor penguins are also thought to be the fastest swimmers, reaching top speeds of about 17 mph although more normally swimming at 3–6 mph.

Although penguins are flightless, they do fly – but they fly underwater. The wings have become thin, rigid paddles with which the bird can push itself through the water. The wing beat is slightly different from that of flying birds in that there is no recovery stroke.

The entire flipper rotates so that the downstroke pushes the water downwards and backwards and the upstroke pushes it upwards and backwards. In this way a bird maintains thrust throughout the wing-stroke cycle. In order to power itself through the water, a penguin has strong flight muscles and, unlike other flightless birds, retains the keel on the sternum.

In order to maximize its swimming speed a penguin might also resort to 'porpoising', leaping clear of the water and plunging back in repeatedly. It does this to overcome water resistance and to save energy. At a certain speed it is more economical in energy terms for the bird to leap out of the water and pass through the less-resistant air for a short distance than to plough on through the more highly resistant water.

It is now generally thought that all the flightless birds – even ostriches and penguins – evolved from flying ancestors. Flight was a special ability that birds acquired and perfected. Flight gave birds the means by which they can now live and survive in such diverse habitats, in such different climates, on every continent and on every ocean from the poles to the equator. Flight also gave them the opportunity to travel the world, and the ability to seek out the optimum conditions to feed well and maximize the chances of bringing up the next generation – something, alas, that their close relatives, the dinosaurs, were denied in some cataclysmic event all that time ago. The legacy of the dinosaurs is the remarkable world of birds.

2

BIRDS OF A FEATHER

MARTHA DIED AT I P.M. (LOCAL TIME) ON I SEPTEMBER 1914. SHE WAS the last of her kind. Once there were many millions like Martha, but during the early part of the nineteenth century man's aptitude for destroying all living things was being exercised, not only in the sea, where whales and seals were slaughtered unmercifully, but also across North America, where small birds were the target. The seals and whales were eventually saved; Martha's relatives were not.

Martha was a long-tailed passenger pigeon and she lived out her twenty-nine years in Cincinnati Zoo. Before the hunters came, wild passenger pigeons were thought to have been one of the most numerous species of birds ever known. The famous American naturalist, John James Audubon, saw them. He described giant pink clouds of them, driven like hurricanes. One flock in Kentucky in 1813 contained many billions of birds. It was nearly 300 miles long and 4 miles wide. It took three days to pass, the birds flying at speeds of 60 mph. The beat of their wings chilled the air. Their droppings rained on the ground. The colonists had a plentiful, if monotonous, supply of food.

The birds were caught in the most cruel ways. Long sticks were used to knock them from a low-flying flock to the ground. One blast from a shotgun bagged a hundred birds at a time. Sulphur was burned below roosts to poison and suffocate them. But perhaps the most cruel and effective method was trapping. A captured live pigeon had its eyelids sewn up tight so that it could not see, and it was tied to a perch which could be manipulated to make the bird flutter. Other birds flying overhead thought the tethered pigeon had found a food supply and dropped in to join it. Then the trap was sprung and three to four hundred birds were caught. The tethered, blinded bird gave rise to the expression 'stool-pigeon'.

By 1889, all the wild passenger pigeons had been killed. The flocks that had once obscured the sun over hundreds of square miles, turning midday into twilight, had disappeared. Groups were bred in captivity but, because of inbreeding, they weakened and eventually died out. In the three hundred years that Europeans had been in North America they had exterminated the world's most numerous bird.

A similar fate befell the Carolina parakeet, another bird that flew in gigantic flocks in the eastern and southern parts of the USA. Like the passenger pigeon, this bird was also hunted, but its ultimate downfall was due to an unfortunate piece of natural behaviour. When a bird was injured or killed, the rest of the flock would gather around, as if willing it to get to its feet and take to the air again. The true purpose of this altruistic gathering is not clear but, presented with such a target, hunters eliminated a flock instantly. The last Carolina parakeet, a male called Incas, died of a 'broken heart' after its mate of thirty years, called Lady Jane, passed away, also in Cincinnati Zoo, four years after Martha.

So, given that birds living in flocks – even enormous flocks – and birds breeding in huge colonies are vulnerable to agents of mass destruction, whether they be: deliberate, such as hunting and shooting; accidental, such as the indiscriminate use of pesticides; or natural disasters, such as freak weather conditions or highly contagious diseases, why should birds group so closely together in such large numbers? Scattered individuals, presented with the same conditions, are less at risk; at least some loners live and continue the line. When a flock is hit, all the birds go at once. Why, then, gather in a flock or nest in a colony?

Clearly, there must be some advantage gained by certain birds in particular circumstances to come together in large groups. In fact, over half of the nearly 9,000 known living species of birds form flocks at some time in their lives. Flocking behaviour has evolved because those individuals exploiting it gain some advantage over those that do not. This is how, in this case, evolution works. In the long term the gregarious survive, the loners do not.

So, is a flock-full of alert eyes better at spotting predators than the pair of eyes of a bird on its own? Do many birds make it easier to find rich sources of food? Is an individual, lost in a flock, less likely to be singled out as prey? Or is a flock more conspicuous than a lone bird? Does the ability to see approaching danger, to be lost in the crowd, and to find food, outweigh the disadvantage of being obvious to predators?

CLUMPS AND INFORMATION CENTRES

The European robin feeds alone. Two robins at a bird table will squabble until one is forced to leave. House sparrows, on the other hand, will flock to the table as soon as the first bird's desire to eat has overcome its reluctance to be in the open, and it flies across to feed. Sparrows eat together.

The difference between these two ways of obtaining a meal is determined by the nature of the food itself and the places where the food is found. Away from the bird table, robins tend to stay hidden. They wait on low branches or under bushes, ready to pounce on beetles or caterpillars that may venture from cover. The food is thinly distributed and there is some advantage to be gained from the bird's excluding rivals and keeping the food to itself. And, by staying hidden, the bird is relatively safe from predators.

Sparrows, however, live mainly on seeds which are found on grasses out in the open. Furthermore, the distribution of seed heads is patchy. If one bird locates a 'clump' of grass in seed, and is seen to be actively feeding, there is some advantage in the other birds' joining it; and there should be enough food for all.

Other birds, searching for food supplies that occur in short-lived 'clumps', such as swarms of insects, schools of fish, ripening fruit, or the carcasses of dead animals, are also more efficient at finding food when in a flock. Each bird watches and is ready to imitate the behaviour of its flock mates. If, for example, a few individuals focus their attention on a piece of ground, such as vultures at a dead body, others will quickly join them. Descending vultures serve as a beacon that enables others to find the carcass. The birds have discovered the whereabouts of food by watching the behaviour of the flock – the flock is an information centre.

Ornithologists following the exploits of guillemots (thick-billed murres) in the Canadian Arctic have watched birds flying out to sea for two hours or more in order to find suitable fishing grounds. If a bird heads off in the wrong direction it could be very wasteful in terms of energy and time, so there is a strong pressure for an individual to use any and every piece of information to make its life easier. And it's easier to follow the crowd.

At any given moment birds are arriving and departing the colony. Those arriving tend to be large groups and fly in a straight line, presumably back from the feeding sites. Birds in the colony can see the direction from which they returned and, when it is their turn to go feeding, head out in the same way.

Those leaving the breeding ledges glide down to the sea surface, bathe and preen and then take off for the open sea. Although they fly away independently, a few miles out to sea they begin to join with other birds until a flock of twenty to a hundred birds is flying along together. The flocks travel in a straight line towards the horizon, each group separated from the next by about a half a minute. They travel in lines or in V-formations like waterfowl but quite close to the water. The lead bird occasionally bobs up to check the heading from incoming flocks, whereupon it might change course; the rest of the flock follows.

A bird that has just returned from feeding, but is not relieved by its mate and must return again to sea, behaves in a slightly different way. It deposits the food with its mate, turns around and flies back out to sea alone. It knows where the food is to be found and has no need for the information centre, and so rather than waste time with an outgoing naïve flock it travels alone, heading directly back to the food source.

A flock of seabirds is not only an information centre for its own species. It attracts others too, including non-avian interlopers. Minke whales are compulsive bird-watchers. To the south of the San Juan Islands, near Vancouver, minke whales look for flocks of gulls and auks feeding on herrings and sand eels. In the shallow water above submerged sand banks, upwellings bring nutrients to the surface and so the fish shoals are more accessible to the birds. Even though the seabirds feed at one site for only a few minutes, it is sufficient time for the whales to spot them and make for the feeding site.

Taken to its logical conclusion, this continuous updating of food source information linked to a degree of cooperation in feeding can lead to birds developing special ways to exploit the food. In the nutrient-rich, icy waters of the Southern Ocean, blue-eyed shags form huge 'rafts' on the sea's surface. The flock swims along together in close formation, each bird dipping its head below occasionally to look for shoals of fish. As soon as one is located, the spotter dives below and all the others follow. In the confusion below the surface a fish has little chance of escape. It may avoid one cormorant but, as it jigs to the side, it is caught by the bird hunting alongside. By hunting in flocks, blue-eyed shags create a better chance both of spotting food and of catching it.

SEABIRD CITY

Seabirds have a better chance of breeding successfully if they get together. One of the most spectacular wildlife events must be that which takes place each spring in the northern hemisphere when seabirds arrive at their island and cliff-side breeding colonies. Canada's eastern Arctic, for example, is a metropolis for seabirds – three and a half million guillemots (murres), a million and a half fulmars and a quarter of a million kittiwakes arrive in late May and early June. Digges Island and Cape Wolstenholme at the northern tip of Quebec's Ungava Peninsula have seabird cities, or bazaars as they are known, containing 800,000 birds. On eastern Digges Island, birds nest on ledges, covering the 300-metre-high, 2½-mile-long cliff face from 2 metres above sea level to the top, and an even larger city extends along a 5-mile-long cliff side at Cape Wolstenholme on the mainland. Across Baffin Bay ten to twenty million little auks or dovekies breed in the Thule district of Greenland, one of the greatest concentrations of birds on earth.

Very few northern seabird colonies are small. They look confusing, they're noisy and they're smelly, but within these great seabird cities, where millions upon millions of birds congregate each year, there is some degree of order.

The birds arrange themselves according to needs, often occupying different levels on the cliff face. Shags and cormorants, with large, scrappy nests, are on the bottom storey along the rocky shore. Guillemots, each with a minute territory, pack tightly along ledges slightly higher up, while razorbills tend to be scattered about on isolated crevices or behind rocks. Still higher, fulmars and kitti-wakes construct their seaweed and guano nests on high ledges, fulmars sometimes preferring the grass ledges at the cliff top. Here, on the high rock ledges and grassy slopes across the top of a small island, nest the gannets. In some locations, like the Bass Rock in Scotland's Firth of Forth and the Skelligs of south-west Ireland, the gannets, each sitting bird just out of beak range of its neighbour, take over vast tracts of the islands.

Gulls and terns prefer more open places – cliff-top plateaux, sand dunes and low, flat islands. Gull chicks tend to wander and would not survive long on a cliff face. Terns like to have a good view and an early warning of approaching predators. Shearwaters and puffins excavate burrows along cliff tops or take over the abandoned burrows of rabbits. But whatever the nest sites, all these birds have one thing in common – they stick together. Why?

Clearly an enormous congregation of birds is a beacon for predators. But those on four legs are eliminated if the birds nest on an offshore island or on inaccessible cliff faces on the mainland. Winged predators are also deterred, but this is a function not of isolation but of timing.

Seabirds in a colony all do what they must do at roughly the same time. They court, mate, lay eggs, raise their chicks, fledge the young and leave the nest site together. The timing throughout the colony is not precise, for there tend to be pockets of birds in synchrony. The groups may be separated by small geographical features, and although the birds in a group may lay eggs on the same day, the entire colony might be less exact. Each bird is influenced by the state of readiness of the bird next door – a phenomenon known as the 'neighbour effect' – and not by any collective behaviour on the part of the colony. This, of course, means that all the birds are motivated by the same things at the same time, in particular, the need to protect their offspring. A highly motivated group is going to be more effective at deterring predators than a pair of nesting birds on their own.

Breeding in a colony can also be more efficient. Many seabirds return to the exact same spot to breed and meet up with their mates of the previous season, but for those looking for a partner it is easier to find a mate at a traditional meeting place. The focus of activity also has an effect on the birds' physiology. The noise and frenetic activity of a healthy colony stimulates the birds' ovaries and testes. They reach a state of readiness to mate earlier, an important factor for birds nesting in temperate regions or in the far north. Even a few lost days can mean the difference between breeding successfully and losing the brood. And, when most of the birds have paired up, an unmated male is less likely to upset a stable, synchronized group which is well into egg laying or chick rearing.

Inland, female pheasants are concerned about persistent males too. Their answer is to gather into small flocks in the territory of a dominant male bird. In a harem they are protected from the attentions of other males and can spend more time feeding. The pheasant has a slow digestive process so, in order to have her eggs ready on time, she must feed constantly. Solitary females can feed for only a quarter of their active day, the rest of the time being spent looking for rampant males or running away from them. It could be that in the seabird colony too the disruption caused by unmated males has a more significant influence on breeding behaviour than we might have imagined. It's quite easy to see that 'selfish' male disturbance might outweigh predation as the main threat to successful breeding.

Another threat is simply competition for food, and it could be this factor, more than any other, that controls the size of seabird cities. If a colony is too small, the information it receives back from the feeding sites is lacking; small numbers of birds provide unpredictable and unreliable information. If there are too many birds, however, feeding sites are quickly fished out and birds have to fly even further from the colony to collect their daily supply. The farther they fly the less food gets back to the chicks, and the less well they grow. At Coats Island, in northern Hudson Bay, for instance, a smallish (but not too small) colony of 25,000 pairs of guillemots feeds its chicks well. At four weeks of age, when they are ready to leave the nest site, they weight 240 grams on average. At Digges Island, however, where 300,000 pairs are breeding, the chicks weigh only 156 grams. And they must be well prepared, for the chicks, with primary feathers not yet grown, must swim all the way to their wintering grounds off the coast of Newfoundland, a journey of over 620 miles. They swim in large rafts and are aided and abetted by their fathers, who help them to feed on the journey. Mother goes separately, and will not see father again until the following breeding season, when they meet up on the same ledge, at the same nest site, ready to start the process all over again. Those youngsters less well-prepared for the journey fail to make their destination. There is probably then some point at which the lack of food and the low survival rate of chicks begins to limit the size of the colony.

There is, however, a slightly more gruesome reason that might also explain colony life and synchronized breeding. With so many youngsters about, there is plenty of food for predators, like Arctic foxes and skuas, and they are quickly sated; some chicks will therefore survive. At Digges Island, the huge guillemot bazaar loses eggs and chicks to glaucous gulls and ravens. The ravens take one egg per hour and cache them under flaps of moss for future eating. One raven has been seen to hide 1,000 eggs and was able to recall the location of each cache. With this kind of predation a small group nesting together would be unable to survive. The greater the numbers the more likely that this superabundance of food will satisfy the appetites of predators.

As it happens, not many predators risk the wrath of seabirds like adult terns and gulls. Their collective onslaught is enough to deter many threatening animals. They dive-bomb any creature approaching the colony, risking capture themselves. Their raucous screams serve to alert the colony and to frighten away the threatening animal.

Highly vocal birds like terns and gulls are sometimes sought out by other less demonstrative species. In Europe, black-necked grebes, scaup, long-tailed duck and velvet scoters sometimes nest in black-headed gull colonies. And in the pampas wetlands of Argentina in South America, silver and Rolland's grebes nest amongst brown-hooded gulls.

Gulls, however, are not ideal birds to live alongside. They are liable to take over grebe nests or steal nest materials, and grebe eggs are liable to be tipped out and damaged during the fracas. But, curiously, the eggs themselves, and later the chicks, are not preyed upon by the gulls, so the benefits of living within the gull colony begin to outweigh the disadvantages. In particular, the interlopers have discovered that there is some advantage to be gained in having these noisy neighbours, for the grebes can interpret some of the gulls' calls. This is a kind of behaviour known as information parasitism. It's a way in which an animal can gain useful infor-mation, say, about predators or food, from another species.

Grebes have a basic problem in that they swim low in the water and their view of the nest site is obscured by reeds and other vegetation. An approaching predator goes unnoticed. But the gulls are flying about the colony and are able to spot a weasel or falcon long before it becomes a threat. The gull alarm calls give the adult grebes time to hide their eggs underneath a layer of weed before they themselves escape to the safety of the water. And the benefit is real – grebes nesting in gull colonies are two and a half times more likely to raise at least one chick than those nesting alone.

SAFETY IN NUMBERS

Safety in numbers is an important function of grouping together, whether birds are on the ground, on the sea or in the air. A bird in a flock is safer than a bird on its own. With many individuals swimming or milling about, there is always a bird or two not feeding and actively looking about for predators. Indeed, as a flock grows, a bird, reassured that an increasing number of eyes are on the lookout for danger, can afford to be less vigilant itself and concentrate more on feeding.

South American parrots, like the red-and-green macaw, will not come down to clay licks in the sides of river banks unless at least forty of their comrades are prepared to join them. The reason the birds lick clay is presently unknown, although clay is rich in minerals such as calcium and sodium, it is alkaline, which might counteract acid indigestion, or it might help the bird digest toxic seeds and thus exploit a food source denied to other seed-eaters. More usually parrots and macaws live in pairs or small family groups of three or four, but at the clay lick, during the dry season between July and September, they need company. This activity, though, is very dangerous – perhaps the most dangerous in the bird's life – for the gathering *does* attract predators, mainly large black-and-white hawk eagles and ornate hawk eagles. They sneak up on the parrot congregations, using the foliage of the mid and understories to conceal their presence, and pounce on the smaller birds as they swoop down to the clay lick. But clearly some advantage is gained by the parrots in forming into a large group, sometimes as many as 500 at a single clay lick – whether it be the presence of more eyes to spot predators or better defence prospects in mobbing. If there was no benefit, why should birds do it, especially as there is also competition for the best places at the lick itself?

Whatever the answer, all macaws do not behave in the same way at the licks. Some find a prime position on the lick site, stay for six or seven minutes and then fly back to the trees. This maximizes their time on the lick but exposes them to greater danger. The bird must balance the need for the clay with the risk of being caught by a hawk eagle. In other words, those that take the greatest risk, obtain the greatest benefits. The alternative strategy is to stay for a couple of minutes at a time, during a half-hour period, thus reducing the risk but also reducing the amount of time licking clay. The birds spend more time flying and squabbling and less on licking, but they are exposed for less time in the open.

While a New World parrot watches for eagles or a tiny European sparrow is on the lookout for a sparrowhawk or the friendly neighbourhood tabby, the African ostrich has much larger worries on its mind. It does not actually bury its head in the sand, but it certainly has its head effectively buried in the grass while feeding, making it easy prey for a pride of lions. The 120-kilogram ostrich, like the 5-gram house sparrow, solves its dilemma by gathering into loose flocks. The larger the group the less often the bird looks up and the more food it can consume. An ostrich eating alone looks about nervously for at least twenty minutes in every hour. Three or more birds together can afford to be less vigilant. Each spends about fifty-four minutes eating and six minutes looking. Heads rise at random, but there is still effective surveillance by each pair of eyes set 2 metres above the surrounding countryside.

Birds in a large flock spot an approaching predator from a much greater distance than do birds in a small flock. The larger a flock grows, the earlier a hunter is detected, and the less it is successful – another reason a flock can spend more time feeding. Birds in a flock are reassured that predators will be detected in good time for them to take evasive action. In an experiment with a model hawk, for example, it has been shown that a group of starlings gain a one-second advantage over one bird on its own – sufficient time to make good their escape. The blurr of wings and general bedlam of a mass take-off is likely to confuse a predator, and give all the individuals in the flock a better chance of escape. And the predator can only catch one bird at a time.

The larger a flock becomes, the larger the area it can safely explore. The flock can forage further from cover. Sparrows in small flocks, for example, will only feed at the edges of fields, close to the hedgerow, preferring to fight and jostle over a small patch of food than to feed at a large 'clump' in the open. Progressively larger flocks move away from the hedge and take advantage of 'clumps' in the centre of the field.

A foraging flock moves by 'leap-frogging' – the birds at the rear flying over and landing ahead of those in the front. In this way the birds at the back of the flock do not try to look for food in an area that has already been stripped.

RANK

In a flock of feeding birds, such as sparrows, the food supply is not apportioned evenly. Dominant birds take the lion's share. By hogging the best part of a food 'clump', they feed quickly, leaving time for preening, resting and reproduction. Birds of lesser rank must remain on the periphery of the feeding flocks, and cannot gain access to the food until the dominant birds have left. Subordinates are then at a further disadvantage because as the flock becomes smaller they must spend more time looking about for predators. In order to gather enough food they must take more risks and are less likely to survive.

On small 'clumps' of food, lack of room means that birds must squeeze together. Most birds have a minimum distance at which they tolerate neighbours – gulls, for example, need about 30 centimetres between individuals, lapwings forage about 3 metres apart, and herons, spaced out along a section of shoreline, need several metres. On a small food 'clump', therefore, inevitably more bill-jabbing or wing-flicking fights break out and it is less likely that a subordinate bird will get a look-in. It could mean a subordinate bird being excluded altogether.

How, though, do the dominants and subordinates achieve and maintain their status in the flock? Surely, if they were fighting all day, they would throw away the advantage they had gained in the first place – too much fighting means not enough feeding. This is demonstrated by yellow warblers in the USA. Dominant birds do no better than subordinates in the feeding stakes because they must spend so much time strutting, chasing and fighting. A bird's answer to this problem is to find a less distracting way to advertise its status in society, whilst retaining a dominant position. Some, it seems, have done just that. They wear their rank, like an NCO's stripes, on their sleeve or, more accurately, on their chest, head or neck.

The rank of North American chickadees and white-crowned sparrows and European house sparrows and great tits, for example, is declared by the width of dark-coloured bands of feathers. The wider or darker the band, the higher the bird is in society. In the USA, high-ranking Harris sparrows have more black feathers on their heads, necks and breasts, and white-crowned sparrows have the brightest stripes on their heads. European great tits of higher breeding have wider stripes down the middle of the breast. These 'badges of status' reduce squabbling when feeding, and enable the dominant birds to declare their rank and obtain the most food unchallenged.

But why do the subordinates go along with it? Why don't they cheat? The simple answer is that it is not worth it. The 'badge of status' *is* only a badge. The bird must still back it up with physical size and maturity. It is no coincidence that those with the best 'badges' are the largest and oldest cock birds. The 'badge' allows other members of the flock to recognize instantly the wearer's status. It reduces the need for flock members to fight for the right to be first to exploit the food. A 'badge' helps dominants and subordinates to conserve valuable energy.

Turnstones do things differently. Each turnstone has its own individual colour pattern. In the breeding season, turnstones recognize their neighbours by the black-and-white pattern of plumage on the head and neck. Theory has it that this identification tag prevents neighbours in a breeding site from continually fighting; they remember the previous encounter and avoid future conflict. If a neighbour oversteps the boundary line, it causes less of a fracas than if an intruding bird from a more distant part of the breeding grounds enters the territory.

In winter, turnstones form into flocks. As with the chickadees, some turnstones dominate the feeding sites, but their status as such is not reflected in their plumage. Instead, individual identity is recognized: dominant and submissive birds recognize each other by their individual plumage differences. Again this is a way of reducing conflict and of saving energy.

As a bird flock moves through a feeding site, it is apparent that some birds do the searching and others simply copy them. In house sparrow flocks, dominant birds tend to be those that actively look for the rich food sources. The subordinates do little of their own food-searching, but follow the dominant birds, sometimes stealing the food from under their bills. Similarly, small groups of tits forage through woodland picking off flying insects resting on leaves.

Suddenly, one bird might search the underside of a leaf and pull out a caterpillar. The other birds then follow its example, and the flock switches from topsides to undersides. The searcher has identified a 'clump' of food, in this case a population of caterpillars chomping their way through their food plant, and the copiers exploit it.

DINNER CALL

What all this means for birds is that those feeding in a flock in the open have discovered where food is to be found, how best to get at it, and how to avoid being caught. Indeed, a bird in a flock spends, on average, about one tenth of its time looking about and nine tenths eating. A lone bird, like a robin, must spend at least half of its time checking for danger. Both sparrows and robins, though, survive. Each bird, in its own way, has found a successful and efficient way, using the least amount of energy, to locate food and eat in comparative safety. In other words, each bird has identified and developed its own strategy to occupy an ecological niche – robins feed alone on insects in the bushes, sparrows forage in flocks for seeds in the open.

Interestingly, a sparrow behaves like a robin when presented with a single item of food, such as a small crust of bread on a bird table. On this occasion, it would rather keep the food to itself than share it with the rest of the flock. Indeed, by keeping quiet it discourages other birds from coming close. Normally, a sparrow is known for its incessant chatter, but the noise stops immediately it has taken possession of the bread.

If food is scattered on the lawn or in a similar place exposed to predators, like the neighbourhood cat, the first sparrow which spots it does not fly down immediately; instead, it perches nearby and calls. Other sparrows arrive and they all descend together to feed. On the face of it, it seems a daft thing for a sparrow to do. The other sparrows are competitors for the food. But the wily sparrow has found that extra eyes are useful and there is always the chance that one of the other birds in the flock will be caught if a predator strikes. On the other hand, if there are too many birds, then there is not enough food to go round. The solution is not to call too vigorously.

The first sparrow calls enthusiastically, but as more and more birds arrive the chirruping calls are produced less and less. The sparrow, it seems, can judge the optimum balance between the advantage gained by safety in numbers and the disadvantage of having to share its food. It has been suggested that the 'food-finding' call of the black-headed gull (normally thought to be a 'keep away' signal) might also be an invitation to reduce predator risk. Ravens also attract other ravens to food sources with a specific call.

In the wild, by calling the sparrow can ensure that a protective flock gathers around while it feeds out in the open; the greater the food source, the more chirruping. With a limited food supply it says nothing but risks being spotted by a predator. The vigour with which the sparrow gives its chirrup is directly related to the amount of food available, and a balance is struck between calling or remaining silent, sharing food or being selfish, and gaining the protection of the flock or not.

Cliff swallows have a squeak that attracts the attention of other cliff swallows. These birds nest in colonies and the colony is thought to be an information centre that gives individuals news about the quality, quantity and whereabouts of food. The view has been that the passing on of information is unintentional, a by-product of birds watching other birds returning to the colony. Those carrying the most food have clearly found the best source; best then for a less fortunate individual to follow those birds.

Now, however, it has been found that the squeak call is used when birds are out foraging, but only under certain weather conditions. If the temperature is below 17°C, the sun is not shining, and the wind is less than 16mph birds foraging in loose flocks start to call. Under these conditions, insect prey is scarce. So, to make the best of what is available, the birds call when they've found a patch of insects. The chances are that a bird will do better by recruiting other birds to the area, watching them chase insects, and tracking the swarms. The swarms are short-lived, so a bird is unlikely to feed on a swarm for any length of time. Competition from other birds exploiting that swarm, then, is not important. It can be shared. But other birds are chasing other swarms. By listening for the squeak call of other successful hunters, each bird is able to forage successfully for longer.

TO FLOCK OR NOT TO FLOCK

There are times when birds might not want to cooperate and some birds change their strategy completely, depending on the circumstances. Throughout the lean winter months, great tits congregate in flocks, while in the spring and summer of plenty they defend nesting territories. In the early part of the spring, when the temperature can yo-yo daily, great tits form flocks on cold days and lead a solitary, and sometimes highly territorial, life when it is warm and sunny.

Pied wagtails are partial to dung flies. During the main part of a summer's day, when the flies gather on cowpats for courtship and mating, each wagtail defends a small territory around the dung. A large number of birds would disturb the flies and would make feeding difficult, so each wagtail fervently guards its own feeding site. In the morning and evening, however, the flies do not come to the dung and so wagtails gather in small flocks to feed on swarms of midges and gnats. These tiny flies are not disturbed by the milling birds, so the wagtails tolerate each other's presence at the food source.

The same is true on estuarine mudflats. Ringed plovers and curlews *look* for their food. A large number of birds would muddy the water and frighten the prey, such as worms, shrimps and shellfish, back into their burrows. Solitary feeders are less likely to disturb the food. Knots and dunlin locate food by *touch*, probing the mud with their beaks. They are unaffected by others nearby and feed in large flocks that may contain many hundreds of birds.

Redshanks do both. At night, when they cannot see their food, they gather in tight groups and probe the mud, wagging their bills from side to side to trap a small gastropod mollusc, *Hydrobia*, which is undisturbed by the patter of hundreds of tiny redshank feet. In the dark, they congregate in the same way as the knots. During the day, when their favourite burrowing shrimps, *Corophium*, can be seen with their tails sticking out of the mud, they forage alone like the plovers. Too many redshanks would disturb the crustaceans to the extent that the birds would be unable to catch them. The distance between birds is determined by the food they are eating.

Rooks hunting for earthworms in a field follow the same rules. They forage in well-ordered ranks, spaced well apart. Too many birds moving close together, like the plovers on their mud bank, disturb the worms and the prey escapes by pulling deep down into the earth.

The great blue heron of North and Central America is very precise in the way it tolerates or rejects others of its kind. Its patience is exhausted after exactly three-and-a-half minutes.

At first a solitary bird will discover an ample supply of fish and begin to pick them off, first by stalking and then stabbing at them with a deft thrust of the bill. Others will notice its success and join in. The rapidly forming flock, acting as a temporary information centre, attacts even more birds until a large flock is fishing happily, side by side, on the shoal of fish. But as more and more birds arrive, there are fewer and fewer fish left to catch. When a bird has to wait for three-and-a-half minutes for a fish, it abandons the site and looks elsewhere. If the fish shoals are too small or too scattered, the birds will avoid feeding in flocks and eat alone.

Sometimes conventions break down and chaos prevails. A dead fish on the seashore will have gulls homing-in from all directions and there is undignified mayhem as birds disregard their normal social graces and struggle and chase each other for a slice of the action.

Family flocks, such as those of the Florida scrub jay and the Australian magpie, in which all the birds are related to each other, tend to remain in stable groups of up to twenty individuals. But most foraging bird flocks vary in size throughout the day. When a rich source of food, such as a tree-full of berries or a worm-rich patch of mud, is located, birds fly in and the flock size increases. As the food is used up, they begin to leave and search for another flock gathering elsewhere, at another food source. In this way, flocks assemble, disperse and reassemble at 'clumps' of food.

BIG FLOCKS, SMALL FLOCKS

Flocks also change size in relation to actual attacks by predators. Flocks of yellow-eyed juncos in Arizona, for example, will come together when harassed by a hawk – the greater the number of attacks, the larger the flock, the more time devoted to scanning, and the less time to feeding; but at least they *can* feed. A jumpy bird on its own spends so much time scanning the sky that it does not have the time to feed at all.

Flock size also determines whether a bird flees at once or waits. In a small flock, it is more likely to decide that discretion is the better part of valour and take no chance. It makes off to the nearest refuge. In a larger flock it can afford to hesitate and gain more information about the threat. The bird in the small flock may use up energy unnecessarily. By responding too soon it might flee from something quite harmless and lose feeding time. One in a larger flock waits for the correct facts to emerge, reacts only to real danger and is able to feed for longer.

Helmeted guinea fowl gather in enormous flocks containing upwards of 2,000 birds – but only in winter in temperate areas and in the dry season in the tropics, for during the breeding season the flocks break up due to the aggressive behaviour of the cock birds. With breeding completed and the relative calm of winter approaching the flocks gather at known food 'clumps', watering holes or roost sites from which they do not travel far throughout the non-breeding period; indeed, they rarely travel more than 1.2 miles from the centre. During the course of the day, however, each flock moves in a particular pattern depending on the activity.

First thing each morning the flock descends from its tree roost and the dominant cock birds strut off towards the local water supply. The rest of the flock follows in single file, the cocks constantly alert for predators, such as baboons or snakes. If danger threatens, the birds gather together in a tight cluster with the younger, smaller birds tending to find their way to the centre of the flock or at a point farthest from the perceived threat. Danger past, the birds fan out and forage. This they do in line-abreast, each bird searching for the favourite food, usually underground bulbs and tubers. When food is discovered, the birds begin to gather around the 'clump', the flock serving to attract in other birds to feed.

So, by maximizing food gathering and minimizing predation, some bird flocks can grow to enormous proportions and quite simply become very effective eating machines. As such they can cause havoc when in competition with people. As often as not, the flocks contain birds of the same species. In most cases, those wise and resourceful ancients, who provided us with easy-to-remember insights into the natural world, actually got it right – birds of a feather *do* flock together; and when they do, it is often spectacular, sometimes a nuisance, and occasionally frightening.

For some people, bird flocks can mean big trouble. An East African farmer will look on helplessly as a 'cloud' of quelea or red-billed weaver birds drops from the sky and, like a swarm of locusts, devours his carefully nurtured crop. In this part of the world, where famine is never far from the door, a ravenous flock can tip the balance between life and death.

Quelea live, roost and breed in large flocks at the times when food is plentiful – from the middle to the end of the rainy seasons.

At this time, the grasslands produce most seeds. But during the dry season, when food supplies are patchy, flocks amalgamate into enormous groups, sometimes over a million strong. They gather to take advantage of the few places where plants still grow. A field of irrigated millet or sorghum is like a magnet, and it can be devastated in hours.

Since 1946, many African countries have been forced to take drastic measures with inhumane killing programmes – the spraying of chemical poisons from the air or the use of flame-throwers and petrol-bombs at roost sites – simply to rid themselves of these pests, but the birds always come back. They are long-distance migrants, constantly seeking out the times and places of plenty. Destroy one flock and there is always another ready to fly in and take its place.

The battle between bird and farmer continues even to this day. A few years ago, the largest known flock of queleas, consisting of more than six million birds, was spotted near Arusha in northern Tanzania. It was estimated that it ate its way through 18 tonnes of grain a day. United Nations aircraft with chemical sprays attempted to destroy the birds but failed to eliminate the vast majority and they went on the rampage elsewhere in East Africa.

In Queensland, Australia, winter flocks of bowerbirds can devastate commercial fruit crops. And in 1985 a serious drought drove hundreds of galahs and other cockatoos from their more usual bushlands into the leafy Wahroonga suburb of Sydney. One delinquent group, behaving like refugees from a Hitchcock movie, took to tearing houses apart. Using their strong beaks and claws, they tore off roof coverings and destroyed wooden eaves and verandah fences. Insurance companies were reported to have refused to reimburse residents for the damage. They claimed the parrot attacks were an 'Act of God'.

In the northern hemisphere, winter flocks of gulls can be an even greater nuisance and a serious danger to human life. They seek out open areas of countryside on which to roost, the all-round view making it easier to spot ground predators. Unfortunately, ideal conditions – ideal, that is, for gulls – are found at airfields. Landings and take-offs to and from the gull roost can present a serious hazard to their more clumsy metal-winged, wide-bodied skymates performing the same manoeuvres.

COMMUNAL ROOSTS

The other great nuisance is the starling. Winter is the time when British cities are invaded by huge numbers of starlings that drop in from the continent of Europe. They have been doing it since 1840, when the first reported starling roost settled down in the city of Newcastle. More recently, several million of them turned Abbey Park in Leicester into little more than an open cesspit. Droppings coated picnic tables, paths, swings and see-saws with a smelly layer of guano. Trees died, local residents complained. The council responded with fire-crackers, playback of alarm calls and a pet fox on a lead. The local human population were disturbed but the starlings were unimpressed.

In Belgium, authorities faced with a similar problem did not pussy-foot around. The cherry crop was threatened and so they called in the military, who placed their faith in some well-placed sticks of dynamite. Three-quarters of a million birds were eliminated in the conflagration, but the birds kept coming back. A decade later saw the starling flock as big and as healthy as ever. Throughout north-western Europe the story is the same.

The rector at St Mary Redcliffe, in the centre of Bristol, doesn't welcome a noisy section of his flock. Every evening he is reminded of the last cleaning bill as the church's exclusive murmuring of starlings flies in from the surrounding countryside and deposits its ammonia-rich and stone-dissolving 'visiting cards' on the turrets, gargoyles and gutters.

Why the birds should come to the church at all is a biological paradox. By arriving at the same place at the same time every day flocks present predators with a predictable, regular and abundant supply of food. The birds themselves must fly out each morning over the same area of countryside that they foraged the day before. Assuming they ate all the food yesterday, they must fly even further today, and so on throughout the year. Competition for food must be fierce, yet they still feed and roost in flocks.

Starling flocks solve the problem by splitting into small foraging parties that explore widely different parts of the countryside each day. The Leicester birds, it was found, fly as much as 15 miles in all directions away from the roost. Dominant birds head for cattle country, feasting on barley in cattle-feed in the morning and late afternoon, and spending the rest of the day searching for leatherjackets. In the evening, the widely separated foraging flocks begin to coalesce. They gather into pre-roost assemblies before heading for the city roost. Then, the whole lot descends on Abbey Park for the night, great swirling clouds of birds acting as a beacon for distant stragglers to see. Sheer weight of numbers causes branches to crack. Foxes, rats and even badgers are waiting below for the casualties to fall down through the canopy. A cherry tree, festooned with noisy birds, once toppled and crushed many of its occupants.

Starlings sometimes travel vast distances each day. A daily round-trip of over 150 miles is not unknown. These large-scale movements each morning gave rise to an intriguing series of discoveries which were made in the 1950s.

During the Second World War, radar operators noticed peculiar rings on their radar screens, which were given the nickname 'angels'. Each morning the rings were seen to appear in one spot and then slowly grow in size until they finally disappeared. It was suspected that 'angels' were the radar images of birds, and after the war, when better radar systems were installed, the radar operators confirmed that this was indeed the case. Careful study of some of the rings showed them to be flocks of starlings leaving their roost sites at dawn and fanning out into the countryside. The rings, though, were not single, but consisted of a series of concentric circles. From this observation, it was found that starlings do not leave the roost in one big rush. Instead the small foraging flocks stagger their exit, each batch leaving three minutes after the previous one, and showing up as concentric rings or 'angels' on the radar screen.

At dusk, the small foraging parties reform into their enormous flocks to roost during the night. The advantages of a large roost appear to outweigh the disadvantages. The mathematics is simple. A bird roosting on its own has a 100 per cent chance of being eaten; two birds 50 per cent, and so on, until a roost of many thousands of birds gives an individual a minuscule chance of being caught napping. A very large and noisy flock will of course actually *attract* predators. But as long as an individual's chances of being eaten are less than if it were living alone, it will continue to live in a flock. And in a flock of thousands of starlings it would need an enormous number of predators to take out the entire flock, and predators never exist in those sorts of numbers. If they did, they would simply eat themselves out of 'house-and-home' and become extinct. Starlings in flocks, therefore, are on to a good thing.

In rural areas, starling flocks can be seen performing their twilight manoeuvres before dropping in to the safety of a reed bed or a stand of trees. But nowadays, with fewer and fewer green sites and more and more built-up areas, starlings have been forced to look for alternatives. In doing so, they have discovered that city life can be much more comfortable. City centres are always a few degrees warmer than the surrounding countryside. Churches and other tall buildings with ledges and window sills provide safe, snug roosting sites.

The distribution of birds throughout the roost is not random. There is competition for the warmest and safest positions, usually the more central places in the roost. The older birds chase out younger birds and take the best sites. Males are dominant over females. The centres of roosts are the exclusive preserve of mature males. Young females are left, quite literally, out in the cold.

Some individuals roost in exactly the same spot each night, while others move around. This distribution of birds within the roost has given rise to a new theory: the less well-fed birds on the outside are there to gain information about food sources from the centrally placed well-fed birds, and in return those well-fed birds are protected from nocturnal predators by the outer shield of less well-off birds.

On cold nights, individuals in the roost huddle closer together. In freezing conditions they can be seen shoulder to shoulder, sometimes forty in a row. In this way, they minimize heat-loss from their inactive bodies. It is particularly important to conserve energy when snow-covered or frosty ground has meant that the day's foraging has been poor. But does the energy conserved in the roost compensate for the energy used in flying to and from the roost site? The calculations have been made for jackdaws and starlings and it seems that it does not. Also, the closer birds are together, the greater the chance of passing on parasites and perhaps disease. In the meantime, nobody knows why starlings – like North American barn swallows, bank swallows, tree swallows and even flying mammals such as long-tailed bats – ignore the science of it all and get into a 'huddle'.

A 'huddle' starts when one bird moves along the perch or ledge and sidles up to its neighbour. This forms the nucleus of the 'huddle'. Other birds land just a few inches either side, facing the same way as the first two, and then shuffle across until they touch. As the birds form up alongside a long line develops.

The most compact 'huddles' are formed by winter wrens in

northern Europe. In warm weather they roost alone, but come the winter they squeeze into any available cavity, such as a squirrel drey, sometimes as many as sixty birds in a single 'huddle'. For tiny wrens to conserve body-heat and survive a harsh winter they must find a warm, well-insulated communal roost. The small golden-crowned kinglet of North America 'huddles' in contact groups in the same way.

Some birds like the appropriately named lovebirds of Africa and the red munia of Pakistan and India do not just 'huddle' at night. They spend part of the day preening each other in very close 'huddles', the characteristic head-nibbling being a means of maintaining peaceful relations in the flock. Waxbill flocks go even further. When one bird starts to preen, all the others follow suit. They do their preening, sleeping, feeding and flying – all in synchrony.

One might think that having found the roost, acquired the best available position, and determined whether a bird should rub shoulders with its neighbour, *that* would be the end of the story. But it is not the case; when the birds go to sleep a whole new set of problems emerge.

DORMITORY SLEEPING

Sleeping birds, even those high on a church tower, are clearly vulnerable to nocturnal predators such as owls. They check for danger by 'peeking'. Every now and again, a sleeping bird will open an eye and 'peek'. And, just as 'looking' rates reduce with flock size during the day, birds in a flock 'peek' less when the roost is bigger.

The study that revealed this remarkable insight into avian nightlife did not involve a researcher perched on a church roof, but was the result of a study of ducks on a Thames-side jetty near Oxford. A predator, such as a cat or a fox, can only eat one duck at a time. Sleeping in a flock, just like feeding in a flock, reduces a bird's chances of being the victim. Ducks closer to the shore, and therefore closer to danger, 'peek' more than those further away. And if several birds are between an individual and the shore it will 'peek' less than if there were no birds in between. Clearly, the birds closer to the shore are more vulnerable and offer some measure of protection for those some distance away. The cat will get one of *them* first.

Not unexpectedly, during the breeding season, male ducks 'peek' significantly more than females. Not only do they have to contend with predators, but they must also watch for rival males who are sneaking in to steal away with the females. As the proportion of females in a flock increases, the 'peeking' rate of males also increases. Males which have paired with a female 'peek' more than bachelor males. They are keen to guard their investment. A third factor might be that male ducks are more brightly coloured than females. They must 'peek' more often because they are more conspicuous to predators. It is, perhaps, relevant that male 'peeking' rates go down after male ducks moult to a dowdy 'eclipse' plumage, when they resemble females, directly after the breeding season.

Herring gulls are the greatest 'peekers'. They will not close their eyes for more than a minute at a time, even though they sleep for five hours a day.

Whatever the reason for 'peeking', sleeping in flocks enables a bird to lower its level of vigilance and, quite literally, get more sleep. Why it should want to sleep so much is not clear, for sleep is a little understood phenomenon. One theory has it that it is a bird's way (and any other animal's, come to that) of remaining still and out of the way when being active might be considered too dangerous or not worth the effort. Whatever the reason, birds vary considerably in the amount of sleep they seem to need. The starling clocks up about forty-five minutes a day, while the smew spends up to thirteen and a half hours a day fast asleep. This great discrepancy between species seems to nullify the theory that sleep is restorative, otherwise most birds would be sleeping for about the same amount of time. There are some clues, however. When the days get longer in spring, some birds sleep less. It seems to be worth getting up to forage or hunt when food availability increases. Also, if the risk of predation is greater, then it is better to be awake and alert.

There is, however, another good reason to roost in a flock. Some birds returning each evening will have eaten well, others less so. If the hungry birds follow the well-fed birds in the morning, they will find the better food sources. The starling roost, like the daytime sparrow congregation and the seabird colony, is an information centre. The less well-off copy the well-to-do and maybe do better. This could explain why subordinates, usually juvenile birds, bother to come to roosts at all. After all, they are left out in the cold and are the first to be taken by predators. Perhaps by staying with the roost they gain information from the older, more experienced birds about the best places to find a meal. The benefits outweigh the risks. This might also explain why daytime foraging flocks increase in size when a source of food is found. The new arrivals are the juveniles that observed the successful adults in the roost the night before, and then followed them to the feeding sites the following day. A study of swallow flocks in Denmark has shown that this is, indeed, the case. It also showed that undernourished youngsters did not follow well-fed juveniles; they are not yet to be trusted. Mature birds are a more reliable source of information.

The same is true of the black vultures of North Carolina. A large, dead carcass, found on a snowy winter's day, is preserved in its natural deep-freeze and provides another meal the following morning. On the evening of the first day, the successful scavengers, returning with full tummies and a supercilious manner, are observed by the less-successful birds. On day two, those birds in the know fly back to their food source and are followed by the rest of the roost. Significantly, the older, wiser birds are early risers and start out for the food first. The juveniles and younger adults arrive later and fight over the leftovers. In the winter, when the weather is bad, it is advantageous for black vultures to roost in flocks. Again, the flock becomes the information centre.

This is further illustrated by two similar species of African kestrels. The common kestrel has its own hunting area where it catches small rodents. The lesser kestrel forms flocks which explore a much larger area searching out concentrations of insects. The common kestrel roosts alone, lesser kestrels get together. Faced with such a scattered food source, lesser kestrels benefit from a little help from their friends. Information exchanged at the roost assists each kestrel to find the best places to explore during the next day.

Some normally solitary birds will form communal roosts, and gain all the advantages the roost can provide, when times are hard. Robins, for example, have been known to abandon their territories and roost together during the harshest winters. Others, like some waders and gulls, forage alone during the day and head back to a communal roost at night. Roost sites can vary – gulls foraging on Bristol rubbish tips, for example, head for islands in the Severn Estuary; terns and pelicans seek the safety of sandbars and small islands, separated from ground-living predators by a reassuring stretch of water; ducks dispense with terra firma altogether and roost on the water itself.

CHORUS LINES

So, roosting in large flocks enables older birds to gain protection and younger birds to obtain information. One of the favourite roosts for sleeping, 'peeking', information-seeking starlings has been under the canopy at Bristol's Temple Meads railway station. Every evening, passers-by are enthralled by the huge flock wheeling and surging, in an ever-changing cloud, across the darkening sky. A local peregrine has a field day. And each morning, commuters waiting for the 8.05 to Paddington are entertained by the noisy, chattering flock as it prepares to leave. At an invisible signal the flock is suddenly silent and then, as if energized by the flick of a switch, one group of birds streams from the station and away into the country. After more chattering, the flock goes silent once more and another batch makes its exit. This behaviour continues until all the birds have left. On the platform below, and on the ledges of nearby St Mary Redcliffe, the legacy of the night's roost is all that remains. In the evening, much to the chagrin of the Station Master and the Rector, they all return.

During late afternoon, when the light is still good, small groups of starlings arrive from fields, gardens and parks up to 20 miles away and gather at pre-roost feeding sites about 3 miles from the main roost. Here they ensure that their gizzards are filled for the long night ahead. As the flocks fly overhead, others join them until flocks containing millions of birds start to form. Eventually they all move towards and circle the roost site, amalgamating into even larger flocks until a gigantic amoeba-like swarm flies nervously to and fro, gathering ever more birds as it goes. The entire company flies as one, swooping down, dropping off the first birds as they fly past the roost, and then surging upwards again into the dusk.

But how do they keep together and not collide? How do they co-ordinate the twists and turns that occur with such rapidity that it is difficult to imagine how normal communication between individuals can occur? Does one 'flight leader' issue commands that are followed by the rest of the birds? Could a message spread through the flock by some undiscovered electromagnetic signal or by extra-sensory perception?

The answer, it seems, is none of those things. A flock of flying birds behaves like a high-kicking chorus line. One bird banks into the flock and its immediate neighbours turn with it. The change of direction is passed from bird to bird, slowly at first and then with increasing rapidity, until all the birds have completed the manoeuvre.

The birds next to the 'initiator' respond slowly because they rely only on their normal reaction times. Birds further away see the approaching wave of movement and can time their response to coincide with its arrival at their position in the flock. By anticipating the manoeuvre, they can change direction at up to three times the speed of their normal visual reaction time. In a flock of dunlin, for example, birds close to the 'initiator' take about 67 milliseconds to respond, while those at the end of the 'chorus-line' take only 15 milliseconds.

A manoeuvre will only take place when a bird, any bird, moves *into* the flock. A change of direction to the left, for instance, is initiated by birds on the right of the flock. Those changing direction *out* of the group are ignored. This, it is thought, is a simple response to predation. Birds of prey tend to pick off individuals that have become separated. To avoid being left out in the open and vulnerable to attack, birds follow an 'initiator' into the body of the flock and in doing so avoid any potentially fatal delay from indecision.

The large-scale movements of the flock also serve to confuse a predator. A bird of prey must be careful not to get caught up with the flock. A mid-air collision could be disastrous both for prey and predator. A tightly wheeling formation can deter an attack. The tighter the flock, the safer each bird will be, and the greater is the need to be closer to its centre – hence the 'chorus-line' effect. Sometimes, though, the 'chorus' splits into two, each part flying either side of the predator and doubling the confusion.

Flocks with a mission tend to be compact and regimented. Starlings at dusk are intent on reaching the safety of their roosting site. Lapwings in loose, scrappy flocks have no particular purpose; those in tight groups are either intent on covering long distances during migration or are preparing to settle to feed or roost. They circle a potential landing site in close formation, first checking for predators, before gliding gently down or side-slipping and dropping out of the sky.

MIXED FLOCKS

Most of these spectacular flying displays are made by flocks containing birds of the same species, but that is not always the case.

In the southern USA, huge mixed flocks of red-winged blackbirds, introduced European starlings, grackles and cowbirds scour the countryside for cultivated fields of corn and other crops. Their evening roosts contain so many birds that whole forests are destroyed by the droppings and an area can be declared unfit for human habitation. Dangerous bacteria grow in the thick carpet of guano. Breathing the spore-filled air can be dangerous and, for some people, fatal. The winter flocks have been calculated to contain over 50 million birds.

A mixed-species flock gains all the benefits of one containing birds of the same species, but with an extra advantage – different bird species exploit different sources of food. There is less competition. Interestingly, the number of birds in a mixed flock decreases as the amount of available food increases. It is a further demonstration that flocking behaviour is closely allied, not only to predator avoidance, but also to feeding efficiency. The less food there is, the greater the need for birds to get together to find it.

In the tropical forests of South America, mixed flocks of insect-eaters and omnivores (those that take advantage of what is available whether it is fruit, nuts, carrion or insects) work their way through the dense foliage, moving at about 0.2 miles per hour. Each species has its own feeding station. There are those in the top of the canopy, some in the lower tree levels, birds in the bushes and still others on the ground. One species heads the battalion – often an antbird. These entrepreneurial birds watch for army ants. When the columns of ants are about to move away from their bivouacs on the forest floor, the antbirds take up stations ahead of the army, ready to intercept escaping insects. There is competition for the best feeding sites at the head of the column, and so a hierarchy of antbirds is established. Large birds, such as the ocellated antbird, take the prime positions just ahead of the ants. The smaller ones, such as the spotted antbird, spread out on either side. In the trees above and in the bushes nearby, the rest of the mixed flock follow along behind picking off the leftovers or simply going about their business higher in the forest canopy.

In another part of the Amazon, two other mixed flock leaders have taken unfair advantage of such a congregation. Birds are constantly on the lookout for predators. Exploit that nervousness and a bird can jump the food queue and make off with the choicest morsels. In the Amazon forests of Peru, the white-winged shrike tanager and bluish-slate antshrike do just that.

These two birds, like the other antbirds, lead mixed flocks of tropical forest birds; indeed, the flocks are thought to contain the greatest mixture of bird species in a single flock – forty or more individuals representing twenty to thirty species (some have been seen with as many as seventy separate species).

Each species has its place in the forest and its own search and capture method. Antwrens and vireos, for example, hop along branches and pick off crickets, spiders and caterpillars found on the tops of leaves. Woodcreepers and ovenbirds climb tree trunks, probing into cracks and crannies for grubs and other insects that hide behind loose bark during the day. Jacamars fly out and catch fast-flying dragonflies and wasps. Nunbirds pounce on insects flying away in the general disturbance. Some birds prefer the treetops, others the lower parts of the forest.

The flock assembles each morning around a core of five to ten pairs of birds. The core is permanent, the rest fly from flock to flock in search of the best pickings. At four-thirty in the afternoon the visitors leave and the core flock settles down to bathing and preening. Although the core flock tolerates the arrival of all the other birds each day, it will strongly defend a territory against others of its own kind. During the day, the visitors will join in too. If two mixed flocks meet at a territorial boundary they will sing 'keep out' warnings at each other, each species singing at its opposite number in the opposing flock. Flocks foraging in the lower parts of the forest will even take things a little further and come to blows.

The shrike tanager is flock leader in the forest canopy, while the antshrike heads those flocks combing the understory. Both birds keep their respective flocks together by constantly calling. But they are not only flock leaders. They are also the sentinels – they watch for danger. The forest is the hunting place for many species of bird-eating forest hawks. One reason the other birds tag along is that these two birds offer some measure of protection. The shrike tanager and the antshrike are first to spot predators and their loud, screeching, high-pitched alarm calls provide ample warning for the rest of the flock. One raucous squawk and they freeze, jump, or race for cover. These two birds, though, have capitalized on their privileged position.

As the flock moves through the forest, flying insects are flushed from the foliage. Katydids (New World grasshoppers), which escape the bird predators by dropping to the ground, are a favourite food. As they go into their escape routine there is a mad scramble behind as the birds jostle for the prey. The fastest and most aerobatic birds reach the prey ahead of the rest, and the two sentinels have learned a simple trick to make sure that it's they who get there first.

When an insect flies out and one of the flock is about to pounce, a sentinel gives the alarm call. But there is no predator about. The bird simply calls 'wolf!' The other birds hesitate momentarily and the sentinel grabs the food.

For some inexplicable reason the other birds seem not to have realized they are being cheated. But then, being deceived is a small price to pay for the safety normally conferred on the flock by the issue of genuine alarm calls. It is sensible for the rest of the flock to freeze or take cover and lose one meal rather than to risk not responding and be caught in the open when it is the real thing.

On the heathlands of Europe, another sentinel – the stonechat – is not a deceiver. It is a paragon of avian etiquette and the life-saver of mixed flocks of meadow pipits, willow warblers, reed buntings and yellowhammers. They all forage together and stay close to the stonechat.

The stonechat feeds by perching on a high vantage point and grabbing insects rising in the warm air or by sitting on a lower perch and pouncing on those foolish enough to scamper across the ground. On either perch, the stonechat not only spots its own prey, but is in the best position to see other, larger, passerine-eating predators. Its 'chack' alarm call, accompanied by frantic wing flicking, not only alerts baby stonechats to stay silent in the nest, but also warns all the other small birds in the area of impending danger.

In the woodlands of the eastern USA, Carolina chickadees feed in the trees and bushes. Following them are ground-feeding eastern bluebirds, dark-eyed juncos and chipping sparrows. The elevated position of the chickadees means that they spot predators first, and when they give an alarm call all four species of birds dive for cover.

DANGER

Most birds in flocks have ways in which to alert flock members of impending doom. Alarm calls are an obvious way, but some birds reinforce the danger signal by visual means. Lapwings, for example, have a white flash under the wings and tail, particularly visible when the birds forage in the gloom of dawn or dusk, or at night when lapwings feed under a full moon.

Alarm calls (see pages 153–7) can also rally small birds and bring them on the offensive, a behaviour known as 'mobbing'. Owls are mobbed by thrushes and finches, and buzzards are mobbed by crows. By gathering into a group, the combined efforts of the less-powerful birds can intimidate a predator to such an extent that it will reluctantly leave the area. And in the same way as flocking during foraging and communal roosting acts as an information centre, the noisy mob provides less-experienced juvenile birds with information about potential predators by alerting them to the danger. They can observe, from close quarters, the hunting behaviour of the predator and, perhaps, learn how best to avoid being the prey.

Owls seem to attract the largest mobs. As soon as one appears, blackbirds, robins, chaffinches and tits will change their high-pitched, non-locatable alarm calls to raucous rattles or 'ticks' that rally all the other small birds in the area (see pages 157–9). The mob will dive-bomb, swoop and screech until the owl flies on. Cock blackbirds will leave their territories and combine their efforts in order to see it off, the only drawback being that they all fight like fury amongst themselves after the threat has passed.

There is, however, a danger that the predator might turn on the mob and seize one of its members. The flock must approach close enough to harass the predator but stay far enough away not to be caught. A large mob can keep its distance. The noise and movement of many birds, such as a flock of cliff swallows, is probably sufficient to scare off the threat. They present a formidable obstacle to a predator simply by milling about and calling nearby. A bird on its own or in a small flock, such as a barn swallow, must take more risks, diving close to the predator in order to create the greatest nuisance.

The pied flycatcher has a two-phase defence system to deter predators. In response to birds, such as great spotted woodpeckers, likely to threaten eggs and nestlings, flycatchers carry out close attacks, known as 'snarling'. Mobbing from a distance is reserved for sparrowhawks and other predators dangerous to adult birds.

Before the breeding season begins, mobbing is at a low level. It increases when the eggs are laid and when the young hatch, reaching a peak just before fledging. If a bird loses its brood, mobbing is reduced. Unmated birds expose themselves much less to threatening predators than do mated pairs, suggesting that mobbing behaviour – at least in this species – has developed to protect offspring even though there is some risk to the parents.

Curiously, the flycatchers' mobbing response is reduced if the birds become habituated to the predator. Experiments were carried out with stuffed owls, and if the model was always flown in from the same direction the flycatchers eventually ignored it. The mobbing response was only evoked if the predator was brought in from different directions.

Sometimes, mobbing birds are caught out. If one is separated from the rest it is likely that the predator will catch it. Merlins, hobbies, buzzards and kestrels have been seen to take advantage of this situation. A buzzard, for example, can roll over while in flight and grab a bird dive-bombing it from above.

And what if a bird *is* caught? What should it do? Starlings scream. But why? What are the benefits?

A sudden loud noise might startle a predator into letting its captive go. Screams might alert the rest of the flock and in an altruistic way warn them to escape. Likewise, a scream might rally a flock to mob the predator. There is, however, another theory.

If a small bird, like a starling, shouts as loud as it can, it will attract other predators. A gaggle of predators are likely to squabble over the meal and the victim has a chance, albeit a slender one, of escape.

SUCCESSFUL INVADERS

The starling, one way and another, is a very successful bird. Indeed, it is thought to be *the* most successful in the world with a global population in excess of 600 million. In the USA at the turn of the century, a misguided naturalist released 100 birds into New York's Central Park. Today, there are over 200 million starlings living right across North America. By living in a flock, the starling is able to forage, unlike the secretive solitary robin, out in the open, and has been quick to follow the agricultural endeavours of the human race across many continents. Wherever land is tilled, the starling is there to exploit the many beneficial insects uncovered by the plough and the pest ones attracted by Man's unnatural monocultured crops. Its ability to probe and prise apart the soil means that it can find and extract food that is inaccessible to many other birds. In addition, the structure of its eye enables it to search the ground for food while, at the same time, scanning the sky for predators.

A bird that is slowly taking over the British countryside is the magpie. Although it is usually seen in ones and twos, and sometimes in threes and fours, there are occasions when up to 100 might come together in a loose, squabbling flock. At one time naturalists thought these magpie flocks were involved in some kind of courtship ritual and they became known as 'marriage meetings', but now, thanks to observations by researchers at the University of Sheffield, we know differently.

In late winter and early spring flocks of agitated birds are seen chasing and calling, and occasionally fighting. Sometimes this occurs when one of a resident pair dies and a territory is only occupied by the survivor. At other times, a congregation begins to gather when a solitary male or an unmated pair drops into another pair's territory. Naturally, the residents challenge the visitors and the subsequent row encourages other magpies to fly in. Eventually, the intruders are seen off, but sometimes they return time and time again, perhaps perceiving a weakness in the resident's defences, until they carve out a bit of their own territory. Each time there is an altercation, the crowd of noisy magpies gathers; why it should do so is still a mystery.

FLOCKING MYSTERIES

Studies of flocking behaviour in birds have come a long way since those early naturalists marvelled at the clouds of passenger pigeons and eskimo curlews. But even so, there are still mysteries – the times when birds behave in ways for which we have no explanation and can only guess at what has gone on.

In a seventeenth-century pamphlet stored in the British Library, there is an account of a fierce and bloody battle that was fought in the city of Cork, on the southern coast of Ireland. It raged for two days in mid-October 1621. There were thousands of casualties as two great armies, one coming from the east of the city and the other from the west, clashed and ripped each other apart. But the soldiers were not people, they were starlings.

Over a period of several days, two huge flocks of starlings were seen to group on either side of Cork. When foraging for food, birds from neither flock crossed an invisible frontier between the two camps. Local city folk noticed that they were making strange calls.

Occasionally, small groups of birds from either side would fly, like reconnaissance patrols, between the two armies – hovering, chattering and observing before returning to their own lines.

At nine o'clock on the morning of 12 October, both flocks rose into a clear sky and began to fight. Bodies rained down on the city. Some birds had broken wings, legs or necks; others had their eyes pecked out. Pairs of birds, locked in combat – some with one adversary's beak thrust into the other's breast – fluttered into the streets. By late evening on the second day the battle was over and the birds disappeared. The next day there was not a bird to be seen.

Rivalry between bird flocks is not only confined to the realms of cryptozoology, for there have been well-documented reports of flocks fighting in South American forests. During the southern winter, resident tropical flycatchers are joined by migrants from Patagonia, and the resulting mixed flocks, containing up to thirty different species, vigorously defend large territories against rival flocks.

The historical archives reveal other incredible tales. In 1736, two flocks of unidentified birds collided over the River Samock, near Preston in Lancashire. A passing farmer was able to collect 180 birds and sell them at the Preston market.

In 1883, three flocks of ravens, each more than a hundred strong and containing both male and female birds, flew at each other over the German village of Ginnheim. The birds pecked at heads and eyes with such force that more than fifty birds fell dead from the sky. A local gardener called at the offices of the *Frankfurt Journal*, told of the battle, and presented the astonished journalists with a large chest filled with dead ravens.

Reports of birds falling from the sky are not uncommon to this day. 'Wrecks' of wayward seabirds, such as little auks, are often the result of freak weather conditions. Migrating birds are blown off course and can end up hungry and exhausted many miles from their intended destination. Many die.

There are also other mysteries. In April 1964, Texans living close to Lake Waco and Cransfill Gap were 'rained' upon by dead birds. Two separate flocks of giant white pelicans crashed to earth at the two sites, located some 40 miles apart, on the same day. The weather was not to blame. There were no hurricanes, tornadoes or any other violent storms. The birds just fell out of the sky, and there was no obvious explanation for the deaths.

In 1971, over 500 thrushes and warblers crashed through windows and into the sides of buildings for three days at Prince Rupert in British Columbia, Canada. At an East Shilton housing estate in Leicestershire, in 1976, dead birds dropped out of the sky, not just for a few days, but over a period of nine months. And perhaps most peculiar of all is the case of 105 dead geese that fell throughout Norfolk, England, in 1978 after an unusually violent storm. Experts said they had 'died of fright'.

More recently, in November 1985, scores of birds were reported to have crashed into houses at Zabljak, a town high in the mountains of Montenegro. Twenty-two birds drowned when they flew in through an open window and ended up in the bathtub with Micun Karadzic, a local resident.

A couple of years earlier, in Sweden, a plausible explanation for some of these mysterious bird deaths was discovered. The birds in question were waxwings, and during a mild winter they went on a feeding spree on rowan berries. Normally the birds would have come to no harm, but the warm weather caused the berries to ferment. The birds, quite literally, were drunk on the alcohol. They took to smashing into plate glass windows and colliding with the sides of buildings. Some stood in a drunken stupor or tottered about in the middle of the road where they were run down by passing cars. These normally very shy birds became quite uninhibited.

But perhaps one of the greatest bird flock mysteries of all is the story of the vultures of Gettysburg. For over a hundred years, more than 900 black vultures and turkey vultures have gathered amongst the monuments, cannons and grapevines at the Gettysburg National Military Park in Pennsylvania. The first birds appeared, so it is written, on 1 July 1863. It was the last day of a mighty battle in which 50,000 men and thousands of horses were killed. The men were buried but the horses, strewn across the battlefield, were left. The vultures were presented with a superabundance of carrion; to them went the spoils of war. Most likely they stayed the winter and scavenged on the frozen carcasses. The following year they returned, and then every year ever since – macabre sentinels of death.

3

ACROSS THE WORLD

Lancelot didn't arrive. Anxious eyes scanned the mild November skies above Gloucestershire but Lancelot wasn't there. After twenty-three years of travel between the west of England and Siberia and flying a total of 130,000 miles, Lancelot was missing, presumed dead.

Lancelot was a Bewick's swan. Each year, during the short and frantic Arctic summer on the West Siberian Plain, he and his long-time mate Elaine had less than 130 ice-free days in which to court, mate, nest, incubate eggs and rear chicks on the grassy tundra – an inhospitable place sodden with meltwater, pockmarked by ponds and shallow lakes, and infested with blackflies and mosquitoes.

By September, or October at the latest, they and their family – for the youngsters remain with the parents for the first autumn and winter – were forced to flee the harsh northern winter and migrate to where the winter is less severe; they joined 2,500 other Bewick's that make for Britain and Ireland each winter. Flying most of the way at a height of about 2,700 metres, they took the same route each year: first along the White Sea coast, and then overland via Lake Ladoga to the Gulf of Finland. By mid-October they were ready to cross the Baltic from northern Estonia to Gotland and southern Sweden, and then they travelled onwards across the southern part of the North Sea and southern Britain to the Rushy Pen at Slimbridge in Gloucestershire, arriving in November. But in 1986 Elaine had arrived alone. Lancelot didn't make a twenty-fourth visit.

Swans and geese are remarkable travellers, and many take advantage of the enormous tracts of tundra that offer breeding birds unlimited space, a sudden abundance of food and few predators. But there are risks. In high latitudes the weather can change in an instant. Spring can be seized unexpectedly in the grip of a wintry storm, causing huge numbers of deaths amongst newly hatched chicks. Life cycles must be resilient enough for there to be occasional years in which an entire population might not breed at all.

And birds must be strong and powerful flyers to cover the vast distances, sometimes over the wildest of seas. In order to make their journeys they take advantage of prevailing winds near the ground and air movements at higher levels in the atmosphere. Swans and geese are among the highest flyers. Many species fly regularly at over 6,000 metres in order to clear mountain ranges. West Greenland and Canadian white-fronted and brent geese must fly up to 3,500 metres to cross the Greenland ice-cap. Others fly high to exploit jet streams.

A group of thirty whooper swans, returning to western Scotland from Iceland, were observed from an aircraft over the Inner Hebrides on 9 December 1967. Both aircraft and swans were flying at 8,230 metres. An air traffic controller in Northern Ireland spotted the birds on his radar screen and confirmed not only their amazing height above sea level, but also their speed: they were flying at a ground speed of 86 mph. The birds took advantage of the wind and weather conditions prevailing at the time. It is thought the flock took off from Iceland at dawn in a ridge of high pressure. They rapidly gained altitude and rode with a fast-flowing jet stream in the lower stratosphere, making the journey to the Scottish west coast in just seven hours.

Even more remarkable was the temperature in which these birds

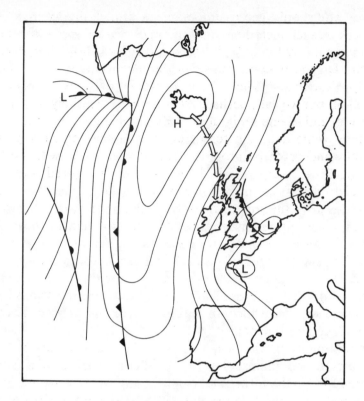

The arrows show the probable track of a flock of whooper swans which, in December 1967, took advantage of a fast-flowing northerly jet stream. The birds started in Iceland on a ridge of high pressure and were seen flying at 8,200 metres over the Inner Hebrides in a temperature estimated to be –48°C. They took just seven hours to fly from Iceland to Northern Ireland.

were flying. It was estimated to be less than −48°C. With the danger of overheating from the continuous action of the flight muscles on a long journey, high flying could be a strategy for keeping cool. Heat can be lost from under the wings or through the mouth during breathing (see page 34).

The air is thinner at higher altitudes, so there is less resistance during flight; a bird can fly faster but without using more energy. Decreased oxygen levels are not a problem because birds are able to make use of the oxygen in their blood more efficiently than other animals. Their only concern is high cloud, for a bird entering a section of sky containing water vapour is in danger of having its wings ice up. Flocks, therefore, will fly over or under clouds.

But why should geese and swans, such as Lancelot and Elaine, embark on such incredible journeys in the first place? What benefits do they gain by flying so far to spend such a short time in the far north? Do the benefits outweigh the inconvenience of a long and perilous excursion? There is, of course, no definitive answer to the question, but we can, perhaps, speculate on the likely way in which Lancelot and Elaine's migration story unfolded.

Many years ago, the temperate winter feeding sites in north-western and central Europe became overcrowded with birds and feeding flocks were attacked by all manner of predators. Man's arrival from Africa might have been the last straw. Some birds, undeterred by the mayhem, simply upped and went, looking for pastures new. Others were pushed. And although Bewick's swans gather in huge flocks during the winter, they are very territorial when it comes to breeding; they need space, and lots of it.

And so, at the end of the last Ice Age, when gradually larger tracts of land became available for colonization, the swans headed north and east. First, they discovered ample living space. There was land enough for one pair of birds to occupy 2,000 hectares of tundra without upsetting the neighbours. Then, they discovered food. These flat, wet plains of western Siberia in spring and summer offered food in the form of tubers, rhizomes, leaves and grass, and it was constantly available throughout the short summer. Continuous daylight allowed cygnets to feed round the clock, and grow faster and fledge earlier than their southern relatives. Thirdly, the northern climate and a well-spaced population of breeding birds reduced the threat from parasites and diseases. And fourthly, there was little disturbance, save the occasional opportunistic Arctic fox (and it was driven away by the male bird while the female led her cygnets to safety at the water's edge). Faced with such favourable conditions, the swans settled and bred; but they couldn't stay. The season was brief, and they were forced south by the inclement weather. The preferred travel option was to return to the ancestral home in north-western Europe.

But even there, some swans found that conditions were not to their liking and they travelled that extra bit further, 'leap-frogging' away from mainland Europe in search of new, less-crowded sites to put down and sit out the winter. Bewick's swans ventured into Britain as recently as the 1930s and the birds at Slimbridge have only found Severn-side conditions suitable since after the war. A small man-made lake and supplementary feeding can prove to be irresistible. Today's population, including Elaine and the late Lancelot, are most likely the offspring of a band of revolutionary swans that stopped off on the way to Ireland. Irish and British birds traditionally swap sites throughout the winter as weather conditions change, and some birds discovered a free hand-out of grain at Slimbridge and made it their main base.

There is, of course, an alternative explanation. The influences on Bewick's swan migration could have been the other way round. Climatic conditions in Siberia before the Ice Age were more favourable than today. During the warm interglacial period, mammoths and cave bears roamed the land and maybe Bewick's swans lived there the year round too. Mammoths and swans were forced south by the spreading ice sheet during the glacial period. When the glaciers receded, the mammoths had been exterminated by early man and the birds gradually found their way back to the traditional home sites to breed; but still had to return south to their glacial and post-glacial sites to wait out the harsh winters.

There is, however, an interesting postscript to the Bewick's story. Bewick's swans mate for life and pairs of birds always travel between the same winter and breeding sites. Young birds fly with the family. What then happens when a young bird takes its first mate or an older bird loses its partner and takes another mate? As pairing generally takes place at the breeding sites, to which sites do they fly in the autumn? Does the pair favour the male's traditional wintering ground or that of the female?

On the breeding grounds the male declares the decision to be his by performing a pre-flight display. He pushes his head backwards and forwards and gives a specific contact call. In effect, he is encouraging his partner to fly the long journey at roughly the same time as he does. This has important implications for the female at their destination.

Single females tend to arrive after the males and therefore miss out on the best feeding and roosting sites. The female's decision-making partner ensures that she is well placed in the hierarchy and will have access to the best sites. But the males do not have everything their own way. In the spring the tables are turned, and it is the female swans who decide when to leave for Siberia.

STAY OR GO?

The Ice Ages have not been the only influence on the evolution of migration. They may have shaped migration routes in the northern hemisphere, but many others birds in other parts of the world have set out on long migrations unaffected by the comings and goings of the ice sheets. Geological movements of the earth's crust may have isolated, over millions of years, feeding and breeding sites. Opportunities may have arisen when geological events have created conditions favourable to nesting at one site and feeding at another. In the Great Rift Valley of Africa, for example, lesser and greater flamingos build their nests on islands in soda lakes, the caustic water preventing predators – including man – from approaching. But they must fly to other lakes in order to feed.

Food, though, is often the governing factor determining whether a bird should stay or go. Overcrowding, shortage of food and over-predation may force birds to seek food and nest sites elsewhere. As each successive site fills, birds must travel even further to find space. By a process of 'leap-frogging' – as one nest site becomes overcrowded or less interesting for some other reason, birds pass over to the next vacant site – it would not take long, on a geological timescale, for a species to find itself far from its original home. Birds making the journey gain advantages over those staying behind. The 'stayers', with less food, are less likely to survive. The 'goers', with untapped food supplies, more space in which to nest and search for food, and in areas where the local predators will not have caught up in evolutionary terms with the new supply of prey, are more likely to thrive and multiply. Eventually the 'goers' out-breed the 'stayers', and, when the species shows a regular to-and-fro movement between the new and old sites, it changes from being a resident to being a migrant.

The change from resident to migrant can sometimes show in a bird's shape and form. The common wheatear is a migrant, flying each year between Eurasia and Africa, but the subspecies found in Somalia is sedentary. The two birds are roughly the same shape and size, adapted to life in semi-deserts and stony hillsides, except that the migrant has substantially longer and more pointed wings than the resident. The primary feathers of the migrant extend twice as far beyond the secondaries as do those of the sedentary bird – an adaptation that allows the wheatear to engage in some remarkable feats of migration.

After the Ice Age, the wheatear headed first into north-west Europe for the summer, some birds reaching as far north and west as Greenland. Yet they still return to the Sahel to spend the winter. Other populations began to colonize sites to the east and today some birds fly as far as Alaska. Each autumn they return to Africa, but in doing so must traverse the entire continent of Asia. It means that these birds spend at least eight months of the year migrating to and from their winter and summer sites.

This adaptation of the wing length is also seen to great effect in the twenty-five known races of rufous-collared sparrows living in Central and South America. Most are residents and have stumpy, rounded wings. Of the remaining birds, one lives in the rarefied air of the High Andes and another is a long-distance migrant; both have long, pointed, more efficient wings.

The travel plans of some birds are not firm, but vary depending on food availability. This can be regular or irregular, and might represent the early stages of a species changing from resident to migrant.

European blackbirds, for example, show inconsistencies in their migration plans. Those in northern central Europe regularly head south to Spain, France and North Africa, but most of the blackbirds in southern central Europe do not take a winter break. Instead, they stay on their breeding grounds throughout the winter. Whether to stay or whether to go is determined by food availability and the risk of starvation. Cold is not so much a problem. When the temperature drops and fat reserves are reduced, a blackbird reduces energy demands by dropping its own body temperature slightly from 41°C to 39°C. It fluffs up its feathers to increase insulation and forms itself into a fluffy ball, which reduces the ratio between surface area and volume, thus reducing further loss of energy. Taking these measures the bird can survive temperatures as low as −30°C, and as long as sufficient food is available and the winter is not too long and too harsh the non-migratory blackbird is first in line for territories and mates the following spring. On the other hand, if the winter is bad, the stay-at-homes die and those birds that did fly south are the only ones to survive and breed.

Interestingly, something not dissimilar is happening to some of the western European populations of lesser black-backed gulls. In the recent past, birds breeding in Britain overwintered in Spain and north-west Africa, but nowadays the birds are remaining in Britain or at the most travelling to northern France.

The mass movements of northern owls and birds of prey are influenced by the availability of small rodents, such as lemmings and voles, and by larger animals, such as the snowshoe hare. Populations of rodents have peaks and troughs in a four-year cycle. So every four years there is a superabundance of voles, enough to sustain the predators during the winter months. In good vole years, rough-legged buzzards and snowy owls, both feeding on rodents, stay in the snowy north during winter, but in lean years they move south.

Similarly, snowshoe hare populations peak every eleven years. So goshawks and horned owls, which prey upon hares, remain in the north every ten to eleven years; but for the rest of the cycle they head south in the autumn in search of alternative food.

Crossbills are less regular. They normally live the year round in the coniferous forests of the northern hemisphere. They feed exclusively on conifer seeds and are totally dependent on the year's crop. If the eating is good the birds stay put, but if the crop fails millions of birds 'irrupt' to other regions. From 1800 to 1965, for example, crossbills 'irrupted' sixty-seven times into south-western Europe. The movement is not considered by some scientists to be a true migration, for the birds do not make the journey every year. Sometimes they travel in successive years, while at other times there may be eleven years between 'irruptions'. Distances vary, but individuals have been known to fly all the way to south-western Spain, some 2,484 miles from their normal breeding sites in Scandinavian forests. Some travel so far, so it is said, that they are unable to find their way back. Others are unsuccessful in chancing upon alternative sources of pine cones. As a consequence the mass movements were once known as 'death-wanderings'. A few birds are lucky: they find rich pickings and stay. They may breed for three or four seasons before the crop is exhausted and they return once more to the north.

'Irruptions' tend to follow particularly good breeding seasons and the mass exodus is usually made by mainly juvenile birds. The reverse is true for some genuine migrants, for not all birds of a migrating species actually migrate. Youngsters will make the first journey away from the nesting sites to the wintering grounds but those not intending to breed during the next season stay behind or travel only part of the way the following spring. For the rest, the benefits of the energy gained from a superabundance of food in the summer breeding grounds outweigh the energy consumed on the long flight, and birds are better able to breed successfully.

LEGACY OF THE ICE

Glaciation in the northern hemisphere disrupted the lives of many birds and forced some to adopt what at first seem to be totally illogical migration routes but, in fact, reveal the ways in which traditional pathways have been extended as the glaciers receded and population pressures forced birds to seek increasingly distant breeding sites.

The pectoral sandpiper, for instance, breeds in large numbers along the arctic coasts of North America and has extended its summer range westwards across the Bering Strait, into Russia as far as the Taymyr Pensinsular. But this wayward population does not take the direct route south across Asia each autumn and neither does it hug the Pacific coast via Kamchatka, through Manchuria to south-east Asia as other east Siberian migrants might do. Instead, these birds follow the Russian arctic coast east, cross over the Bering Strait to Alaska, join the North American population, and *then* fly south all the way to the southern half of South America, not deviating from the traditional route even though there are plenty of easier options available for gaining access to suitable winter quarters.

Perhaps even more remarkable is the flight path of the migrating arctic warbler. The original population of this small olive-green bird, about the size of a wood warbler (13 centimetres long) but with a pale front, white wing bars and pale legs, lived in birch and conifer forests in north-eastern Siberia. It extended its summer range in two directions: some birds went east to Alaska while others flew as far west as Norway (today they arrive as regular as clockwork between 18 and 25 June).

But, come the autumn, the Alaskan birds do not follow other North American birds south along the Pacific coast, and the Norwegian birds do not head off towards the Mediterranean and the sunnier climes of Africa with the rest of the European migrants. Both populations head back towards their ancestral summer home, join up with Siberian birds and overwinter in south-east Asia, in places like Indonesia, Malaysia, the Philippines and north-west New Guinea. The Norwegian birds faced with a 7,763-mile journey to the Malay archipelago, set off before many of the other migrants, the chicks leaving the nest in early August and following their parents south and east not long afterwards. Indeed, this race of arctic warbler flies so far across the world that it is thought that if it had to travel any further it would not have time to breed at all.

Interestingly, the summer range of the willow warbler of north-west Europe and Siberia overlaps with that of the Siberian–Scandinavian populations of the arctic warbler. But, in the autumn and winter the two species are completely segregated. Willow warblers go exclusively to Africa south of the Sahara, and the arctic warblers to south-east Asia. It is thought they evolved from the same ancestral stock but that at some point during a glacial period an eastern population became isolated from a western group by the advancing ice sheet. The western warblers were forced into Africa and the eastern ones to south-east Asia. When the ice retreated, the birds returned to the north but were separated geographically by the vast Asian continent and eventually evolved into two distinct species. Today birds from each of the two groups are reunited each summer in Siberia's northern forests (although they do not inter-breed), but each autumn they separate once more to follow their own paths south.

THE JOURNEYS

The main pathways of bird migration can be split into three major systems: 1. Eurasia to and from Africa; 2. North America to and from Central and South America; 3. north-eastern Asia to and from south-eastern Asia and Australia. By far the most studied system is that between Europe and Africa where over 60 million birds have been ringed and over a million have been recovered. Such intense studies have even allowed researchers to estimate that over 5 billion birds migrate between the continents each year.

But why should all these birds from the tropics be on the move at all? Surely conditions in Africa are conducive to successful breeding and rearing; indeed, many species of birds live there all the year round. Why then should those tiny migrants, such as swallows, swifts and warblers, that reach northern Europe each spring from Africa and return there once again in the autumn, set out on such arduous journeys? The likely answer is that these birds originated from populations in Africa and that competition for food – as with the swans and geese in the Arctic – encouraged some birds to fly north where competition is less, predators are fewer, a seasonal abundance of insect food appears each spring and summer and there is more daylight in which to catch it. And they have been so successful in adopting this strategy that today, after a good summer's breeding, an estimated 90 million house martins, 220 million swallows and 375 million sand martins set off for Africa, outnumbering, it is thought, the resident species that stayed behind.

So, whatever the reason and whichever way migration stories have unfolded, the need to find food or living space – whether influenced by climatic change or overcrowding – seems to be the main stimulus to travel. As of this evolutionary moment, most bird migrants demonstrate a whole range of travel plans to maximize their exposure to plenty of good food and fair weather in order to breed successfully each year. Departure times vary from species to species. Small birds, such as passerines, prefer travelling at night. The air is more stable, the danger from predators – which rely to a great extent on sight for hunting – is reduced, and there are fewer distractions to slow down the journey. They can feed by day. Small insect-eating birds, such as swifts, swallows and martins that scoop up aerial plankton whilst flying, of necessity must fly by day. Ducks and geese travel both by day and night. Larger birds, including storks, cranes and raptors that rely on thermals to gain height and subsequently distance with little effort, must also fly by day and rest by night.

Distances travelled vary considerably. Short-distance migrants include the cream-coloured courser and the bunting-like bar-tailed desert lark. Both breed in the northern Sahara in spring but are forced north to the Mediterranean coast of North Africa by the heat and drought of summer. Further to the south, the pennant-winged nightjar also migrates relatively short distances, from one side of the equator to the other, to feed on swarms of flying termites that emerge at the time of seasonal rains. From September to November the western population breeds in southern Africa, from Angola across Zambia to northern Mozambique, while the eastern population nests in southern Tanzania and Central Africa. The male is conspicuous because of the elongated ninth primary feathers on each wing, which are over twice the length of the bird's body. In February, the western birds head for the Sahel and the eastern birds may be found in southern Sudan, Uganda and Kenya where the males lose their long feathers during the moult.

In the USA, the trumpeter swan – the largest of the swans with a wingspan of 3.1 metres and weighing up to 17.2 kilograms – breeds in the Rockies at the Red Rock Lakes in south-western Montana and Yellowstone National Park on the Montana–Wyoming border, yet flies no further than local lakes and streams fed by hot springs to spend the winter. Even though the area may be covered in deep snow, the warm waters do not freeze, allowing the birds to feed there alongside bison and elk that also move into the hot-springs areas to spend the winter.

Short migrations are often ones of altitude rather than latitude or longitude. In South America, the grey-flanked cinclodes, one of the shaketail ovenbirds, builds its nest in the high Chilean Andes at about 3,500 metres, yet frequents the narrow coastal plain through-out the rest of the year. In the Himalayas, the white-capped water redstart frequents the banks of fast-flowing mountain torrents, breeding at 220–400 metres and overwintering at 60–240 metres. Similarly, in North America, pine grosbeaks, black-capped rosy finches, and grey-headed juncos breed in alpine or subalpine levels of the Colorado Rockies in summer and descend to lower levels to avoid the snows of winter.

The North American blue grouse does it the other way round. It overwinters in the evergreen mountain pine forests of Idaho, where it feeds on needles and tree buds, and nests just 300 metres down the mountain in forests of deciduous broad-leaved trees. Here young leaves and developing flowers provide a rich source of food early in the breeding season. During the height of summer, female grouse and their offspring descend further to take advantage of insects and berries in the valleys. In the autumn all the birds return to the pine forests.

For some birds the desire to migrate can be so strong that those in captivity still attempt to make their traditional journeys. Pinioned geese at Slimbridge, for example, make one of the shortest seasonal migrations of any bird – from one side of their pond to the other. But they make the brief journey at the same time as their free-flying relatives in the wild.

EPIC JOURNEYS

At the other end of the distance scale is the arctic tern, the champion of bird migrants. It flies from one end of the world to the other, exploiting the superabundance of food during spring and summer in both hemispheres. And those birds nesting farthest north, up to 82°N and some within 450 miles of the North Pole, fly the farthest south, an annual round trip of over 21,750 miles, achieved by a bird not much larger than a pigeon. Apart from passage through temperate and tropical latitudes, they experience a lifetime of perpetual spring–summer seasons, flying to where the sun never sets and where it is always a time of plenty.

One of the most exciting ringing returns was from a bird ringed in Anglesey, North Wales, in June 1966. It must have followed the European and African Atlantic coasts, turning east across the southern section of the Indian Ocean, before being caught again near Bega in New South Wales, Australia, at the end of the year, a distance calculated to be about 11,222 miles. A single bird, based on the ringing returns of a twenty-six-year-old adult which ended its days aboard a Soviet whaling ship in the Southern Ocean, must have migrated a distance of well over a million miles during its lifetime.

The whimbrel and sanderling can almost match that feat. Birds breeding in the far north of Alaska may stop off anywhere on the Pacific coast of the Americas, between Vancouver and Tierra del Fuego, to spend the winter. They might even foresake the mainland for offshore islands like those in the Galapagos archipelago where whimbrels and sanderlings join semipalmated plover, ruddy turnstone, wandering tattler and northern phalarope as the six most common North American waders to visit the islands each boreal winter.

The list of long-distance migrants is like a who's who of the avian world; indeed, about half of the world's known species of birds migrate; that's about 4,000 species winging their way across the globe. There are many birds that join the terns and waders in travelling enormous distances and some take the most circuitous of routes.

The short-tailed shearwater or 'mutton bird' makes an annual 20,000-mile figure-of-eight migration in the western Pacific, flying with the minimum of effort by using the prevailing winds and arriving at just the right time at places where food is seasonally abundant. It breeds in vast numbers on islands in the Bass Strait, and in Tasmania, New South Wales, Victoria and Southern Australia during the southern summer from November to March. It flies to Japan via New Zealand and Fiji during April and May, reaches Kamchatka and the Bering Sea from June to August, crosses to the Pacific coast of North America in September and then heads south-west back across the Pacific Ocean to Australia during October. The return journey is made in such a rush that all the birds arrive home at the same time. Over 60,000 birds an hour have been seen arriving at breeding sites.

In the Atlantic Ocean, the large and powerful great shearwater follows an equally extraordinary long-winded loop migration. This 53-centimetres-long pelagic seabird with a 111-centimetre wingspan arrives between September and November at Inaccessible, Gough and Nightingale Islands and Tristan da Cunha (there is also a new colony starting up on Kidney Island in the Falklands) to breed. Each April, with egg-laying, chick-rearing and fledging complete, the adult great shearwaters start out on a transequatorial migration, first to the coastal waters of South America, then north to Bermuda between May and July, reaching the Grand Banks off Newfoundland in the period July to August. Some birds go as far north as the Arctic Circle before swooping round to Greenland and across the north-east Atlantic, where birds are found in large numbers off the south-west of Ireland in the autumn. As the northern winter approaches and the southern spring sets in the birds head south once more to the islands of the southern Atlantic.

Another remarkable journey is undertaken by the eastern race of the American golden plover, a 25-centimetres-long shorebird. After a three-month breeding season in the Canadian Arctic, birds follow the coast to Labrador and then head out to sea towards the Lesser Antilles group of volcanic islands, a non-stop flight over the Atlantic Ocean of more than 2,300 miles. Not content with conditions in the West Indies, the birds continue their journey through gaps in the Guiana Highlands, across the Amazon Basin and Matto Grosso, and follow the River Paraguay through Uruguay and on to the Pampas of Argentina. After a three-month stop, the birds head out over the Gran Chaco, follow the Andes to the Isthmus of Panama, cross the Gulf of Mexico from Yucatan to Texas, and follow the Mississippi north to the Canadian Arctic, a round trip of over 15,500 miles.

Curiously, juvenile birds miss out the Atlantic section of the route and take the Texas–Yucatan–Panama route into South America.

The lesser snow goose or blue goose (on account of a recent mutation that introduces a slate-grey colour to the plumage of an increasing number of birds) migrates from the Canadian Arctic to the Pacific and Gulf coasts of the USA and back each year. One population to the east of the Rockies flies from breeding sites on islands to the north of Hudson Bay, via the Great Lakes, to the marshes of Louisiana and Texas where they spend the winter. But their return journey takes them up the Mississippi river system and on a route to the west of the southerly migration. And when they move, they move fast. In 1952 a large flock was spotted leaving St James Bay, at the southern end of Hudson Bay, at dusk on 16 October. Next day, an airliner collided with geese at 1,800–2,400 metres above Lake Huron and air traffic controllers warned other aircraft of the hazard. On 18 October the flock was monitored flying at a height of 900 metres over southern Illinois, and by the morning of 19 October the birds were landing at Vermillion on the Louisiana coast. They covered the 1,680 miles at an average speed of 30 mph, which meant that the flock flew 685 miles each day.

This monitoring of bird flocks across North America has shown that often huge numbers of birds migrate at the same time. The phenomenon is known as the 'grand passage', and by noting the time flocks set off and the time they set down an estimate can be made of their flying speed. Ducks were found to be amongst the fastest long-distance flyers. On 23 and 24 October 1957, attention was focused on an enormous flock of about half a million ducks heading out on a broad front from breeding sites in eastern Saskatchewan and Manitoba. Funnelled down the Mississippi valley, the birds made rapidly for the bayous of Louisiana, flying at 460–850 metres by day and at 150 metres at night, and arrived during 24 and 25 October. The scientists monitoring the flock's progress revealed that the 1,500-mile non-stop journey had been achieved at an average ground speed of 40–50 mph. The birds had flown 993–1,180 miles each day, a speed that surpassed the fastest known passage by a homing pigeon that, in 1925, was displaced from its loft to a distance of 1,006 miles and took just a day and a half to reach home.

But not all migrating birds are as large as geese, ducks, plovers or shearwaters. Perhaps some of the more remarkable journeys are undertaken by some of the smallest birds. European barn swallows traverse the Sahara Desert each spring and autumn, spending the winter in Africa and the summer in northern Europe. Their migration was recognized as long ago as the sixth century BC. The Greek poet Anacreon recorded the return of swallows to Egypt in the autumn and realized that this was one of their winter re-treats.

So well studied have their movements been in recent years that different populations can be pinpointed with some accuracy. German swallows, for example, overwinter in Central Africa, whereas British and Russian swallows fly farther south and 'leap-frog' other European birds to overwinter in southern Africa.

British swallows have been traced to an area around Johannes-burg.

These same studies have also revealed that small migrating birds may sometimes pay the price for long-distance travel. In October 1974 migrating swallows and house martins were cut off by unusually heavy snow in the Alps. The normal high pressure system over Europe was positioned out in the Atlantic, allowing a series of depressions to bring cold north-easterly winds to blow across Europe. Birds trapped in Denmark sought refuge in south-eastern Britain, and exhausted birds were reported in houses. Window ledges became makeshift roost sites.

Heavy weather over the sea may blow some birds off course and they flop exhausted onto the decks of ships. Small birds are susceptible to bad weather even in their sought-after wintering sites. In November 1968, for instance, the weather turned unusually cold in southern Africa and few insects were on the wing. Migrant birds, arriving exhausted and hungry from the north, starved, yet local non-migrants survived.

On their return north in the spring the southern African birds recross the Sahara, putting down and resting at oases on the North African coast before their flight over the Mediterranean. Many don't make it. Swallows account for the greatest number of bird fatalities during the desert crossing. They fly lower than most bird migrants and are thought to run into problems with rising body temperature during the flight across the desert, one of the hottest places on earth. When they reach the Mediterranean these low flyers, passing over a rough sea, may become engulfed in waves.

The birds tend to fly downwind (although they have been known to fly upwind during the autumn migration – an adaptation to low-level feeding without stalling), travelling in huge flocks. On reaching Europe they follow the 9.5°C isotherm north,* flying by day, feeding on insects in flight, swooping over pools to drink on the wing, and stopping off at reed beds overnight.

*An isotherm is an imaginary line that joins together places with the same temperature, in a similar way that contours join together places of the same height on survey maps and isobars join together places with the same atmospheric pressure on weather maps.

MYTHS AND REALITIES

Swallows are considered by European countryfolk and those still in touch with nature and the natural seasons to be the harbingers of summer. Their arrival in the British Isles can be as early as March. In March 1977 a high pressure system over the western Mediterranean provided the birds with a southerly tail wind, and not only brought unusually warm weather to north-western Europe but also carried red Saharan dust to Northern Ireland and Scotland. More usually the first swallows are seen in Britain in April and these early arrivals are greeted with caution, giving rise to the warning – directed, perhaps, at those who would like to cast their clout – that 'one swallow does not a summer make'. Shakespeare, in *The Winter's Tale*, noted that the swallow's normal ETA was unlikely to be March:

> . . . Daffodils;
> That come before the swallow dares, and take
> The winds of March with beauty;

And Tennyson was moved to reflect in *The Princess* on the swallow's incredible journey:

> O tell her, Swallow, thou that knowest
> each,
> That bright and fierce and fickle is the
> South,
> And dark and true and tender is the North.

At one time, before formal bird ringing was commonplace and the movements of individual birds could be monitored, it was suggested that small birds did not migrate at all; it was said that they hibernated. Swallows, for example, were supposed to spend the winter months underwater. No less than the founder of the sciences of comparative anatomy and palaeontology, Baron Cuvier (1769–1832) believed that swallows became torpid in winter and hibernated at the bottom of the water in marshes. There were also reports from other eminent scientists, such as Professor Etmuller of Leipzig in the 1750s, who stated that a common fishing practice in northern lands was to break the ice and catch the hibernating birds in nets trolled beneath the surface.

These eighteenth-century accounts were influenced, perhaps, by the writings of Olaus Magnus, the naturalist Archbishop of Uppsala in Sweden – the very same archbishop who wrote about the gigantic kraken, a sea creature said to be several miles across. In 1555, he published his *Historia de Gentibus Septentionalibus et Natura* and reported that swallows hibernate in pools of stagnant water. Similarly, the great diarist Samuel Pepys (1633–1703) wrote of swallows being brought up in nets and coming back to life when placed next to a fire.

Even the likes of the Revd Gilbert White, of Selborne in Hampshire, England, supported the notion of swallows hibernating, not under water, but in crevices, caves and buildings. He was struck by the way birds disappeared in bad weather and reappeared when conditions became more favourable. In autumn he noted that all Selborne's swallows and house martins vanished, but on a sunny day some would again be on the wing. What he had not appreciated was that birds breeding farther north would be passing through southern England on their way south. The birds that he'd thought had come out of hibernation on fine days were not Selborne birds at all but those on passage. Nevertheless, White meticulously records, in his *Natural History of Selborne* published in 1788, hibernating swallows, swifts and martins recovered from the masonry of churches, in dry stone walls and behind crumbling cliff faces.

Similarly, Bishop Edward Stanley quotes instances, in his *Familiar History of Birds* published in 1865, of Scottish swallows dug out of a dried-up pond, packed into the hollow of a tree, and huddled together in the roof of a barn. He also tells of martins in a sandbank and a corncrake in a mud wall. Samuel Johnson, reflecting these opinions, was quite emphatic:

> Swallows certainly sleep all winter. A
> number of them conglobulate together by
> flying round and round and then, all in a
> heap, throw themselves under water and
> lie in the bed of a river.

Curiously enough, in the winter of 1974–5 unusual weather systems brought unseasonally mild weather to Britain, and swallows, house martins and whinchats, were spotted in January. It would be difficult to establish whether those birds had overwintered and even hibernated in Britain or had flown north earlier than usual, thus introducing a tiny element of doubt into the swallow hibernation debate.

But, despite the genuine belief of nineteenth-century naturalists in hibernating hirondines, the scientific community has found little evidence to justify the stories as fact and today the only bird known to hibernate is the common poor-will of North America; although some nightjars, swifts and hummingbirds are known to enter a state of torpor for a couple of days. Eight white-throated swifts, for example, were found in a crevice in the cliffs of Slover Mountain, California during a particularly cold spell in January 1913. And in Australia the white-backed swallow, banded whiteface, red-capped robin, white-fronted honeyeater, and mistletoe flowerpecker have been discovered surviving cold nights in the Australian desert in a state of temporary suspended animation.

The poor-will discovery was made on 29 December 1946 when an apparently dead bird was found in a vertical rock crevice in the Colorado Desert of southern California. Its body was cold and still, and had no perceptible heartbeat, yet, as it was placed back in its crevice, the bird opened one eye. Closer investigation revealed that the poor-will's body temperature drops from 35–44°C when it is active to 18–20°C and sometimes lower during hibernation. The reduced body temperature means it need use up less stored body fat during the lean and cold winter months and therefore have a better chance of surviving until spring. Often birds will return to the same hibernation site for several years. And although the scientific community had been rather late in recognizing the common poor-will's overwintering ability, it had not gone unnoticed amongst local folk. The Hopi Indians had long called it 'the sleeper'.

But the swallow and its relatives, despite the beliefs of many eighteenth- and nineteenth-century naturalists, do not normally hibernate, nor bury themselves in ponds or mud-walls; they migrate. And even more astonishing has been the way naturalists believed that small birds, like swallows, were able to fly such long distances. It was said that they hitched a ride on the backs of larger birds, a proposal taken quite seriously in the early 1880s when the learned journal *Nature* received and published several letters from reliable and sometimes eminent sources.

Professor E.W. Claypole started the ball rolling with a cutting from the New York *Evening Post* dated November 1880. It contained a letter from an anonymous correspondent who told of a priest on the Mediterranean island of Crete who, in the summer of

1878, claimed that local people saw southward-migrating sand-cranes carrying tiny birds on their backs. Observers on the ground or in fishing boats, it was said, could hear the passengers chirping.

Dr John Rae followed with another letter to *Nature*. This time the story was from the Cree tribe of North American Indians. They told of finches flying to Hudson Bay on the backs of Canada geese. The small birds were supposed to have flown up when startled by locals shooting at the landing Canada geese. In the American literature Dr James Cushing Merrill contributed another North American tale. He told of the Crow Indians' belief that sandhill and whooping cranes carried the little *napite-shu-utl* – what Merrill thought was a small grebe. One in ten birds were reputed to carry hitchhikers.

Similar stories abound in avian literature and legend. Indeed, the wren is credited with flying from Scandinavia to the east coast of Britain on the back of the short-eared owl, and wildfowlers in East Anglia told of goldcrests – Europe's smallest bird – being carried on the backs of larger migrants. The Tartars of south-central Russia had stories of migrating cranes carrying corncrakes to warmer climes each autumn. And a British sea captain sailing through the Straits of Gibraltar claimed he saw a flock of geese migrating north with small birds the size of larks rising from their backs; passengers aboard verified his report.

THE MIGRATION TRIGGER

In reality, migrating birds of all sizes and shapes are generally believed to fly under their own power and must prepare well for their long journeys. Some passerines and shorebirds, such as dunlin, even increase the size of their flight muscles before setting off, and reduce them after their arrival at their destination. But how do they know when to do this? How do they know when it is time to migrate?

How a bird knows when to migrate is not fully understood, although day length, weather conditions and food availability have all been implicated as triggers at one time or another. A favourite explanation at present involves the amount of light and dark to which a bird is exposed – progressively longer days and shorter nights in spring, progressively shorter days and longer nights in autumn and so on. This is fine for birds in temperate regions where the day length is strongly seasonal, but in equatorial latitudes there is little seasonal variation, yet birds wintering in those regions also know exactly when to migrate to the north. To account for this, and the fact that migratory birds kept in cages show migratory restlessness and moult at the same time as their wild relatives, it is thought that there must be some kind of internal timing mechanism, either set once a year, say, in spring, or set for longer periods, maybe several years at a time.

In Germany experiments were carried out to test this theory. Garden warblers were exposed to different photoperiods – 10, 12 and 16 hours of daylight – for three years, but they still showed migratory restlessness and moulted at the normal times. This suggested a long-term clock. In a longer experiment, blackcaps and garden warblers were exposed to fixed periods of daylight for eight years, yet they still moulted twice a year as do birds in the wild exposed to normal seasonal daylight conditions. There was however one surprise: the laboratory birds had an annual cycle of ten months rather than twelve – a phenomenon known as the circannual rhythm, meaning 'about a year'.

The bird 'year', however, is an actual year and so there must also be some kind of mechanism by which the internal circannual rhythm is synchronized to the external seasonal rhythm. In the laboratory the researchers were able to do this by exposing captive garden warblers to day lengths that they would normally experience in the wild at about 40°N – a latitude within the summer breeding range of warblers. By manipulating day length they could even get the birds to moult on a six-monthly cycle instead of the usual twelve. So the seasonal pattern, they concluded, is set by an internal clock which is modified by environmental changes. And this clock controls not only when some birds migrate but also the direction in which they are heading, switching course corrections on and off when appropriate (see page 124). Now the researchers are looking for the clock itself.

It is thought that the pineal body at the base of the forebrain – a small gland that René Descartes considered the seat of the soul – responds to changes in day and night length and produces the hormone melatonin. More melatonin is produced at night than by day, so that during the year the amount of the hormone circulating in the bird's body varies from season to season. During the year, therefore, the gland might be considered a 'rhythm generator'. It sets the bird's circadian rhythm. Even very small sections of pineal tissue show all the characteristics of the gland itself. It is thought that each cell in the gland is a kind of 'rhythm generating oscillator' and that all the cells are synchronized to produce melatonin.

When melatonin levels reach a certain threshold – at some point when levels are decreasing in spring or increasing in the autumn – the bird's body knows that it is time to migrate. Individual birds of the same species have their own threshold. Individual Bewick's swans overwintering at Slimbridge, Gloucestershire, for example, always arrive and leave on roughly the same date; and those arriving first stay the longest. It has also been found that young Bewick's acquire their parents' migratory threshold, although it is not clear if this is by learning it or if it is passed on in the genes.

Evidence from work at Radolfzell in Germany suggests that the urge to migrate is an inherited characteristic. Researchers there have crossed migratory blackcaps with non-migratory ones and discovered that the offspring showed a pattern of migratory restlessness halfway between that shown by the parents.

PREPARING FOR THE FLIGHT

Knowing when to migrate is only part of the story, for a bird must prepare its body for the flight some time in advance of its departure date. To do this and to take on fuel for the journey, a bird must eat far more food than it needs for normal day-to-day activities (apart from swifts, which are constantly on the wing, whether migrating or not). A bird's body weight might increase substantially before it sets off on migration, anything between 30 and 100 per cent depending on the distance it must fly before refuelling. Flying is energy-draining, and a small songbird might use up 0.8 per cent of its body weight for every flying hour. But for birds putting on large reserves of fat the potential flying time without refuelling can be enormous.

Those that double their body weight, for example, might remain airborne for 100 hours or more, important for birds that must cross oceans or deserts non-stop. A bird can travel 34 miles on one gram of fat – compared to 96 miles for a fish and 9 miles for a mammal – so a 100-gram wader carrying 30 grams of fat can travel 1,000 miles, sufficient to cross the western Sahara from north to south or vice versa.

The tiny ruby-throated hummingbird must cross the Gulf of Mexico on a non-stop flight and half of its body weight consists of stored fat. British sedge warblers, heading for West Africa, carry a similar load.

In the Pacific, the western race of the golden plover travels from the South Pacific, including Australasia and South East Asia, to the Arctic, and must fly non-stop over vast tracts of ocean. In April, northward migrants have been caught and ringed at Wake Island (to the west of Hawaii) in the north-west Pacific and after weighing have been shown to be carrying fat reserves that could take them another 4,000 miles without refuelling, sufficient for them to make the Aleutian Islands or Kamchatka. Birds have been recorded flying the 2,050 miles from the Aleutians to Hawaii – perhaps the longest uninterrupted flight travelled by any bird – in just 35 hours.

Whether a bird should or should not put on weight for migration is under the control of another hormone, prolactin. Its release stimulates a bird's appetite and determines whether the liver should synthesize fat. The fat is carried in the blood as low-density lipoproteins and transported to the cells of the 'fat pads' where it is stored. Warblers store fats at a rate of 5 per cent a day, but use it up at a much faster rate.

A classic study of blackpoll warblers, on their annual long-distance migration from Canada to South America and back has given some indication of the way migrating birds gain and lose weight before, during and after their journey.

The birds set out from Alaska and Canada in the fall and gather inland in the US state of Massachusetts. They follow weather fronts south-eastwards across the North American continent arriving in New England with a body weight of about 10–13 grams. Here they feed and rest for a couple of weeks whilst doubling their body weight. The fuel is body fat, stored in fat pads below the skin and amongst the bird's viscera. They gain weight, not by increasing the number of fat storage cells in the fat pads but by storing fat in existing cells, slowly at first to about 16–19 grams and then, in the last couple of days, putting on body fat rapidly to 20–23 grams in order to sustain them on the second and most hazardous stage in their remarkable journey.

On a suitable cool, dry and calm evening at the end of September and beginning of October, most of the birds launch themselves out into the Atlantic Ocean and fly 2,500 miles over the open sea. Radar stations have tracked the birds flying at 600–1,250 metres on a heading 10 degrees east of south. With a slight tail wind they can expect to average 25 mph on the journey over the sea.

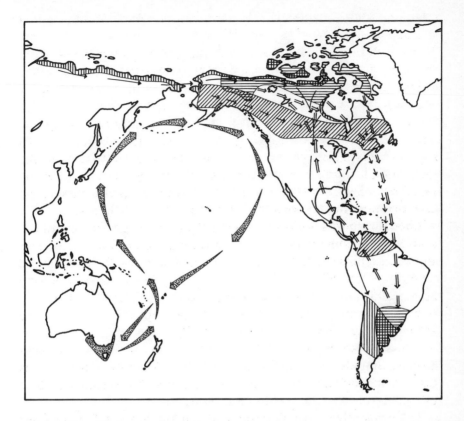

The map of the Pacific region and the Americas shows the routes of some long-distance bird migrants.

Stippled arrows:	*The annual figure-of-eight migration across the Pacific Ocean of the short-tailed shearwater.*
Vertical hatching and long arrows:	*The pectoral sandpiper breeds in the Arctic and over-winters in South America. Birds in northern Siberia forsake the easy route south along Asia's Pacific coast and fly to North America before heading south.*
Horizontal hatching and open arrows:	*The North American race of the lesser golden plover breeds in the North American arctic and winters in South America. Birds head south over the western Atlantic but return to the north via the Central American land route.*
Diagonal hatching and short arrows:	*Blackpoll warblers breed across North America in summer but head out over the Atlantic on their way south in the autumn, returning via the islands of the West Indies in spring.*

On Bermuda – about 750 miles south of New England – researchers have caught and weighed the tiny migrants and found them to be in good shape with average body weights of about 16 grams. Using this information they were able to work out how long and how far the birds could travel on the fuel they were able to take on board before setting off on their sea journey. The calculations revealed that they could fly non-stop for 110 hours and easily reach the South American coast before the fat reserves ran out and they became exhausted. This means that blackpoll warblers can take the most direct route south, and have the option to stop off at Bermuda or along the West Indies island arc in the event of bad weather.

The return journey is different. They go island-hopping through the Caribbean before heading north through Florida and across mainland North America.

REFUELLING

Some birds do not put on large amounts of fat at all. Instead, they might feed during the journey – swallows, for example, do not take on extra food reserves, fly by day, and eat on the wing; or they might take advantage of winds and air currents, cranes and honey buzzards, for example, soaring on thermals to cross the Bosporus and the Straits of Gibraltar; or they make short hops from one refuelling stop to the next, taking advantage of changes in local conditions and food availability. Song birds, heading north during the northern spring, time their arrivals with improvements in the weather and the flowering of plants and the emergence of insects. In the autumn, the availability of stocks of fruits, berries and nuts influences the southward movement of some song birds.

Another remarkable and well-timed journey is made by the tiny rufous hummingbird. This 3-gram bundle of muscle, bone and feathers can exist on a diet of nectar, yet obtains enough energy to fly the length of North America from Alaska, where it has spent the summer, to Mexico, where it overwinters, a round-trip journey of more than 3,750 miles.

It even migrates *over* the Rocky Mountains, but the extraordinary thing is not how it finds its way there and back, but how it times its arrival at refuelling stops along the route just as particular flowers are coming into blossom.

Refuelling stops and rest stations are important to long-distance bird migrants. By timing their arrival at sites where a seasonal abundance of food is readily available, birds heading towards higher latitudes in order to breed are able to feed up, gain body weight rapidly and be away quickly, thus reducing their stop-over time and gaining valuable extra days at the breeding site. At Delaware Bay on the east coast of the USA, northward-flying waders have learned, down the eons, to coincide their arrival at the Bay with the shoreward migration of thousands of creatures that will provide the birds with food.

In late spring each year, horseshoe crabs – not true crabs at all but animals related to scorpions and spiders – head for the beaches of Delaware Bay. They have spent most of the year foraging in the muds and sands at the bottom of the bay or on the bed of the nearby Atlantic Ocean but in spring they are ready to spawn. On the spring tides of early May the male crabs arrive first. They form a line several crabs deep and maybe a couple of crabs high along the edge of the sea. They are packed so tightly that tens of thousands of individuals can be found along a mile stretch of beach, and along undisturbed beaches the line of crabs can be uninterrupted for several miles.

As the tide turns the females arrive. They seek places in which to deposit their eggs, but on their emergence from the sea they become the focus of male attention. The thick black line breaks up and the males clump around the females, each vying with neighbouring males for the right to mate. The female, with a winning male firmly attached, digs a hole, maybe 20 centimetres deep in an attempt to avoid the probing bills of shorebirds, and lays up to 80,000 eggs. The male fertilizes the eggs and the crabs return to the sea. There may be up to fifty nests for every square metre of beach, a superabundance of food for any creature that might exploit it; and the creatures that do just that include gulls, song sparrows, cowbirds, grackles, mourning doves, house finches, starlings, house sparrows, pigeons, raccoons, foxes, moles and eleven species of migrating waders.

The migrants come from Brazil, Patagonia, Chile, Peru, Suriname and Venezuela, even as far south as Tierra del Fuego. They are on their way to breeding grounds in the Canadian arctic and they are in a hurry. The first to reach the north get the best breeding sites and can best take advantage of the endless days and abundance of food. Over 1.5 million birds arrive at Delaware Bay in May, the numbers peaking between the 18th and 24th. They eat their fill and depart. By June, all the birds have flown.

Most birds probe about in the sand, plucking up single eggs that have not been buried deeply. The turnstones, however, go digging. All along the tideline they excavate the crabs' eggs, and squabble for possession. Birds with brightly coloured crowns win the day, and the food. If a hole is left for more than a minute the other birds jostle for position. Sanderlings often follow the turnstones and they, in turn, fight to defend the prime feeding sites. Semipalmated sandpipers are more tolerant of each other and do not fight; several may share a vacated hole. Laughing gulls, which nest in the marshes along the coast, patrol the beach and spot turnstones that linger too long at particularly rich sites, and then swoop in to take over. The waders avoid the squabbling gulls, and must also keep an eye on the sky for peregrine falcons attracted to the confusion.

At night the birds leave the shoreline, where they may be packed 100,000–250,000 to a beach, and fly eastwards to roost in the tidal marshes and outer Atlantic beaches. The tiny crabs' eggs are turned into stored fat. Even though each egg provides little nutrient in itself, there is such a glut of food that migrants can double their weight before they resume their flight north. In order to put on sufficient weight they must gobble up eggs at a rate of one every five seconds. And, as it takes 135,000 eggs for each 50-gram sanderling to double its weight to 100 grams during the stopover, it has been calculated that 50,000 sanderlings consume 6 billion eggs weighing 27 tonnes in just a fortnight. Some overindulge and put on so much weight they can hardly take-off, simply bouncing along the ground until they finally get airborne and are ready to tackle the final 2,500 miles of their long journey to the Arctic.

Staging posts such as Delaware Bay, through which over 80 per cent of the North American population of the red knot are funnelled, are important for migrating birds; indeed, without them the journeys would be impossible. Another important staging post is a 70 mile-long stretch of the Platte River in Nebraska.

At sunset in the third week of March, three-quarters of the New World's population of sandhill cranes packs into the Great Bend area of the Platte between Overton and Grand Island, to the west of Omaha. At night they roost by the river and by day fatten up on corn debris, worms, snails and insects from the cornfields and river meadows nearby.

They begin to trickle in during late February, when snow is still on the ground, but the great arrival from wintering sites along the Gulf Coast of Texas, the playa lake region of west Texas, New Mexico and Mexico itself is in mid-March. Bird-watchers from all over the USA converge on the Platte, eager to see the amazing spectacle and to watch the cranes dance; and they don't have to leave their cars – this, the largest gathering of cranes in the world, can be seen from Interstate Highway 80.

In amongst the sandhills are very rare whooping cranes. They are part of a captive breeding programme in which the second eggs (which are normally abandoned by the parents) from caged birds in Maryland are fostered by sandhill cranes. All the surviving whooping cranes are the descendants from a small remnant flock of fifteen birds that lived in what is now the Arkansas National Wildlife Refuge in Texas. Now there are over a hundred birds, and each year they join the sandhills at the Platte River on their way to Wood Buffalo National Park in Canada's North-West Territories.

On warm afternoons along the Platte River stop-over, all the cranes soar high in the sky, and as the days go by and the temperature gradually rises they fly higher and more often until, in early April, the flocks take off and head north. Refuelled and refreshed, the birds are ready to cross the great northern forests and the featureless tundra where there are few refuelling stops. They migrate to breeding sites on the lands bordering the Arctic Ocean, from Hudson Bay in the east to Siberia in the west.

Elsewhere on the North American continent there are several similar refuelling points that serve the 20 million migrating birds crossing the USA and Canada each year. In May, 6.5 million western sandpipers and 3.5 million dunlin stop off at the intertidal mudflats of the Copper River Delta in Alaska, one of the few sites on the Pacific coast that can take a million or more shorebirds at each sitting.

At Mono Lake in California, 750,000 eared grebes arrive on a single October day, and at Cheyenne Bottoms, in Kansas, nearly all the Baird's sandpipers, white-rumped sandpipers, stilt sandpipers, long-billed dowitchers and Wilson's phalaropes flying the inland route pack into the 11,000 acres of wetlands to refuel. In mid-July, 70 per cent of the world's population of semipalmated sandpipers descend on the Bay of Fundy on the north-east coast, where they probe for small crustaceans.

Other major staging posts are at Gray's Harbor, Boundary Bay and Bowerman Basin in Washington, San Francisco Bay in

California, Stillwater in Nevada, Klamath Basin on the California–Oregon border and Izembek Lagoon in Alaska, where all the Pacific coast population of brant (brent) geese feed up on eel grass each autumn before heading south for southern California. Each of these important wetland areas is a link in a chain of staging posts that stretch from wintering sites in the south to breeding grounds in the north. The chains are part of regularly used 'flyways' – bird highways in the sky.

FLYWAYS

In 1950, American ornithologist Frederick Lincoln was analysing bird ringing returns when he noticed that North American ducks, geese and swans tended to fly north and south along regular corridors – the Pacific flyway in the west, the Central flyway to the east of the Rocky Mountains, the Mississippi flyway following the course of the Mississipi–Missouri River system, and the Atlantic flyway in the east. He thought at first that individuals adhered to the same flyway each and every year, but more recent research has shown this to be an oversimplified view. Generally it is felt that birds starting on the migration head out along a broad front but that the configuration of land and sea tends to funnel the bulk of migrants along the flyways. The flyways have no definite boundaries and birds flying one route often overlap with those on another.

Skeins of Ross's geese, for example, leave their breeding grounds bordering Queen Maud Gulf in the Canadian arctic each autumn and fly south either to the Great Slave Lake or Lake Athabasca, their first staging posts. Stage two takes them to the Canadian–USA border in the north of Montana, and the third and final stage sees them heading over the Rockies to wintering sites in the Sacramento and San Joaquin valleys that run down the centre of the state of California. This population frequents the Pacific flyway.

Another population of Ross's geese, breeding on Southampton Island in the north of Hudson Bay and on the mainland near the town of Churchill, follow the Mississippi flyway. Unencumbered with mountains, deserts or vast tracts of water, it is the most used route north and south. Huge numbers of pintails, mallard, Canada geese, American robins and myrtle warblers travel the same flyway. Lake Winnipeg and points along the fertile Mississippi basin act as staging posts. This population of Ross's geese overwinters in the marshes and bayous of the Mississippi River delta around New Orleans.

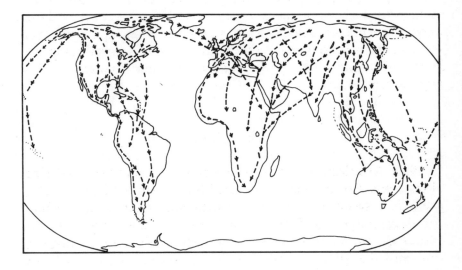

The main north-south flyways across the world during the northern autumn.

On the North American continent, the geography generally enables birds to fly directly north and south, but on the continent of Europe, mountain chains and seas run west to east. So the larger autumn migrants, such as raptors, storks and cranes, which tend to soar using thermals and would fail to find rising columns of warm air over the sea, usually have a south-west or a south-east component in their journey. Faced with the Mediterranean, they seek easy crossing points, the birds from north-western Europe funnelled across the Straits of Gibraltar, and those from central and eastern Europe finding the Bosporus before heading south across the Bible lands of the eastern Mediterranean and thence into Africa via Egypt.

The crossing points are the focus of attention not only for the bird migrants and their human followers – the seasonal army of bird-watchers that line the route each spring and autumn – but also for avian pirates. Eagles, falcons, hawks, storks, cranes and even large griffon vultures are mobbed by flocks of herring gulls. Some are forced down into the water and can drown. Young and inexperienced song birds heading south in the autumn may be intercepted by

Eleonora's falcons. These fast-flying killers migrate to the Mediterranean from Madagascar each spring but they do not breed immediately. Instead they wait for the autumn influx of naïve young songbirds, abundant food for growing Eleonora's chicks.

In the spring, the northward migration of smaller birds takes place along more direct routes although they still tend to avoid wide expanses of sea. Tunisia–Sardinia–Corsica–northern Italy is one route across the Mediterranean, while a little to the west Algeria–Balearic Islands–southern France is another, the birds using the Rhone Valley to squeeze between the Alps and the Massif Central and reach breeding sites further north. Birds travelling north through Spain seek out mountain passes in order to cross the Pyrenees. Waiting for them all along the Mediterranean are the guns of the macho sharpshooters.

But some routes are not so obvious. It was always thought, for example, that a flock of 30,000 knots feeding at Balsfjord, 30 miles to the south of Tromsö in arctic Norway, was part of the Siberian breeding population. That was until a group of scientists from Britain began to look into the matter more carefully.

They discovered that thirty out of thirty-eight birds with rings had started their journey in April and early May from the east coast of Britain, at places like the Wash. When they set out they weigh about 190 grams, but when they arrive at Balsfjord, after a 1,100-mile flight across the North Sea and along the Norwegian coast, they have lost about 20 per cent of their weight. They feed on the mudflats along the shores of the fjord – the only one in the area which is ice-free in May and with suitable feeding sites – for about two to three weeks and then continue on their journey. It was at this point that the scientists were in for a surprise, for in late May, instead of going towards Siberia, the birds headed north-west to breeding grounds at Peary Land in north-east Greenland. Further studies revealed that another population, breeding in arctic Canada, also winters in western Europe, using Iceland as a staging post.

Staging posts are also evident in trans-Saharan flights by the small song birds that spend the summer in Europe and the winter in Africa. At first it was thought that these migrants made the crossing in one go, but now we know that small birds like redstarts and garden warblers seek out oases, dry valleys (wadis) with rich vegetation, and shaded rocky areas after their first night overflying the desert and put down to rest during the day. If their fat reserves are low they may become active by day and feed up on insects or fruits. When they are in good shape they continue their journey on a subsequent night.

On the Asian continent the Himalayas and neighbouring mountain chains form a natural ecological barrier to north–south migration. Most birds find routes through passes or around the edges of the mountains, although the bar-headed goose goes right over the top and small flocks have been seen flying above Mt Everest.

Along the eastern fringe of Asia, birds can avoid flying over the deserts and mountains of Tibet and Mongolia by hugging the Pacific seaboard, where they can fly north–south and vice versa without any geographical hindrance. Each autumn, the eastern Siberia populations of knot and sanderling head south through Manchuria and Korea in order to island-hop through the Philippines and finally disperse to wintering sites in Australia. Some birds even reach New Zealand, an amazing journey.

One of the few land birds to make the same journey is the needle-tailed swift, breeding in central Asia and overwintering in Australia. The rest, including eastern populations of barn swallows, sand martins, ospreys, red-throated pipits and red-backed shrikes, tend to make landfall in the islands of south-east Asia or, like the wryneck, the black kite and the buzzard, pull up at the southern extremities of the continent. Ducks, such as the pintail, pochard and tufted duck forego a flight over the mountains and spend the winters on lakes to the north of the Himalayas.

A curious pattern of migration and choice of route is shown by two distinct populations of brent geese. These small geese prefer to hug the coast during their migrations, but birds from breeding sites only 373 miles apart head off in the autumn in completely opposite directions. Those on the Taymyr Peninsular follow the western Siberia coast to Scandinavia and then on towards wintering sites in north-west Europe, including the British Isles. But those around the Lena Delta, not far to the east, follow the east Siberia coast to the Chukotskiy Peninsular before turning south along Kamchatka and through the Kurile Islands in order to spend the winter in Japan or Korea.

In North America, this east–west split in the migration of neighbouring populations of brent geese is repeated. The birds breed along the arctic fringe of North America, including the complex of islands to the north of Canada. Come the autumn, the geese breeding to the west head for Alaska and then south down the

Pacific coast of North America to California and Mexico. The eastern population, however, flies out over Baffin Bay, across Greenland and the Denmark Strait to Iceland, and then heads out over the North Atlantic to winter in Ireland. Here east meets west, for the Canadian arctic arrivals rub shoulders with those from Siberia.

WEATHER FORECAST

The route a bird may take and the decision whether to set off or not depends very much on the weather, and birds are diligent weather watchers; their very lives depend on getting the weather forecast right. And they go about it much the same way as we do: they watch the sky and check out the current meteorological conditions. Whether a bird migrates at all could depend simply on the weather. This is more important during the autumn migration, for in spring adverse weather is likely to be encountered not at the beginning of the journey but at the end. A mild winter on the tundra, for example, could mean birds staying put. A late snowstorm might trigger movement south in the New Year rather than the previous autumn. And birds ready to migrate early in the season are more fussy about conditions than the late starters, who must head out whatever the weather in order to avoid being trapped. Those that do decide to up-and-away watch out for long periods of favourable flying weather – clear skies and following winds.

Clear skies in themselves might stimulate movement, for in higher latitudes they are often associated with a drop in temperature which provides the stimulus to fly to warmer climes. Birds tend to accompany anticyclones or 'highs' or fly with the ridges of high pressure in the gaps between depressions or 'lows'. Anticyclones also mean light winds, ideal for migrants that wish to avoid being blown off course. On the eastern side of an anticyclone over Britain in autumn, for example, the light winds blow from the north, assisting the southerly movement of birds at that time of year.

Stronger winds, associated with depressions and cold and occluded fronts, are only useful if they are blowing in the right direction. Wheatears, redpolls and lapland buntings from Greenland and Iceland take off on a ridge of high pressure that often follows a depression, but on their flight towards Scotland to the south-east they take advantage of the north-westerly winds following the depression and have a curved flight path rather than a direct one, following the direction of the winds in the weather system. Larger birds, like the whooper swans, fly high to avoid buffeting at lower levels, but take advantage of the light winds in jet streams following depressions. Alaskan birds follow strong north-westerlies at a height of 1.9 miles, and travel with ease from the Beaufort Sea to Canada.

Across the northern hemisphere, winds following cold fronts and blowing from the north-east or north-west are important for the autumn migration south. In Sweden, night-flying song birds take advantage of the winds behind cold fronts, such as might occur when an anticyclone is positioned over Britain or over the northern part of the North Sea. They assist the birds' passages across the southern Baltic. Those, like thrushes, finches and goldcrests, heading for Britain are helped across the southern part of the North Sea by the wind.

The winds and wind direction also play an important role in the migration of 100 million North American bird migrants in the western Atlantic. It may seem odd that small birds, such as blackpoll warblers (see pages 112–13), should head out over the sea and cross directly from North to South America without putting down in, say, Bermuda or the West Indies. Indeed, the non-stop flight is approaching the limits of migration for birds with such small fat reserves. But they do it, and they do it with the assistance of the wind. Columbus saw them doing it in 1498. He was on his third voyage to the New World and spotted song birds 180 miles from Trinidad.

The birds fly first to the Atlantic seaboard of North America and wait at the coast for a cold front to pass. In its wake are clear skies and strong north-westerly winds. After sunset in late September and early October huge numbers, up to 12 million a night, all leave together and launch out into the Atlantic itself. For 10–20 hours they take advantage of the tail winds behind the frontal system. Heading generally in a south-east direction over the ocean, the migrants gradually overtake the front and, after passing through a section around the Sargasso Sea in which the winds can vary, they hit the north-east trade winds. These winds bend their track back towards the Americas on a south-west heading and push them directly onto the South American mainland.

Shore birds, leaving the coast of Nova Scotia each autumn, use the same strategy. Samuel Nelmes reported seeing them in the autumn of 1833. He was on board the *Carib* about 300 miles east of Bermuda when he reported seeing flock upon flock of plovers pass by, all heading south-east. In more recent times, observers on Bermuda have seen vast flocks passing the island at a height of about 1¼–3 miles. But if they kept that compass heading and relied, as the songbirds do, on the trade winds to push them back towards the west, the birds would not reach land and would drop exhausted into the sea. The further north the birds' departure point is, the more likely they are to be blown east over the ocean. They must therefore abandon their constant heading at some point in their migration and reorient from south-east to south. This course correction will then bring them back to land.

Migrating birds have been seen overflying Antigua at 4 miles on their way to South America. By the time they reach Barbados they drop down to 3,000 metres and at Tobago they are at about 300 metres, ready to land on the mainland. The journey from Nova Scotia of more than 2,000 miles takes the birds about 80 hours. (The human equivalent would be a series of four-minute-miles for 80 hours; and, using an analogy with an automobile's fuel consumption, the bird is travelling at 1,158,696 kilometres to the litre or 720,000 miles to the gallon.)

Because the birds are at the limit of their migratory capability any untoward event is going to seriously upset their travel plans. A tropical storm encountered en route may see some birds heading back to the North American mainland or putting down on a Caribbean island or a passing ship to sit it out. Others may be blown out to sea where they perish; feathers in the stomachs of deep-sea fishes are witness to these disasters.

Arctic terns from the Canadian arctic also use the prevailing winds to hitch a ride, but they go the whole way. They do not fly directly south along the US east coast like the song birds and shore-birds; instead they head out across the Atlantic Ocean, riding the strong Westerlies before turning south down the Atlantic coast of Europe and Africa. Some birds take advantage of winds blowing the opposite way south of the equator and recross the Atlantic to fly south along the South American east coast.

In the main, birds tend to avoid crosswinds, although they can sometimes compensate if one is encountered en route. Some North American land-birds follow the prevailing wind in whatever direction it goes, as long as the general direction is south; whereas larger waders and wildfowl tend to stick to their set course, despite

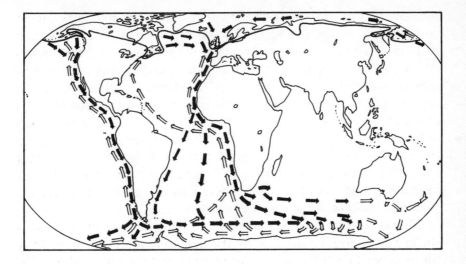

The migration routes taken by the Arctic tern. Birds breeding the furthest north tend to fly the furthest south. North American birds follow the prevailing winds across the North Atlantic before heading south. Birds breed north of the continuous line right across the holarctic.

(filled arrows)   *Autumn–winter migrations*
(open arrows)   *Winter–spring migrations*

the wind direction. If the wind is strong they might, at the very least, drift away from their flight path, and at worst, are blown totally off course. The vagrants so sought after by bird tickers in the south-west of England are often unfortunate individuals, taken unawares and blown far from their normal nesting or wintering sites, and therefore, disorientated and confused, often condemned to die.

One bird that was blown off course in 1967 was Albert. Albert is a black-browed albatross that, for the past twenty-five years or so, has been joining a gannet colony at Unst in the Shetlands each breeding season. Unfortunately, Albert is unlikely ever to breed because the others of his kind are many thousands of miles to the south, breeding on sub-Antarctic Islands in the Southern Ocean. Somehow or other Albert was blown off course and found himself (or herself, as Albert's sex is unknown) not in the southern hemisphere where he should have been but in the north. With an 2.4-metre wingspan Albert needs good winds to give him lift, but at the equator, where

125

the doldrums prevail, it is difficult for the large bird to return south. So Albert is trapped, and until another aberrant wind blows an albatross of the opposite sex across the equator he will remain unfulfilled and not breed. Instead he sleeps the summer away, sitting on a mud platform by day, perched on 122-metre-high cliffs at Herma Ness at the north of the island. In August the lonely bird leaves, only to return again in February.

Albert is not the first albatross to have been blown so far away from home. One was spotted on Fair Isle in 1949 and another over Chichester Harbour in 1974. And in 1860 an albatross visited Myggenaes Holm in the Faroes for thirty-four years, until it was met by an ignoramus with a gun and was shot. The local fishermen referred to the bird as the 'king of the gannets', and thought that killing it would bring them bad luck, just as Coleridge had written in the *Rime of the Ancient Mariner*.

DISASTERS

Heavy gales and stormy seas sometimes push huge numbers of birds off course and 'wrecks' of dead and dying seabirds appear on coasts or inland. The auk family seems to be particularly vulnerable. In British waters alone there have been more than a dozen major wrecks of guillemots, razorbills and puffins.

On 11 May 1856, for example, severe north-westerly gales pushed large numbers of the larger auks towards the north Norfolk coast and many perished. Over 240 birds were recovered from a 2-mile stretch of foreshore. And in the autumn of 1895, enormous numbers of razorbills were blown inland in Argyleshire.

Some wrecks are a mystery. On 28 September 1971 Canadian newspapers carried stories about thrushes and warblers crashing through windows in the town of Prince Rupert, British Columbia. Eider ducks fell on Brewer, Maine, in 1979; mallard near Walker, Iowa in 1978; scaups, canvasbacks and redheads on St Mary's City, Maryland in 1969; and Canada geese on Derby in 1974 – an event which included one goose crashing through the window of a startled inmate listening to Frankie Lane's 'Cry of the Wild Goose'.

Sometimes, unusual weather conditions can bring spectacular falls of birds. In late autumn 1937, Scandinavian fieldfares were crossing the North Sea, heading for the British Isles. But strong winds blowing anticlockwise around an unusually deep depression to the south of Britain swept the birds off to Greenland. Today, some of their descendents still live in southern Greenland.

In September 1965 an even more complex weather system pushed migrants onto the British east coast. A ridge of high pressure built up over Scandinavia on 1 September, providing suitable north-easterly winds for night-flying song birds to reach British shores, and northerly winds for birds setting off from sites further east to fly south into Europe. The winds were part of a weather system dominated by a depression over the Alps; but this was no ordinary depression. On 2 September, instead of moving to the east or north-east, as is normal, it moved in a north-westerly direction causing strong north and north-easterly winds to blow across the southern North Sea. Meanwhile, the high pressure ridge persisted over Scandinavia.

By the morning of 3 September, the low pressure area had pushed against the ridge of high pressure creating a very complex weather system, and by midday the main low was centred over the southern North Sea and a secondary low had formed over south-east England. Thick cloud dominated the sky south of a line from the Humber to Denmark. During the afternoon, the winds over East Anglia backed from north-north-west to south-east and were filled with heavy rain. All the migrants, that would normally be heading south-south-west or south on their way to Europe and had been lulled into a false sense of security by the Scandinavian ridge of high pressure, were caught unawares. Millions were blown off course and onto the British coast. Some didn't make it alive and were washed ashore, having dropped exhausted into the North Sea and drowned. Others flopped onto dry land. An estimated half-a-million birds landed on a 25-mile stretch of Suffolk coast alone. Walking 2½ miles along the shore, one ornithologist reported an estimated 15,000 redstarts, 8,000 wheatears, 4,000 pied flycatchers, 3,000 garden warblers, 1,500 whinchats, 1,500 tree pipits, 1,000 willow warblers and 500 whitethroats. People in local towns were surprised by redstarts landing exhausted on their shoulders. Within a few days conditions changed, and the birds, interrupted so rudely and so catastrophically by the weather, resumed their migration south.

Caught over the open sea, the Scandinavian migrants had no choice but to plough on and attempt to make land-fall, but normally in bad weather most birds simply put down and wait it out – although birds *have* been seen to start a migration in fog, rain and overcast skies: they simply rise above the fog bank or cloud to where the sky is clear and conditions are more favourable. Others, including some of those foolhardy waders and wildfowl, often don't start at all until tail winds are available to whisk them away to the south. Ducks on staging lakes around Ohio have been seen to gather in large, compact rafts, all pointing into the wind and waiting for conditions to change. Indeed, the size of a migrating flock may depend on the weather. When skies are cloudy, flocks tend to be bigger. A large number of birds, it seems, can navigate with a greater degree of accuracy than a bird on its own.

But how *do* they navigate; how do migrating birds find their way?

FINDING THE WAY

The navigational and orientational skills involved in bird migration are still, to some extent, a mystery. We have still to probe the avian brain sufficiently well to expose the mechanisms by which a bird like a guillemot is able to migrate vast distances over land and sea yet find its way back unerringly to the exact place where it bred the previous year. Swallows locate last year's nest and re-use it. Arctic terns fly across the entire world and return each year to the same scrape in the sand. And, in one classic experiment, the navigational talents of two Manx shearwaters were exposed. They were taken from their burrows on the Welsh island of Skokholm and transported to Boston, Massachusetts and Venice, Italy, where they were released. Travelling at 243 and 265 miles a day respectively, often over unfamiliar terrain or featureless ocean, the two birds returned to the very same nesting burrows from which they had been taken. The Boston bird returned home well in advance of the letter telling of its release.

How on earth did they do it? It's a question that has intrigued naturalists for centuries, but in recent years clues as to how it all might work have begun to appear.

The experimental techniques are numerous; pigeons are fitted with magnets that disturb the earth's magnetic field; starlings are held captive in cages with moveable mirrors that can change the apparent position of the sun; sparrows are released from cages carried aloft by helium balloons and recaught on the ground; indigo buntings sit in darkened planetaria and watch pinpoints of light on a domed ceiling; night-fliers are tracked by military radar; day-flyers run gauntlets of binoculars; and many migrants are caught, ringed, released and caught again and again. But no matter what the method, all have contributed in some small way to the present feeling that birds have not one, but several navigational aids and back-up systems with which to find their way about the globe.

The relative importance of each system has yet to be assessed and the way they are integrated or calibrated is still being worked out, but researchers are beginning to put together some parts of the jigsaw.

Many migration experiments today involve birds that have been hand-reared. Curiously, species that migrate show the predisposition to do so, and even in captivity they behave, rather conveniently, just as their free-flying cousins do in the wild. They moult to grow feathers with which they will not fly, put on weight ready for a journey they cannot make, hop in the direction that the wild birds take, and stop this migratory restlessness when the wild birds have arrived at their destination. Unlike their wild relatives, birds in the laboratory can be subjected to all sorts of controlled changes in their environment and their behaviour observed. The magnetic field around the cage can be changed, as can the direction of sunlight hitting the cage or an artificial pattern of stars on a planetarium roof.

But, from early times, the bird that featured strongly in navigation experiment was not a wild bird nor a hand-reared version, but a semi-domesticated bird, the racing pigeon. Pigeons have been known to take just one day to find their way to the home loft from a release point some 620 miles away, travelling at a speed of about 50 mph. In order to achieve such a speedy and accurate return, the birds would have had little time for random searching, and would have had to follow a direct flight-path, a process requiring both a compass and a map.

This extraordinary navigational skill is all the more intriguing when it is realized that the racing pigeon is a domesticated version of the rock dove, a bird species that shows very little seasonal migration in the wild. Wild rock doves in the Mediterranean were thought to have been the ancestors of the domestic pigeon. These birds nested on cliffs and had to search far and wide to collect grain which they brought back to the nest. Their homing abilities probably sprang from the need to find and return to the nest site after foraging.

Subsequently, the racing pigeon has provided some early clues about bird navigation and has been used for over 2,000 years to carry messages for the military. Part of the birds' early training was to take them progressively greater distances from the loft in order to familiarize them with local topography, a learning process that could be extended by taking parent birds with their fledged offspring to create a series of beacons for longer journeys. Geese and swans also seem to do this. Family parties, containing parents and the current year's offspring, fly together, the younger birds learning the route from one staging post to the next.

Those birds migrating along regular flyways can 'pilot' from one landmark to another. They can remember the geography, such as mountains, valleys and rivers along the route. American hawks, flying across the Isthmus of Panama, for instance, show signs of having some knowledge of the ground conditions below. When crossing Mexico they deviate from the direct route to avoid the harsh landscape of the Sierra Madre and fly along its western margins closer to the coast.

The sense of smell could be useful; petrels and other birds with an acute sense of smell might recognize local olfactory cues. And the sense of hearing might be used. Pigeons have been shown to be able to detect very low frequency sounds – as low as 0.1Hz or one cycle in ten seconds – so that waves crashing on the shore or the wind passing through canyons could provide recognizable infrasonic signatures. And birds flying overhead might hear seasonal congregations of animals on the ground. Night-flyers could recognize choruses of frogs or toads at their traditional breeding sites.

But what if a bird hasn't been that way before? Young cuckoos are nest parasites and are therefore denied access to their parents; and the adult cuckoos fly to Africa a couple of months before their offspring anyway. The young birds could not possibly have learned the route from them. There must be in-built, innate instructions that rely on other navigational cues to help some young inexperienced migrants head off generally in the right direction. Clearly, for some birds, there is more to orientation and navigation than simple familiarization, particularly if you have no geographical cues to follow.

Scientists in a light aircraft once followed migrating gannets over the sea in an early attempt to pick up cues for navigation. They soon realized that islands are too few and changes in sea colour, salinity and temperature are too variable. It was thought therefore that birds flying to oceanic islands or crossing featureless deserts would more probably rely on celestial cues. In the day sky the sun is the most obvious feature, at night the moon and stars, although in order to take advantage of them animals must have some appreciation of their apparent movement across the sky. And to do that they must calibrate their position against a constant reference source – most likely the earth's geomagnetic field.

MAGNETIC SENSE

The importance of magnetism in bird navigation was demonstrated in Germany in 1965 and later in the USA in the early 1970s. When magnets were attached to the backs of pigeons the birds were unable to orient on cloudy days. Brass bars had no effect. In another experiment, ornithologists placed small coils on either side of a pigeon's head. Powered by minute mercury batteries, the coils could be used to produce a controllable earth strength magnetic field. By reversing the polarity of the field a pigeon could be made to fly in the opposite direction to its loft. The researchers eventually discovered that minute fluctuations in the earth's magnetic field, as small as a five-hundredth of the strength of the natural field, can upset a bird's compass heading.

This was interesting, because previously observers had indicated a link between sunspot activity and the speed with which racing pigeons returned home. Sunspots are known to affect the magnetosphere, causing detectable fluctuations in the earth's magnetic field.* Slow returning birds, apparently showing orientation difficulties, are more noticeable on the days following sunspot activity.

Similar problems are experienced by birds flying close to magnetic anomalies or magnetic storms. Pigeons released in the iron-rich Kyffhauser Mountains in Eastern Germany, for example, set off for their lofts in the wrong direction before rectifying their mistake. And migrating birds flying over a large alternating-current radar antennae system in Wisconsin were found to change altitude or direction suddenly when the equipment was operating. Birds heading north jigged to the left.

Young birds probably begin to detect and appreciate the earth's magnetic field whilst still in the egg. In Sweden, pied flycatcher nests were surrounded by an artificial magnetic field, offset from the

---

*The magnetosphere is the asymmetric shield around our planet which is controlled by the earth's magnetic field rather than the sun's; it is thin facing the sun and thick away from it.

normal geomagnetic field, during incubation and nesting. Two months later, at about the time the fledglings normally headed south on their autumn migration, the researchers found that at the start of their journey the young birds headed off in a direction which complemented the offset. This was evidence supporting the hypothesis that a magnetic sense might provide a primary, innate reference frame from which other learned compasses could be calibrated.

The field, so some scientists believe, is thought to be detected by particles of magnetite coupled either to stretch-sensitive spindles in the muscles of the neck or to nerve endings in the connective tissue around the brain. Such particles have been found during dissections of white-crowned sparrows and pigeons. Dissection of the bobolink – a long-distance, transequatorial New World land migrant – revealed iron-rich deposits in the sheaths of tissue surrounding the olfactory nerve and bulb, between the eyes, and on bristles in the nasal cavity. Changes in field strength are thought to cause minuscule movements of the particles which are sensed by the nerves. They enable a bird to sense a geomagnetic grid that shows itself as fluctuations in the geomagnetic field, such as the angle of the field or 'dip'.

In Germany, robins were found to use the inclination of the earth's magnetic field for orientation by sensing the angle between the magnetic lines of force and the direction gravity (dip). The smallest angle between the two is north. A magnetic grid possibly represents a bird's magnetic map of the world. From it it can establish its present position and set out on a basic, genetically determined compass heading to where it is supposed to go.

Young inexperienced travellers do just that. In tests with night-flying savannah sparrows it was found that young birds that have not been on migration before rely on geomagnetic information to set their course. More experienced birds learn to use other sources of orientational information. Indeed, learning ensures that young birds gain the detailed knowledge that fills in the gaps left by their innate instructions. Many young birds accompany their parents to learn migration routes, others make solo exploratory flights that cover increasingly larger areas of countryside around the nest site, and still others learn simply from experience on their first migration flights.

In one classic experiment, this shift from innate magnetic to learned visual cues was tested. Starlings breeding in the Netherlands fly west and south-west to overwinter in north-west France and southern England. In one test, a batch of adults and youngsters were captured and released in Switzerland. The adults, which had learned enough to appreciate where they really were rather than where they thought they were, adjusted to the change and headed north-west to their normal winter sites. The youngsters, guided only by their innate geomagnetic compass, headed for western France and Spain.

This compass heading is controlled by a bird's biological clock, most likely set by an internal pacemaker and modified by changes in day length during the year (see pages 109–10). The most westerly population of European garden warblers, for example, are programmed to fly south-west in August and September to head for the Iberian Peninsula, generally south in October to fly from the Straits of Gibraltar to equatorial West Africa, and generally north the following April to return to Europe across the Sahara. In experiments in Germany, caged birds, deprived of seasonal cues, were found to show the same directional shifts in migratory restlessness at the same time as their wild counterparts. A young, inexperienced bird's entire migratory urge and direction is switched on and off by an internal pacemaker, ensuring it is in the right place at the right time. But it is a mechanism that can be overridden. If a bird is flying over a hostile area, like a desert, and is running out of fuel, it can ignore the internal urge to keep to the clock and set down at an oasis and refuel. And as it gains more experience, it can take advantage of all sorts of environmental cues.

SUN, MOON AND STARS

As a bird learns about its environment, it can switch to navigational aids other than magnetism. Geographical landmarks and the position of the sun, moon and stars ensure that the migrant gets to where it is programmed to be going. The sun compass overrides all other sensory cues.

In the 1950s, scientists from the Max Planck Institute showed that birds could orient to the sun. They first noticed starlings in a cage taking an interest in the northerly part of their enclosure in spring, the direction in the wild of their springtime north-westerly migration. This is known as an 'intention movement'; a bird stands with its body oriented in a particular direction or it pecks at a particular part of the cage more than other parts, or it might flutter its wings and fly a short distance in a preferred direction. This behaviour has been used by scientists studying bird migration.

In the German experiments, a screen placed around the cage, but allowing a view of the sky, did not stop the behaviour. In another experiment a circular cage with mirrors was constructed and the starlings exposed both to the direct rays of the sun and to the sun reflected in the mirrors. Whether observing the direct sun or a reflected image apparently shining from a different direction, the starlings always maintained the same angle to the sun or to the direction of the sun's reflection. This angle varied with the time of day, demonstrating that birds, even those in captivity and isolated from the outside world, still compensate for the sun's arc across the sky and appreciate the passage of time by some internal clock.

In other experiments in Germany, the internal clock of pigeons was tested by changing birds' diurnal rhythms. Under normal circumstances the midday sun is considered to be directly south by birds in the northern hemisphere and a control bird, with its day-night rhythm unaffected, released some distance from its loft would fly directly home. If, however, the bird had its clock advanced by six hours, the noon setting was treated as west, rather than south, and a released bird would fly 90 degrees to the left of its homebase. Interestingly, if the sky was overcast, the phase-shifted birds headed straight for home and not 90 degrees to the left. They had been using a compass other than the sun.

There have been several stabs at explaining the way birds appreciate the position of the sun in the sky. One hypothesis suggests that the bird notes the movement of the sun along a small section of its arc and can work out where it should be at its highest point, i.e. at midday, and then work out where it is at present and where home is. The higher the sun is in the sky at noon the lower the bird's latitude (closer to the equator). The difference between the sun's position at midday and its position where the bird first learned its cues for celestial navigation (probably its nest or roost) will give longitudinal information. Other explanations are variations on this theme but all rely on: extraordinary feats of memory in order to remember the sun's movement across the sky at home; amazingly fine observations of the sun's present position; and tremendous mathematical skills in order to make the comparisons between its learned position and its present one.

An unusual structure in the bird's eye has been proposed as a possible sun detector. There is a comb-like body, known as the pecten, which covers the blind spot (the place at the back of the eye where the retinal nerves leave to form the optic nerve). It is a pigmented body fed by many blood vessels, but with no nervous or muscular tissue. The pecten might be a sort of sextant that can be used to measure the sun's angle. In fact its function is unknown, although the general feeling is that it has something to do with bringing more blood, and therefore more oxygen and nutrients, to the eye without the bird having to clog up its retina with blood vessels. The pecten is smallest in diurnal birds and largest in nocturnal birds of prey.

Whatever the method a bird uses, its appreciation of the position of the sun is fundamental to its life. But if the sun is hidden and there are enough blue patches in the sky, polarized light is available, and it too might provide orientation cues. Experimenting with polarized light is fraught with problems, for light reflecting from the surfaces in experimental cages, whether matt black or blotting paper white, can present birds with minute differences in light intensity rather than differences in polarization. Nevertheless, the cue is available and birds might be using it, not necessarily day-flying birds but nocturnal ones.

Many birds migrating by night, such as European robins, American white-throated sparrows, yellow-rumped warblers and blackcaps, take off at sunset or shortly after, during the twilight hours. At this time they have many sources of orientational information available, including wind direction, local geography, early evening star patterns, the geomagnetic field and, on a clear evening, sunset itself. And the setting sun, its position calibrated by the bird's magnetic compass, offers at least two important cues – the glow of the horizon and polarized patterns of natural skylight. The latter is very obvious at sunset and sunrise, and can be used to derive the position of the sun. As the sun sets in the west, the band of maximum polarization runs north–south in a broad ring around the earth, and at this time of day, if the weather is clear, it is the most prominent cue available for a bird, or any other migrant for that matter. Any bird in the northern hemisphere, say, heading north in spring or south in the autumn, could start its journey in the correct direction simply by setting a course parallel to the axis of polarized light – a cue, incidentally, that can be upset by volcanic dust in the atmosphere, as happened in 1982–3 after the violent eruption of El Chichon in Mexico which threw 12 million metric tons of dust into the upper atmosphere and created prolonged sunsets at Ithaca, New York, where tests with pigeons were being undertaken.

But a bird must also appreciate the change in the sun's azimuth during the migration season and therefore the change in position of either sunset glow or axis of polarization. And, indeed, birds can. Robins ringed in Falsterbo, at the southern tip of Sweden, at the end of the autumn, for example, set off at an angle to the setting sun up to 27 degrees different from those starting to migrate early in the season.

And it was at Falsterbo that a curious orientation puzzle was discovered. Researchers who had been watching robin orientation and the importance of polarized light found that newly arrived robins stopping over in Falsterbo on their way south preferred initially to head off in a completely different direction from those caught at Ottenby, about 186 miles to the east on the southern tip of the Baltic island of Oland. The Ottenby birds migrated in the expected direction, i.e. generally south but the Falsterbo birds, normally migrating to the south-west, headed north.

The reason for the discrepancy turned out to depend on the condition of the birds – whether they had large or small fat reserves – and on their flight path before their arrival at the ringing sites. Ottenby birds are mainly from easterly breeding populations in Russia and are on their way to winter sites in southern Europe. Their flight plan takes them over the Baltic, with a short stop at Ottenby, and then a further flight across the remainder of the Baltic. They are also better stocked with fat reserves, indicating that they are well prepared for the sea-crossing.

At Falsterbo, however, the birds arrive mainly after travelling overland routes and in short hops. They have little in the way of fat reserves. Suddenly confronted with the sea, they pull up short, and may fly 12–50 miles north along Sweden's west coast. Here they seek out resting sites and refuel, and spend several days preparing themselves for the sea-crossing. When they are ready and weather conditions are right, the birds continue on their migration towards south-west Europe, taking off in the evening and flying into the night.

During the night itself, the pattern of the stars provides a nocturnal compass. In the northern hemisphere, birds recognize that stars in the Pole Star cluster are in the same position in the sky because they are above the earth's axis of rotation.

Orientation experiments in planetaria have shown that some birds, even newly hatched birds, adjust their direction if the artificial night sky is rotated. In the USA, indigo buntings were exposed to a summer night sky that revolved around a star in the constellation of Orion, rather than the normal Pole Star. In the autumn, the same birds were exposed once more to the novel sky rotation and they showed directional tendencies appropriate to that sky. The birds had learned the positions of the stars. Indeed, gull and tern chicks have been seen sitting in their scrapes in the ground and gazing at the heavens as they learn their star maps.

Not all birds follow this rule, however. In planetarium experiments, in which star patterns and the magnetic field have been altered, the bobolink – another night flyer – seems unimpressed by the changing celestial cues. The tests were carried out in spring, and when celestial north and magnetic north were the same the birds showed a consistent tendency to head north on their normal migration heading. If the celestial north remained the same and the magnetic north was artificially reversed to become magnetic south, the birds' preferred direction was south. They had ignored the celestial cue in favour of the magnetic one and did not begin to reorient to the correct stellar cues for two to five days. This behaviour is similar to that seen in European robins, but not in European warblers and New World savannah sparrows, which tend to respond more readily to visual cues.

For those birds urgently watching the night sky, the stars may not necessarily be the most important feature. Curiously, when a bird is setting off, the stellar compass, even in night-flying migrants, is subordinate to the solar compass in a bird's hierarchy of navigational cues.

In experiments in the southern USA, savannah sparrows were exposed to sunsets deflected from the true direction by mirrors followed by a normal clear night sky. The birds chose to orient at the appropriate angle to the apparent direction of the sunset and not to the correct star pattern. Similarly, when placed in enclosures around which the local magnetic field could be altered and exposed to a shift in the apparent position of the sun, the birds preferred to follow their sunset compass. The results suggest that savannah sparrows set the direction for their nocturnal migration by the sun – using either horizon glow or polarized light – and then use the stars as celestial cues to ensure they continue on the same course in the dark. Birds, it seems, make very few course direction decisions during the night, and merely use the stars to ensure they are maintaining the heading that was established before they took off.

If the early evening solar compass is unavailable because clouds are obscuring the sunset, but the sky clears later, some birds can orient to the stars and take off in the correct direction.

When the evening sky is hidden at sunset and stars in the night sky are also obscured by clouds, birds have a third navigational cue available – the wind. Under these conditions night-flying song birds tracked by radar across New York state have been seen to set off downwind, sometimes in the opposite direction to that which they really want to take.

In a controlled experiment, migrant white-throated sparrows, some with frosted lenses placed over their eyes and others with normal vision, were released from a balloon and tracked by radar. Those that could see properly did not rely on the wind and flew off on their expected migratory path. The birds whose vision had been disrupted and so were deprived of any visual cues headed downwind, even if the direction was inappropriate to their normal migration route.

With other navigational cues absent, but with an overriding desire to migrate, birds in the New York area have a more than 50 per cent chance of heading in the right direction during the spring and a less than 50 per cent chance in the autumn. The wind does not give a reliable compass heading, but it will help get a bird to where it wants to go for at least half the time, sufficient odds for the bird to want to rely on it and to override its more accurate magnetic sense. How it determines wind speed is still a mystery, and something quite remarkable if you consider the controlled experiment in which birds orient downwind within a few seconds of their release.

This apparently odd behaviour of following a directional cue that might be inappropriate to a bird's intended migration route has led some scientists to suggest that the calibration of sun and star compasses is not a once and for all event, set at some point in the bird's early life, but must be revised and reset every few days throughout the bird's life.

There is one more curious piece of navigational behaviour shown by some birds, particularly warblers. Sometimes these birds set off deliberately in the wrong direction, taking a westerly bearing that is the mirror image of the easterly bearing they would normally take. This strange behaviour, where the birds get the angle with respect to north–south correct but reverse the east–west component has been seen in North American warblers and Siberian wagtails. The reason for the reversal is yet another mystery of bird migration, observed but yet to be solved.

As for our present understanding of the principles of bird migration, orientation and navigation, we can, perhaps, draw a few conclusions. During a bird's lifetime, and varying from species to species and under different atmospheric conditions, there is a shift in emphasis in what navigational aids it uses. Scientists have recognized that a bird has a 'compass' sense with which it orients and maintains a course heading and a 'map' sense with which it determines its position relative to home. Some birds, like the homing pigeon, have a compass and a map, but the map sense is little understood. Others use only a compass. For some species, the earth's geomagnetic field seems to provide sufficient directional information for a young bird, pre-programmed with a genetic flight plan, to find its way about. Others simply learn routes from parents. As a bird gets older, it learns visual compasses, using the sun, stars and moon or ground geography; and if all else fails it can fly with the wind. Birds, like NASA spacecraft, have back-up systems to get where they're going and it has made them amongst the most successful long-distance travellers on earth.

But even birds, like NASA spacecraft, can be fooled by the simplest thing. The Bewick's swan contingent at Slimbridge, Gloucestershire, had been leaving for Siberia a month earlier than usual. The staff at the Wildfowl and Wetlands Trust headquarters were understandably concerned. Birds flying north too early will be confronted by bad weather and some would probably perish. Why, wondered the staff, were they leaving prematurely? After some careful thought the light dawned, quite literally. The floodlights on the lake remained on until 10 p.m. The swans were confused. They thought that the longer days of spring had arrived and that they'd better get moving. Today, the lights are turned out at eight-thirty and the Bewick's leave on their incredible journey north and east at precisely the right time.

TRADITIONAL POSTSCRIPT

When they arrive in some parts of the world migrating birds are assured a warm welcome. Throughout Europe, white storks are considered the harbingers of spring and the mythical bringers of babies. There are festivals to celebrate their arrival and in Denmark the stork on its chimney top nest used to be a national symbol! In southern Germany and Alsace, the bird is thought to bring good luck. Storks and people live side by side, the latter providing the former with nest platforms like a cartwheel on a pole or a wooden platform on a roof top.

In California, however, another smaller migrant, travelling from wintering sites in Argentina, has embarrassed its human hosts and sparked off a local row. Each spring for the past 200 years the swallows have arrived at San Juan Capistrano, to the south of Los Angeles. The mission there recorded the arrival of the birds as long ago as 1777, and in recent times people from all over North America have flocked to the town to join in the week-long festival in the birds' honour. There was even a popular song written in 1939 about the event. Local radio stations play 'When the swallows come back to Capistrano' constantly. But in 1989, and each year since, many of the birds have overflown San Juan Capistrano and settled for the summer at an imitation French chateau called 'Heaven's Gate' at Malibu, 75 miles to the north. Although swallows still arrive at Capistrano, traders and shopkeepers are understandably worried that the 'arrival' is not what it used to be.

4

SOUND SENSE

THE PIGEON IS A MUSIC BUFF. TRAINED PIGEONS CAN DISCRIMINATE between the musical works of two recognizable composers – Johann Sebastian Bach and Igor Stravinsky. In tests, birds were encouraged to peck at discs when exposed to tape-recorded extracts from the works of the great composers. If they heard Bach's Toccatas and Fugues in D Minor and F for organ they pecked at one disc, and if they were played Stravinsky's 'Rite of Spring' they pecked at another disc. They could not only distinguish between the great composers but also differentiate between Bach and Stravinsky sound-alikes, and they were right for about 90 per cent of the time.

Dietrich Buxtehude and Alessandro Scarlatti sounded to the birds like Bach, while Antonio Vivaldi, Eliot Carter and Walter Piston they considered to have hints of Stravinsky. Humans tested with the same works considered Vivaldi to be Bach-like.

So, do birds hear things as we do and do they analyse them in the same way? Alas, it seems not. Starlings have been presented with sequences of musical notes which they have been taught to recognize. But if the sequences are transposed to a higher or lower octave the birds cease to respond to them. Indeed, if the tune is shifted up or down by as little as a quarter of a tone they cannot discriminate the sounds. If a human is presented with a tune, but in a different key to the one in which he first learned it, he can still recognize it. Birds, unlike most humans, use something other than relative pitch to discriminate sounds, but that something is just as remarkable. They sense something closer to absolute pitch, an ability possessed only by a few highly gifted musicians.

Birds also recognize timbre – the equivalent ability in humans of distinguishing between a piccolo, flute, oboe or bassoon and of telling apart two distinct human voices. Timbre is created when a fundamental note, say 500 Hz, is combined with harmonics. A second harmonic would be at 1 kHz and a third at 1.5 kHz. When the harmonics are featured or suppressed, the notes are given different tonal qualities. Birds can recognize fundamentals and harmonics, which suggests that they can also recognize tonal qualities in their calls and songs. In the sixty-nine separate song syllables of a zebra finch, for example, researchers have found twenty-nine timbre variations. This means, as one researcher put it, 'that birds can detect, learn, remember and produce remarkably subtle changes in a complex sound.' And that is an amazing thing for such a tiny-brained organism to do.

Compared to those of birds, man's auditory capabilities may seem puny. In human hearing, individual pulses of sounds fuse into a perceived continuous tone at about 20 discrete units per second; in the bird the figure is 200 units per second. A simple experiment with the whip-poor-whill, a North American nightjar, showed how birds are able to pick up more detail in a song than we can.

The whip-poor-whill's name is onomatopoeic. It describes a three-note phrase which the bird sings time after time. When the song is recorded, slowed down and analysed, however, it turns out that there are not three sections but five. Does the bird itself, though, hear three or five? There was an intriguing way to find out.

The mockingbird imitates the whip-poor-whill, so a recording was made of a mockingbird copying its song. When the recording was checked it too showed five phrases. The mockingbird had heard much more than its human observers, and it is likely that the whip-poor-whill itself hears the same.

Birds can also hear the minutest sounds, quite inaudible to the human ear. An owl, hunting at night, locates its prey by detecting the minute rustling sounds made by a mouse or vole as it moves through the grass. By cocking its head to one side, a blackbird can pick up the imperceptible sound of a leatherjacket burrowing below the lawn, and a ringed plover can hear the micro-noise made by some marine invertebrate scrabbling about in the mud.

Even more intriguing is the frequency spectrum across which birds can detect sounds. The pigeon has shown it is able to hear very low frequency sounds – much lower than the sounds we can pick up – but how it uses this sensory information has yet to be determined. And at the other end of the audio spectrum, the oilbird and the cave swiftlet (see pages 163–5), produce very high-frequency click sounds and use echo location in order to find their way in and out of the labyrinth of caves and tunnels in which they nest and roost, much in the way of bats. But perhaps the most audible evidence of birds' ability to produce and make use of sounds – audible, that is, to man – is bird songs and calls.

EARLY CALLS

Bird-calls range from high-pitched warnings to low-pitched booms, but their function is more easily recognized than in songs, for calls are usually given in specific contexts, and are stereotyped, that is, they are reproduced without variations. There are calls associated with threat, courtship, flight, alarm, begging, bonding, identification of partners or offspring and many other forms of behaviour. Geese honk, owls hoot, doves coo, gulls mew and cuckoos, well . . . cuckoo.

The most common bird-call must be the chirp of the ubiquitous sparrow; the most evocative of place are probably the calls of gulls, so reminiscent of the seaside; the most beautiful surely is the haunting tremolo of the black-throated diver; and the most irritating calls, most agree, are those of some tropical species known collectively as 'brain-fever birds' on account of the monotonous nature of their performance and a tendency to call throughout the hottest parts of the day.

Calls feature very early in a bird's life. Some birds actually call whilst still in the egg. Young quail chicks synchronize their hatching by calling. The eight eggs per nest are laid over a period of a few days and so, because they are incubated under the same conditions, the first bird to hatch out would have to wait two days or so for the last chick to hatch. There is a danger, then, that the first of these precocious birds would start to wander before the rest were ready and the brood would be in considerable danger – a predator could pick them off one by one. So, instead, the unhatched chicks call to each other and arrange to emerge together; indeed, they all hatch out within six hours of each other.

Guillemots also call from inside the egg, several days before hatching. The egg is not in a nest, but lies balanced on a ledge. The calls the chick makes from inside the egg ensure that the parents return and incubate the right egg. The bird inside, though, is not only calling, it is also listening. It must learn its parents' calls, and will respond only to their calls when it is on the ledge or later down on the sea after fledging.

American white pelican chicks also call from inside the egg, and they do so to tell mum that they're too hot or too cold. An unhatched chick is little able to control its own temperature and so it must motivate a parent to do the job for it. In the case of the pelican, the parent might actually stand on the egg or sit on it. Up until the moment the chick is ready to hatch, the parent can monitor the temperature through the skin of its webbed feet and cover the eggs – usually two – to warm them up or expose them to cool them. Just before hatching, however, the parent does not remain in such close contact with the eggs. A special call from the first-laid chick encourages the parent to move back in order that the little one can break out. As long as the temperature remains normal, the chick calls once or twice per minute. If, however, the egg temperature drops or rises, the calling rate increases and the parent can step in to adjust the temperature.

Young gulls cannot beg for food unless exposed to maternal feeding calls. In one experiment, a clutch of eggs was exposed to maternal feeding calls, while another clutch received no sound stimulus at all. After hatching, it was found that those chicks which had heard the mother's feeding call pecked at her bill for food. The other chicks did not.

During incubation and brooding, female mallard ducks make a species-typical maternal call to which the unhatched ducklings respond. The mother duck does not start making the call until the embryo duck's head projects into the airspace of the egg, at about seventeen to nineteen days after laying. The hatchlings, then, are aware of their species call some time before they emerge and respond immediately to the maternal call when called out of the nest. This preparation before hatching equips the precocious duckling with an important homing signal to which it can head when danger threatens.

In experiments with unhatched ducklings, it has been shown that those exposed to mother's clucking before they hatched respond to decoys emitting the species call, and will imprint on a decoy; but they do not react to silent decoys. Repetition rate (pattern) and frequency modulation (tune) are salient features for recognition, although it has been found that the calls used by the mother duck before and after hatching are slightly different. There are more notes per burst and more harmonics in a call given after hatching.

The call can be so important that a mother's appearance might be less stimulating than her call. In other experiments, ducklings were visually imprinted on a stuffed duck model soon after they had hatched. They were presented with a red-and-white striped box and the stuffed model, both of which had loudspeakers hidden inside. If the speaker inside the box played the mother duck's 'assembly' call the ducklings would rush towards it, totally ignoring the more visually attractive stuffed bird. Another test was done, not with a stuffed duck but with a silent real one. The ducklings behaved in the same way and preferred the box making the right sound. If, however, the ducklings were presented with a real mother duck making the right sounds they went unerringly to the real thing, ignoring the calling box. They clearly responded to the combined audio-visual stimulus to the exclusion of all others.

As for the ducklings themselves, they emit two quite distinct calls – the 'contentment' call and the 'distress' call – which play an important role in keeping the family together. The contentment call is first given by the duckling inside the egg. It has short note durations and a fast repetition rate and is low in pitch. Later, it is given in the presence of other ducklings and when the mother's call is heard. The distress call is only heard after hatching. It has longer note durations and a slower repetition rate, and is higher pitched. It is given when a duckling is isolated from its group.

The call can mean the difference between life and death, the danger not necessarily coming from a predator. The mother herself is programmed to respond to her offspring in a certain way, and if things are not right she may go berserk and destroy her own youngsters. Sound, it seems, is sometimes at the top of the hierarchy of communication signals a bird might use.

In experiments with turkeys, for instance, a deaf female laid eggs, sat and incubated them normally, but behaved in a very odd way when they hatched. She was unable to recognize her own chicks and proceeded to kill them. Normally, the youngsters' calls induce recognition and suppress the mother's natural aggression. Despite having visual information, the deaf mother was dominated by her aggressive behaviour. There have been similar classic tests with chickens, in which a chick was isolated from its mother. It was placed in a bell jar and could not be heard from outside. Although the hen could clearly see her offspring, she ignored it and walked away.

Parent–offspring recognition is not necessarily instant upon the hatching of the chick, but is dependent upon the lifestyle of the species. Experiments in which young of various ages are swapped between nests have shown that in some colonial birds, such as gulls, brood exchanges can be tolerated until the chicks are about to move out of the nest. In the herring gull, this parent–offspring recognition takes place about five days after hatching, whereas in the kittiwake recognition does not become effective until five weeks.

In Japan, pre-parent recognition begging behaviour was found to be three times longer and more pronounced in island fledglings of the varied tit than in mainland birds. The exaggerated behaviour and extended parental care have probably evolved as a result of the low availability of food and high density of birds on islands.

In a field experiment on North America's west coast, researchers looked at the parent–offspring recognition behaviour of sand martins (bank swallows). Swapping like-aged chicks from nest to nest showed that in this species transfers could be made without upsetting the parents until fifteen days after hatching. At sixteen or seventeen days the swapped chicks were rejected. The researchers identified a change in calls at fifteen days. At this time, the immature begging call changes to a 'signature' call, each chick having its own distinct call.

Other west coast researchers studied the protective behaviour of parent ring-billed gulls. They found that straying chicks give audible cues to their parents. The little ones always wander off in the same direction, so a parent gull knows in which general direction to start looking for its wayward chick. On finding it, the parent only responds if it is its own chick emitting its own particular call.

Ring-billed gulls nest in dense island colonies. They are highly territorial. Neighbouring gulls might kill a stray chick so it is important that contact between parent and offspring promotes protection for the chick. With unhatched eggs or young in the nest the adult gives 'long' or 'mew' calls. Chicks respond to the mew call by returning to the nest site. Mew calls are also given during the feeding of the young. It is thought that perhaps food is the underlying motivation which encourages chicks to respond to parents' calls. Playback experiments have shown that laughing gull and razorbill chicks can also discriminate the voices of their parents from those of other adult birds.

RECOGNIZED IN A CROWD

The need for a young bird to acquire the ability to recognize individuals in the confusion of, say, a seabird colony is paramount. Until wildlife sound research began in earnest, vision was thought to be the main way in which one bird might find another. Many birds have the visual acuity to spot their mates at a distance of 200 metres, but field work in the 1960s showed that sound plays an important role too.

In an attempt to identify the relative importance of sound and vision in seabird recognition, W.H. Thorpe of Cambridge University, a pioneer in the study of animal sounds, visited the Bass Rock in the Firth of Forth. There he was confronted with an enormous colony of noisy gannets. Even in the gannet's simple, squawky call, Thorpe found that there was enough information for the individual to be recognized by others in the colony. While recording gannets on their craggy cliff-top nests he noticed that, when one of a pair returned with its catch, it flew to the bottom of the cliff, hung in the updraft and moved up the cliff face as if going up in a lift, calling all the way. The gannet remaining on the nest paid no attention to the rising current of birds until it heard the unmistakable calls of its returning mate. It became excited, and began calling back. Thorpe concluded that each bird could recognize the calls of its own mate as distinct from those of others. He found that only the first part of the call, the first tenth of a second, was needed.

A similar study was conducted with sandwich terns; this time the way chicks spotted parents was studied. The parent terns locate the nest site with the help of their visual memory. They give the 'fish' call when approaching the area, but only their own offspring react. The young quite obviously recognize, Thorpe discovered, three distinct sections in the call of the parents.

Male and female emperor penguins have distinctive calls, not aimed at the young, but at their partners. A pair may spend weeks apart during the incubation and brooding periods during the long Antarctic winter (see page 218). One bird stays with the egg or youngster and the other goes to sea to fish. When one partner returns, the reunion must be quick; time is of the essence where survival in such a harsh climate is not guaranteed. Male and female must be able to recognize each other in the general mêlée of the colony. To help the process, male and female emperor penguins have different calls. In fact, it's the only way a human observer can tell them apart (outside of watching which one lays the egg) for male and female emperors, the largest of the penguins, are identical in shape, size and colour. Amongst much shuffling, head bowing and beak tilting a pair of emperor penguins deliver a loud, braying trumpet duet, each producing a very distinctive sound. The male penguin's call is built from long pulses of sound, each pulse 100 to 500 milliseconds long. The female's call has short pulses, 30 to 100 milliseconds long.

KEEP OUT CALLS

Pied wagtails vigorously defend winter feeding territories and use a particular call to help in that defence. The birds establish their patch in the autumn. Typically, each feeding territory extends about 300 metres along the edge of a river meadow, encompassing both banks of the river. The food, which is so vital for winter survival, is washed onto the river bank, and each day the territory holder walks along the shore picking up any food debris it can find. The walk is very precise, for the bird avoids walking over the same patch of ground too soon after a foraging excursion. The longer it leaves that piece of shore, the better chance it has of finding food there on the next visit. If it returns too soon it is less likely to be successful and the energy used to forage is wasted. So, in order to maximize its foraging potential, each territory holder walks down one side of the river, crosses to the other bank, and walks back up.

It is vital for the territory holder to keep out intruders or they could upset his carefully executed plan. It is also important for intruders to know if a territory is occupied. A territory holder, on his regular foraging patrol, will have depleted the food systematically, leaving little for an intruder. He too would be wasting his time if he began to forage in an occupied territory. So intruders and residents talk to each other and save energy. Intruders, landing in a territory, call out 'chis-ick', which means in pied wagtail language 'Is there anybody there?' The territory holder replies with a 'chee-wee', and that is usually that. The contest is brief. There is no point in an intruder's staying if a resident is already exploiting the available food.

When an intruder gives his 'chis-ick' call and receives no answer, he waits for about 20 minutes while his confidence builds before he too is ready to give a 'chee-wee' call in defence of his newly acquired patch of riverbank.

CALL REPERTOIRES

Individual recognition and keep-out signals are just two functions of bird-calls. Social calls may keep a flock together. Alarm calls warn others of danger. Mobbing calls summon help. Feeding calls are exchanged between mates. And there are roosting calls, nest-site calls, begging calls, threat calls and so on, each call associated with a particular event in a bird's life. Many bird-calls, unlike songs, tend to be very simple, almost monosyllabic, and relatively easy to understand. A blackbird, for instance gives its 'pinking' call in response to a prowling neighbourhood cat. The meaning is clear – watch out!

Less clear are the 'all-purpose calls' given by birds like the black-throated diver or common loon. The loon has four distinct calls – the tremolo, wail, yodel and hoot – but contained within the calls are subtle variations, each with a separate message. Different styles of tremolos, for instance, indicate different levels of arousal. Low-frequency tremolos indicate a low-level of anxiety, while high-frequency tremolos reveal a very agitated bird. Low-intensity tremolos might be given when a mate returns to the nest, while high-intensity calls, followed by a dive or a take-off, are given as alarm calls.

Contact with a partner is frequently preceded by a wail. It is often given at night and might open and close a night chorus. The hoot is a very low-level contact call between members of the same family. It is a call sometimes given by parents to reassure chicks that they are nearby.

The spectacular yodel is an individual's call sign and it is made mainly by the male bird. It has some role in territorial defence and in establishing an individual's space. In spring, a resident bird will yodel at an intruder. In summer, yodels are heard amongst summer flocks to tell others in the flock that they are too close. For ornithologists, the calls can be used to indentify known individuals; the vocal equivalent of bird-ringing.

This subtlety in meaning has been found in many other birds too. The 'kuk-kuk-kuk' pre-departure call of the kittiwake (black-legged kittiwake) has been the focus of interest of a research team in south-west England. This call appears to be the way in which one kittiwake tells another kittiwake 'I'm just off now.' The response of the partner can vary. If the spouse is disapproving there's a lot of head-tossing and a squabble may ensue that puts the would-be wanderer firmly in his place. But if everything is OK and approval for take-off is given, the mate replies with 'ki-ti-wa-ak,' the four-note call that gave rise to the bird's onomatopoeic name. This characteristic kittiwake call, however, seems not to have just one meaning. The team found that birds use the same call when fighting, returning to the nest, and when a predator is about. Kittiwakes, it seems, have a small vocabulary but each utterance may have a lot of meanings depending on the context. Other birds have larger call vocabularies. Working on the call vocabulary of several species of birds, Thorpe was able to show that some birds have up to fifteen different calls. (The chaffinch has fifteen calls but more recent work has shown that the song sparrow has beaten it with seventeen.)

The passerines come top of the list with the highest number of calls, and as analysis techniques improve and increasingly more species are examined, the call vocabularies of birds appear more and more sophisticated and meaningful. Indeed, our traditional understanding of bird-calls must, in many cases, be revised.

LEARNING CALLS

Traditionally, calls were thought to be inherited and not learned, but this view of bird behaviour has had to be modified in the light of recent work in New York. The bird under scrutiny was the North American goldfinch. One of its calls, a flight call, is used by members of a pair to maintain contact during the breeding season. The female goldfinch is in the habit of incubating the eggs for long periods of time. The male feeds the female, and as soon as he returns to the nest the female begins to beg. The study revealed that the begging behaviour starts long before the female can actually see

THE CALL VOCABULARY OF THE CHAFFINCH

Nature of Call	Call	Remarks
1 Flight call	'Tsup' or 'Tupe'	A short penetrating call. Low pitch with single higher harmonic. Associated with flight or preparation for flight.
2 Social call	'Chink' or 'Spink'	Clear ringing call in two parts. Helps separated birds to meet again.
3 Escape call	'Cheenk'	More shrill than 2. Used as escape call and during courtship by newly paired males.
4 Aggressive call	'Zzzzzz' or 'Zh-zh-zh'	Low buzz uttered during attack and fighting in a few captive males.
5 Alarm call	'Tew'	Most frequent of three alarms. Common in young birds and more rarely adults of both sexes.
6 Alarm call	'Seee'	Extreme alarm in breeding male. Pure tone rising and falling and difficult for predator to locate precisely.
7 Alarm call	'Huit' or 'Whit'	Commonly at rate of 30 per minute. Male chaffinches in spring. Moderate danger.
8 Injury call	'Tseee'	Squeak given by birds hurt fighting.
9 Courtship call	'Kseep', 'Tsit', 'Chwit', 'Tzit'	Short and high-pitched in bursts of three simultaneous descending notes. Male gives it courting female at pair-formation in early part of season.
10 Courtship call	'Tchirp' or 'Chirri'	Coarse chirp. Replaces 9 during courtship later in season.
11 Courtship call	'Seep'	The only extra call of female during breeding season. Short and high-pitched but composed of only two notes.
12 Begging call	'Cheep'	Soft note of nestlings.
13 Begging call	'Chirrup'	Loud and penetrating call of fledglings.
14 Intermediates	'Huit'/'Seee' 'Huit'/'Chink'	Occasional intermediates between alarm and social calls of mature birds.
15 Sub-song	'Chrrp' and variants or low-pitched rattles grouped together in various ways	Chirps and warbles of birds in first summer.
16 Song	'Tchip-tchip-tchip-Cherry-erry-erry-Tchip-Tcheweeoo	Trills and a terminal flourish lasting some two to three seconds. January or February to June, and September and October.

the male. She hears, from some distance away, the flight call that accompanies the male's bounding flight.

Analysis of the male's flight call revealed that it is much more complicated than other bird-calls, and that individual goldfinches have calls with subtle variations. Analysis of a flight call a year later, during the following breeding season, showed that at the beginning of the season a pair of goldfinches modify the structure of their flight calls to a common pattern. One bird, the male in fact, imitates the calls of his partner. They then maintain this modified pattern throughout the breeding season, using the calls as a kind of naming system. This capacity to learn new calls is maintained by the male goldfinch throughout its life. The advantage to the male is that it can establish a bond with a new female if a mate dies or moves away.

Further research has revealed that in the cardueline finches many calls in the repertoire are learned. Finches reared in acoustic isolation produce calls which seem normal to the human ear. The modifications through learning are quite minor, however, and involve detail in the call structure that our undiscriminating ear cannot immediately pick up. None the less, the modifications are sufficient for individual finches to tell each other apart according to the structure of their calls.

The twite – another small, streaked finch – also has calls that appear to be learned. Mated pairs have calls in common which are different from those of other mated pairs. These calls are used to make contact when in flocks.

Similar learned components have been discovered in chaffinch calls. 'Chink' calls from birds raised in captivity are different from those given by birds in the wild. Not having heard the 'chink' call of others, the hand-reared bird is at a disadvantage and consequently produces ill-rehearsed and variable sounds. A laboratory chaffinch has even been known to learn the 'cheep, cheep' of a house sparrow. Dialects have also been found in chaffinch rain calls; birds in separate areas giving quite distinct calls. Dialects can only occur if the call is learned.

Manx shearwaters show local dialects. A population has only to be separated from another for as little as six years for the human observer to appreciate the subtle dialect differences in the calls. Shearwaters on one island have different calls from those birds on neighbouring islands.

Clearly, then, birds are able to copy calls, even the calls of other species, and learning through copying is necessary for the proper development of calls within a repertoire.

ALARM CALLS

No single problem, a researcher once wrote, in anti-predator behaviour has attracted more theories and produced fewer facts than that of the evolution and function of alarm calls. One thing *is* clear, however, and that is that they are very easy to recognize.

The redshank – a European wader – is a champion of alarm callers; it is often known as the sentinel of the salt-marsh. It is first to spot danger and first to raise the alarm. Its alarm call is shrill and, unlike most other bird-calls, it warns not only other redshanks but also other bird species; curlews, plovers, dunlin and gulls soon follow with a chorus of concern. In the mass confusion a predator is often distracted and may be deprived of a meal.

In the wood, the jay is usually first to warn of any approaching threat. A day-flying owl will evoke a hard rattling call from the jay which serves to encourage other birds in the trees to join in and, together, noisily mob and chase away the predator.

In the urban garden, the robin is often first to spot the neighbour-hood cat, to which it gives a clearly audible 'tick tick' alarm. But to a crow flying overhead, it gives a whispy, untraceable call. All the other birds, though, seem to hear it and become agitated.

Bird alarm calls seem to fall into three types: those like that of the redshank are clear shrieks of despair which travel a fair distance across the marsh or estuary; those of the jay are hard-edged and raucous and draw the attention of neighbours to the area of excitement; and the hawk alarm of the robin travels short distances and is hard to pinpoint.

The third group of calls – those that are hard to locate – have been of particular interest to researchers. Chaffinches have come under scrutiny and have been found to have several alarm calls, including the 'chink-chink' call and the 'pink-pink' call. For most other calls, the transmission range is maximized, but for these signals the opposite is required, or at least a compromise between communicating with individuals that need the message and with those that would become a threat if they picked up the signal.

The least locatable of chaffinch alarms is a call given by the male chaffinch to the mate and young in the nest when danger threatens. It is a very high (7–9 kHz), thin whistle which has the curious property of being extremely difficult for a human observer to locate. Analysis of the call has revealed that it is designed in such a way as to reduce the cues that might enable a potential predator to pinpoint the calling bird. It is not completely non-locatable, for it is not possible to produce such a sound, but it does minimize the cues available.

A bird uses three basic cues for locating the source of a sound, all involving some comparison between sounds reaching its two ears. The time of arrival of sounds is important; so, too, is the intensity of the sounds. The head casts a shadow, so if sound is coming from the left, the left ear will hear that sound slightly before the right ear. The sound will also be slightly louder in the left ear than in the right. The third feature is a difference in phase at each ear. Sound travels in undulating waves with peaks and troughs. If the same sound is coming from the left, the peaks might hit the left ear at the same time as the troughs hit the right ear. By comparing this phase difference the direction from which the sound has been coming can be identified.

In order for a bird to locate a sound source, the sound must contain easily detectable abrupt discontinuities, the moment of arrival of which can be compared at a bird's two ears. Using that comparison a bird can locate the source of the sound. But predators can do the same thing. Therefore the chaffinch must modify its call so as to eliminate or, at least, minimize the cues available to its enemies. It does this by producing a call which gradually fades in, reaches a climax and then slowly fades out. The high-pitched nature of the whistle also makes it difficult for comparisons of phase. Wavelengths shorter than the distance between the ears mean that a receiver cannot be sure if it was hearing the dip of the trough directly after the first cycle peak, or if another cycle or two had intervened.

Unfortunately, the picture is not as simple as it might at first seem. Predators, trying to keep one step ahead of the prey's anti-predator systems, have a trick or two in reserve. It is quite possible that predators such as hawks and owls may not be carrying out these kinds of comparison. The way they localize sounds may rely less on a pressure-receptor system than on a pressure-gradient or particle-displacement system. In this way, a predatory bird can locate a sound source simply by scanning with one ear. The diurnal goshawk and the nocturnal barn owl can accurately locate small birds, such as the chaffinch, emitting their thin, supposedly non-locatable alarm calls. Barn owls, for example, have been shown to locate clay-coloured thrushes by the 'sect' alarm call.

But they don't always get it right. At a convalescent home for injured birds of prey in Michigan, red-tailed hawks and great horned owls were put to the test. They were presented with the mobbing calls of the red-winged blackbird and the 'seet' alarm call of the American robin. The raptors located the source of the mobbing sounds with considerable ease, but the alarm calls fooled them. At the start of the call they were about 84 degrees off the mark, but by the end of it, after much head turning, they were 125 degrees adrift. The error is probably due to an inherent design fault in the avian ear and to the size of a large owl's head.

A bird's ears are not isolated from each other like our ears but are connected. Sound entering both ears, then, can hit both ear drums, on the front and on the back. If the sounds on either side of the drum are shifted in phase by 180 degrees, they cancel each other out. So, although a sound hits both eardrums, it might not be heard by them both. If, say, the sound is cancelled from the ear nearer the source, the bird will only hear it with the ear further away. The sound will appear to the bird to be coming from the opposite direction. The problem is exacerbated by the fact that the diameter of the owl's head is twice the wavelength of the robin's 'seet' call, making it even more difficult to locate.

In North America, the black-capped chickadee has a similar non-locatable alarm call. When a predator approaches a flock of these birds, an alarm call, known as 'high zees', is given. It is of the type that fades in and out and has a pure tone frequency of about 8 kHz that attenuates rapidly in the environment. It is also given at an intensity which travels to other members of the flock but no further. Because of its high frequency, the call can also be beamed at a receiver and away from a predator. Interestingly, the evolution of this call is not thought to be related to ensuring the safety of relatives and offspring. Youngsters often disperse many miles away to other flocks. It is also thought not to be used to panic the flock, for chickadees tend to freeze when they hear the call. Rather, the clue seems to be in the long-term monogamous mating system of this species. Mated pairs of chickadees tend to stay close to each other in the same flock and alarm calls might be directed at the mate, to protect it from predation. In this way a pair of successful breeding birds try to ensure they survive together until the next breeding season.

These ventriloquial properties of small bird alarm calls must be important, for thin, high-pitched, fade-in-fade-out calls have been evolved independently by a host of other bird species. Not only that, but the call says meaningful things to birds of quite different species.

Alarm calls are unusual in that they can communicate across species boundaries. A chaffinch in the top of a tree might spot a sparrowhawk and give its 'hawk' alarm call, which would transmit the presence of danger to a great tit, which in turn signals to a wren and so on. And the alarm calls of these different species are so alike that inexperienced bird-watchers often confuse the different calls. The 'wheet' call of the chaffinch, for example, is almost identical to the 'anxiety' call of the chiffchaff, the willow warbler and the redstart.

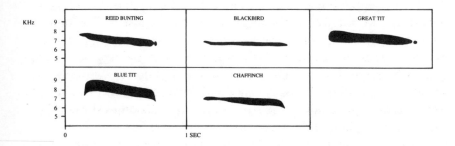

Sonograms of the alarm calls of small birds in responding to potential predators flying overhead.

On the East African savannah, not only other birds take note of the alarm calls of the superb starling; vervet monkeys listen in too. Young vervets have a 70 per cent chance of falling prey to a python, leopard or large eagle and need all the help they can get to survive. Superb starlings are good at spotting these predators and, like the vervets themselves, have distinct alarm calls for terrestrial and aerial predators. The vervets respond to the bird alarms as they would to their own – if a snake or leopard approaches, and the starling calls out, the vervets head for the nearest tree and climb to safety. If an eagle flies overhead, the appropriate alarm sends all and sundry scattering to the bushes where they are safe from the powerful talons of an aerial predator.

But whatever the nature of the call and no matter who is giving it, alarm calls are given more enthusiastically when there is an audience than when the caller is alone.

Like the vervet monkey, the farmyard rooster has different patterns of alarm and escape behaviour depending on the predator.

Escape from a terrestrial predator, like a racoon, clearly must differ in strategy from that appropriate to an aerial predator, like a hawk. The fox or racoon only sees in the horizontal plane and it is safer for a chick to freeze in order to avoid detection. To the hawk alarm, chicks run for cover, any cover, for the raptor spots its prey from the air and it is safer just to get out of sight. But, interestingly, the rooster needs to be in the presence of other chickens before it will call in alarm. If it is alone, it freezes or takes cover with little or no calling, no matter how strong the stimulus.

Ducks shriek or, rather they quack. Female ducks quack a lot in spring. It was thought at first that the frequent calling had something to do with attracting a mate or territorial proclamation, but more recently an alternative explanation has been suggested. The quacking is an alarm call, not to warn others of an approaching predator, but to *attract* predators and flush them from hiding. A female quacks long and hard at dawn and dusk, the times when predators are about, and she will quack away with or without the presence of her partner. Significantly, she stops quacking as soon as she lays her eggs. It is thought that the loud, single-note quack is directed at predators, and is a means by which the female ensures that there are no hidden predators nearby before establishing her nest site. This reduces the risk later that she and her hatchlings will be taken by surprise.

MOBBING CALLS

If an owl or other bird of prey corners a victim, all is not lost. Birds have a second stage of alarm to add to their defences – it is called mobbing (see page 85). Owls approaching a feeding or nesting area in the daytime, for instance, are mobbed by the many smaller birds in the area. Thrushes, jays, nuthatches and chaffinches make mock attacks, swooping in on the intruder, retreating, circling and attacking once more. Characteristic harsh calls of alarm are emitted during the harassment. Like the 'chat' call of the stonechat, these mobbing calls are easy to locate and serve to rally potential defenders from the surrounding countryside.

Mobbing may work in a variety of ways. The noisy attacks may inform others that danger is threatening. They might tell the predator itself that it has been spotted and that there is no chance of a surprise attack. Mobbing might also drive the predator away so that it hunts elsewhere.

A more cynical interpretation might suggest that a bird producing raucous mobbing and alarm calls is attracting as many other birds to itself as possible, so creating an artificial 'selfish-herd' situation. By manipulating other birds to congregate around the predator, an individual reduces its chances of being caught.

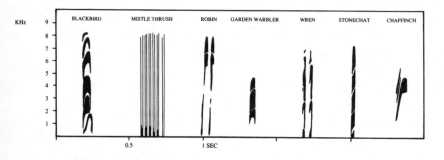

Sonograms of the mobbing calls given by small birds in response to the arrival of an owl.

Mobbing calls are short, square-edged, and have a wide range of frequencies present. This helps orientation for others, as the broad frequency spectrum gives phase and intensity difference information to the receiver. The square-edged start-and-stop points in the call provide time-difference information.

Mobbing calls might also have another function, that of teaching youngsters about the enemy. A young blackbird, exposed to danger without having had any experience of mobbing, shows a weak response to the threat. If it is able to watch and listen to mobbing behaviour by birds of its own species, then the next time it is exposed to danger it mobs more strongly than it did initially. In tests, young blackbirds could be taught mobbing behaviour by hearing the mobbing calls alone. Their response to danger could also be enhanced by playing them the mobbing calls of birds of another species.

Mobbing, though, doesn't always work. Owls sometimes take advantage of such behaviour. There have been several reports of a male owl flying noisily down a woodland clearing, attracting the attention of all the small birds in the area. As usual, they respond by mobbing him. The female of the pair, meanwhile, has been waiting and watching in a nearby tree. As the birds congregate around her mate, she swoops down and grabs one.

BOOMERS

While many small birds call in the higher registers, some of the larger birds reach for the other end of the sound spectrum and call at very low frequencies. These are the 'boomers', and their calls can travel long distances. The booming 500 Hz note of the bittern – a large, well-camouflaged heron-like bird – can be heard several miles away from the reed beds in which it is hiding. In one case a bird was reported to have been heard from over four miles away.

The male sage grouse from North America is another boomer and it has an acoustic trick with which it can impress the hens. Many cock sage grouse gather together during the early part of the breeding season and give their annual performance of dance and song. The males compete with each other for mating stations on the arena floor, an area called a lek. Females visit the lek when ready to mate and are attracted most to the males occupying the central sites. In order to sound the loudest and deepest, and therefore be most attractive to a female sage grouse, each male has an inflatable throat pouch in which it amplifies its booming lek call. The loudest and deepest calls are most probably given by the largest, oldest and most successful breeders, and they perform in the key positions at the centre of the lek.

Another noisy performance is given by the cock capercaillie, a giant in the grouse family. Ornithologists thought that it too should be a boomer, but at first hearing it didn't appear to be. Like the sage grouse, the male capercaillie performs at a lek. It fans out its tail, raises its head to the sky, and lets rip with a rather inconsequential series of pops, clicks and burps, not unlike beer being poured from a bottle. But, to scientifically minded bystanders this outburst seemed rather odd. The cock obviously puts a great deal of energy into the call and, indeed, is seen to shake all over. The other curious thing is that it inflates its enlarged oesophagus like a balloon, just as other grouse species do.

The sage grouse's call can be heard from a mile away, but the insignificant call of the capercaillie is barely audible to the human listener just 200 metres away. Also, the sage grouse's voice is lower than his mate's, and, it was reasoned, so should the voice of the cock capercaillie be. The hen capercaillie has a deep voice, so for the cock's voice to be deeper it would have to be in the depths of the infrasonic range. The only way to find out was to record the capercaillie's voice and then analyse the tapes. This done, it was found that most of the main elements in the call are below 40 Hz and therefore inaudible to the human ear.

This explained the seemingly insignificant call, but how does the bird make the very low-frequency sounds? Physicists explain that the production of such a low-frequency sound, on the organ pipe principle, would require an oesophagus of great length, much longer than the actual length of the bird. But an anatomical investigation of the capercaillie's vocal tract revealed that the bird overcomes this difficulty in a rather clever way. It has a Helmholtz resonator in its throat. This is a closed tube. When air is blown across the mouth, in the same way that a jug-band blower plays a jug, it produces a deep booming note which, in the case of the cock capercaillie, is so deep that we cannot hear it.

Similar anatomical modifications allow the whooping crane and trumpeter swan to produce low resonating notes. The Australian trumpeter manucode – one of the birds-of-paradise – has a long, coiled vocal tract and produces a low-frequency call, and the cock plain chachalaca has one more coil than his mate to produce a sound that is one octave lower than hers.

The rare New Zealand kakapo, a nocturnal, flightless, ground-living parrot, is a boomer. The male projects its low-frequency call by building its own version of the Hollywood Bowl. Like sage grouse and capercaillies, male kakapos gather at leks in the breeding season and boom, sometimes a thousand booms an hour for six or seven hours a night. The sound is amplified by air sacs that make the birds look almost spherical when calling, but this still does not account for the loudness of the signal. This is achieved by calling from excavated hollows, once thought to be dust baths. Further investigation revealed that the bowls are the right shape, like an outside auditorium or amphitheatre, to reflect the sound far and wide.

INSTRUMENTALISTS

Not all bird-calls, however, are made as vocal sounds. The 'drummers' in the bird world use their feet, beaks, wings, feathers and even tools, such as twigs used as drumsticks. The coot stamps its feet in the water to frighten away rivals, the peacock accompanies its visually flamboyant tail display with stiff feather rattling, the mute swan has whistling wing-beats that are thought to keep flying birds in touch with each other, the stork and albatross clap the mandibles of the bill together and the wood pigeon claps its wings.

The frigate bird rattles its mandible in alarm and the owl chick clicks its beak as a warning. The red grouse takes off with an explosive whirring sound thought to startle predators, a diversionary tactic that gives the escaping birds a few seconds to escape. The lapwing 'zooms' during its acrobatic courtship flight and the short-eared owl claps its normally silent wings below the body during its nuptial display.

The snipe makes a fluttering or 'bleating' sound as it descends out of the sky. As the bird falls rapidly through the air with its tail expanded, two modified feathers sticking out either side of the tail vibrate in the air flow at eleven times a second. The American woodcock precedes its vocal flight call, during 'roding', with a trilling sound produced by modified outer primary feathers in each wing. And the male ruffed grouse leans back on stiffened tail feathers and claps his wings against the air to make a thumping sound that gets faster and faster, until the drum roll reaches fever pitch at twenty thumps per second and can be heard over 500 metres away.

The broad-tailed hummingbird similarly produces a whistling sound with its high-speed wings. The air passing over the wings is directed through slots at the tips of the ninth and tenth primary feathers, and the resulting trill is used as a territorial proclamation signal. This was discovered by gluing up the slots and watching what a muted hummingbird would do. The result was that intruders had an easier time in taking over the territory as the resident bird became less aggressive. It couldn't hear its own 'keep out' sound and was confused. When the glue was removed with acetone the resident bird regained his status and chased away all intruders.

The tui and bellbird from New Zealand – two antipodean honeyeaters – produce similar wing noises, but their sound production capability is related to their ability to attract females. Male tuis have wide slots, and the wider the slots and the greater the noise, the more attractive the bird is. Young tuis with smaller slots haven't a chance and are well down in the pecking order. Bellbirds have a similar hierarchical system. But an interesting observation made by workers at the University of Auckland is that the tui, bellbird and a third honeyeater, the silent-flying stitchbird, compete for the right to feed from flowering trees. The tui, which has the widest noise-producing slots, has first call on the nectar-producing flowers, the bellbird is next in line, and the silent stitchbird must be content to feed on the leftovers.

Woodpeckers hammer out a rapid pattern of sounds on hard resonant surfaces, such as tree trunks, using a strong bill. They drum on different trees and produce different quality notes, but it is the temporal pattern of the drumming that is important to other woodpeckers. Some birds drum fast, others slow, and yet others speed up during the performance. The great spotted woodpecker drums accelerando, whereas the lesser spotted woodpecker drums with constant time intervals, although these vary from winter, when it drums slowly at ten to twelve beats per second, to spring when the rolls are faster. The black woodpecker of central and northern Europe produces a drum roll of forty beats, which lasts for a couple of seconds, and black woodpeckers in different geographical regions have drum rolls of different durations – distinct drumming dialects.

Drumming appears to be important during courtship, to bring female woodpeckers into breeding condition, and for territorial proclamation. Playback experiments using drumming sounds will elicit drumming behaviour in great spotted woodpeckers, and it has been shown that within the drumming pattern there are factors which identify individuals. Each woodpecker has its very own drum pattern, so a male and female can instantly recognize each other, as well as their neighbours, by sound.

Drumming is thought to have evolved as a byproduct of feeding behaviour. Woodpeckers attack the trunk of a tree in search of beetle larvae and other wood-boring insects, hammering their beaks into cracks and crevices. But why don't they get a headache?

High-speed film shot at 2,000 frames per second (normally film goes through the gate at 25 frames per second or thereabouts) of an acorn woodpecker in action has revealed that its bill slams into a tree trunk at 6.1 m/s (about 15 mph). One peck takes one thousandth of a second, and deceleration on impact is in the order of 1,000 g. (An astronaut experiences 3.5 g at take-off and it takes 1 g to overcome the earth's gravity.)

The film also revealed that the woodpecker blinks for the few milliseconds before and after the bill hits the tree, protecting the eye from splinters or simply keeping the eye in place. The bird also has a few practice stabs before letting rip.

The woodpecker's brain is very light, weighing not more than an ounce and it is packed into a cranium (brain case) of spongy bone. Muscles act as shock absorbers. But the secret is in the accuracy of the stab. By stabbing in exactly the same spot and not deviating to one side or the other, the woodpecker reduces shearing forces that would otherwise twist and tear the tissues. Also, the bird's neck is held very tense at the moment of impact.

Another avian percussionist is the male palm cockatoo of Australia. He does not use his bill or his head, but makes and uses drumsticks fashioned from twigs. During courtship, he pirouettes whilst hitting a hollow eucalyptus log with a stick held in one foot. In this way the palm cockatoo, the Buddy Rich of the bird world, impresses his future mate.

ECHO LOCATION

For some birds, sound production has taken on a quite different role. In a way, they communicate with themselves. Like bats and dolphins, they use sound to find their way about, particularly in the dark. They bounce sounds off obstacles or targets in the environment in order to orient and navigate. Most spend a part of their daily life in caves.

In South America, one cave-dwelling bird is known as the guacharo – 'the one who cries and laments'; in Trinidad it is called the diablotin – 'little devil'. It has been the source of supernatural stories and superstitions. But the creature with the truly sinister reputation is none other than the 35-centimetre-long oilbird – a neotropical bird which looks somewhat like a cross between a nightjar and a hawk. The raucous screams of hundreds of milling birds, echoing round the galleries in which they roost and nest, have conjured up images of devils and the lost spirits of the dead.

Oilbirds get their name from their unusual chicks – they are half as large again as the adults. They gain weight from oily fruits such as palms, and were much prized, for cooking and lighting oil, by the inhabitants of Caripe in northern Venezuela where *Steatornis caripensis* – the fat bird of Caripe – was discovered for science by Alexander von Humboldt in 1799.

The oilbird possesses an unusual guidance system. It not only makes loud alarm and contact calls but also emits rapid bursts of clicks with the tongue. Inside the cave the bird will let rip with a series of staccato clicks. The sounds bounce off any objects, such as walls or boulders, and by calculating the time the echo takes to return, it can accurately locate any hazard in its flight path. Each click consists of a burst of pulses, the separation of which we cannot appreciate until the call is analysed in the laboratory. Unlike the sounds made by a bat, the oilbird's clicks are not ultrasonic, and can be heard by people. The noise created by a disturbed colony is deafening.

In experiments in darkened flight cages, oilbirds have been shown to be able to use their clicks, as bats do, to avoid obstacles in their flight path; if their ears are plugged they crash into things. When executing a complicated manoeuvre, such as landing on a nest-site ledge, the bird's click rate increases, in the same fashion as small bats; the more clicks, the more information gained from the returning echoes.

The sounds emitted by oilbirds fall unevenly between 1 and 15 kHz, with a dominant frequency range between 1.5 and 2.5 kHz – within the human hearing range and thus making them poor echo locators. The smallest object they can discriminate by echo location is about 20-centimetres in diameter. In tests, they crashed into 5- and 10-centimetre discs, indicating that it is only the larger objects in their environment that they are able to avoid.

Once outside their dark caves, oilbirds do not use click-guidance but instead rely on very sensitive night vision and smell to find the aromatic fruit trees on which they feed.

Another avian cave dweller, the cave swiftlet from south-east Asia, leaves its cave not by night but by day, swapping day and night shifts with the local population of bats. Cave swiftlets are related to the common swifts that visit Europe in summer, but they are smaller and have a tubbier body and shorter wings. Like the oilbirds they use click sounds for echo location in the dark. They are diurnal, hunting for insects by day and returning to the caves to roost or nest at night. But their echo location capability apparently allows them to stay out longer after sunset, and to set out before sunrise, giving the colony a chance to exploit a larger area of food reserves than would be possible if they were using vision alone.

Some species of cave swiftlets emit impulse bursts, like the oilbirds, while others give pairs of clicks, like the *Rusettus* fruit bats except that they are in the human hearing range. One species, the uniform swiftlet from the Solomon Islands, New Caledonia and the New Hebrides, produces clicks between 4.5 and 7.5 kHz. With such a relatively low-click frequency, the swiftlets can expect to receive a less-detailed picture than that obtained by high-frequency clicking bats. Nevertheless, in tests the uniform swiftlet was able to avoid 6-millimetre-diameter wires in a darkened experimental flight cage.

Some populations of cave swiftlets live in the largest caves in the world in the Gonong Mulu National Park in Sarawak. Near the cave roof they construct bowl-shaped nests (the main ingredient of birds'-nest soup) which are firmly attached to the walls. Here the birds and the chicks in the nest are safe. But when it comes to fledging the young cave swiftlet has a fundamental problem – it must learn to fly and navigate in the dark using sound. On its maiden flight the swiftlet must fly well and have a workable echo location system in order to negotiate successfully the passageways and galleries to the cave entrance. Any error can be fatal. Waiting in the slimy covering of wet guano on the cave floor is a nightmarish collection of hungry animals.

There is a giant cricket with powerful legs and huge jaws. It is quite capable of tearing a swiftlet apart, and has been seen to enter a nest, seize an egg in its jaws, and smash it against the cave wall. Crabs forage in the guano heaps. They play tug-of-war with ditched birds, sometimes ripping them in two. Giant dinner-plate-size toads take a chick in one gulp.

Each evening, at the vast cave entrances, flying animals change shifts. The bats that share the upper parts of the caves with the swiftlets are on their way out to feed, while the swiftlets are returning to roost. Bat hawks, dark peregrine-sized birds of prey, swoop across the cave entrance and tear through the teeming flocks. The swiftlets spiral in from great heights, attempting to foil the hawks. Inside the caves, another hazard must be avoided. Cave racer snakes, coiled tightly around stalagtites and stalagmites, pluck swiftlets from mid-air.

As many as a million swiftlets might be nesting in a single cave. Each day, together with the bats, they gather insect food from a vast area around the cave, bringing nutrients for the entire cave community. If it were not for the swiftlets and the bats, and their amazing ability to 'see with sound', this extraordinary and diverse group of animals would not exist at all.

NIGHT SINGERS, CALLERS AND NIGHT HUNTERS

The continuous churring call of the nightjar is so much like the mating call of the natterjack toad that many a misguided bird-watcher has been looking up when he should have been looking down. Nightjars are crepuscular, that is, they are active when the light is fading at dusk and in the eerie half-light just before the dawn. They take advantage of the insects that are on the wing as night-time falls. Likewise bat hawks watch and wait for the comings and goings of prey at cave entrances at dawn and at dusk. Many birds, more than you might think, are true creatures of the night.

The New Zealand kiwi (see page 52) forages like a hedgehog at night, and the oilbird (see pages 163–4) feeds on fruit during the hours of darkness. The potoo, one of the tree-nighthawks of Central and South America, catches insects on moonlit nights, much in the way of flycatchers. It watches from a suitable, elevated vantage point, dashes out to catch passing prey, and returns to the perch to eat it.

Small bird migrants, though actively feeding by day when insect prey is in abundance, fly across the world by night. Some seabirds go fishing by day but avoid the attentions of most land-based predators by returning to their nest sites under cover of darkness. Little penguins file through the sand dunes to nesting burrows inland. For shearwaters and other petrels, which also return to land at night, sound comes into its own. Deprived of visual cues, these birds rely on sound to recognize each other and on smell and sound to find their way home.

Manx shearwaters fish in the open sea by day and arrive at their cliff-top nest burrows on offshore islands at night. They are long-lived and have the same mate each breeding season, but they have a devil of a job to find each other and the burrow in the dark – 'devil' being an appropriate word to use when describing shearwaters. Their eerie, screeching calls are so frightening that some have described them as coming from 'banshees of the night', the source, no doubt, of some ancient tales of witches and warlocks.

Manx shearwaters nest in rabbit burrows on cliff tops, particularly on offshore islands. While one partner stays to incubate the single egg or look after the nestling, the other goes to sea. To avoid gull predation, the adults return in the dark. So, in order to find the correct burrow a pair of birds call to each other, the bird in the burrow acting as a sound beacon on which the incoming bird can home in.

Each shearwater has its own, individual call. Partners who recognize each other quickly at the beginning of the breeding season get down to business earlier and are more likely to fledge their offspring successfully before the end of the season. The young, however, do not respond. Unlike the tern chick, which can directly influence the behaviour of its parents from its scrape in the sand, the young shearwater is stuck down a burrow and has little scope to move towards a parent and solicit food. Indeed, chicks can be swapped from nest to nest and they will continue to be fed, oblivious of the new male and female calls the foster parents are making.

Also, the calls made by male and female shearwaters differ, and the response to those calls differs, depending on who is the receiver. Males respond more to male calls and females to female calls. Males are clearly threatened mainly by rival males, so the male call is aimed in their direction. The female is in danger of having her burrow taken over by another female, so her calls serve to repel other females.

Another blood-curdling night-time caller is the loon or black-throated diver (see page 149). In northern lands during the short summer nights of mid-May to mid-June, divers fill the air with choruses of wails, yodels and tremolos. At night, the still air above the lake surface provides ideal conditions for long-distance trans-missions. First one bird starts up, then its neighbour, and then maybe birds from other lakes nearby join in until the divers of an entire lake system are chorusing together. What the birds are saying to each other is not clear. The romantics would have us believe that it is a chorus of joy, but the sceptics amongst us would probably point out that spring is the time of year when many loons are establishing territories, finding mates and preparing for nesting, and that the night-time chorus has the much more mundane function of proclaiming a territory.

While the shearwater's raucous screeches bathe a Welsh cliff top with strange and eerie sounds and the black-throated diver floods a Canadian lake with its tremulous utterances, the urban garden may find itself reverberating to the beautiful peformance of an unexpected nocturnal songster.

The European robin sings all the year round. It does not, however, sing the same song. In mid-December, British birds start with their spring song. Its function is to vigorously defend a territory and attract a mate. In mid-July, after the moult, the song changes to the winter song. This is a diluted version with the sole function of defending an autumn and winter territory, an important task if a territory holder is to have sufficient food throughout the dark, cold winter months.

The robin also sings at night. It is most probably the bird singing the night away at the bottom of your garden and not, as some suspect, a nightingale. There is even some speculation that the nightingale that sang so wonderfully in Berkeley Square was not a nightingale at all but a little cock robin. Streetlights and floodlights are the usual stimuli for nocturnal song, but a sudden noise can induce a slumbering robin to burst into life and sing. Robins were reported to have been disturbed by explosions during the London Blitz and they started to sing as the bombs rained down.

Perhaps, though, the most evocative of night-time calls is provided by the tawny owl. It was Shakespeare who, in *Love's Labours Lost*, misled many generations with the lines:

> Then nightly sings the staring owl, Tu who;
> Tu whit, tu who – a merry note,

In fact, the long, hooting call of the tawny owl might be better written phonetically as 'hoo . . hoohoohoohoohoohoo'. The naturalist D.A. Orton would agree, for he has documented the nocturnal vocabulary of the tawny owl; no mean achievement for someone working with a bird that is so elusive that it can only be sexed by another of the same species.

The familiar hoot is delivered by both sexes, the male's call being 'softer, breathier and more flute-like'. When the calls are heard coming from many directions it can be assumed that several males are engaged in territorial proclamation. When a harsh call is heard it means that the female has taken an interest in the territory too. If the calls are broken up and disjointed, this signifies that the male has located his mate and is to present her with a gift of a mouse.

The 'ke-wick' call is also given by both sexes, although a female might 'ke-wick' and a male might respond with a hoot. The 'ke-wick' call is a contact call, used by incubating females to say that they are hungry and to keep young birds in check, and by males to challenge other males. With eggs or young in the nest the male softens the call to what Orton describes as 'oo-whip'.

These long-distance calls are often accompanied by softer sounds, as well as hisses, mews, grunts, twitterings and high-pitched screams – altogether a more complex 'language of owls' than the Bard would have had us believe. But while owls may find each other and keep in touch by the calls they deliberately make themselves, they find their prey by the sounds other nocturnal animals make accidentally.

Owls are able to locate the whispiest of sounds. Many species hunt mainly at night, so coupled with their keen night-vision capability is a remarkable sound location system that makes them highly successful night hunters. It has been said that of all animals tested for their ability to localize sound sources, the owl is the most accurate. It can localize sounds both in the horizontal and the vertical dimensions. A filtering and selection system to the brain, processing the sound signals heard by the bird, allows the barn owl to locate its prey even in total darkness.

As an aerial predator, the owl must be able to evaluate the position of its prey from above. The barn owl's target is often a small mammal. In 95 per cent of owl pellets examined, field mice have been identified as the principal food. Mice are quite noisy as they go about their nocturnal foraging. They scuttle through their runways in the undergrowth, brushing against things in their path and making minute rustling noises. They often squabble, squeaking away in both the audible and ultrasonic frequencies. It is these high-frequency components of a rustle or a squeak that the owl uses to locate its prey with such accuracy.

It might be expected that high frequencies would travel only for short distances, attentuating faster in air than lower frequencies. Also, high, hard-edged sounds bounce more readily off grass stems and twigs, which should make them more difficult for the owl to detect. The owl, however, has many tricks up its sleeve, or rather in its face, to outwit even the quietest mouse.

The barn owl's face is basically a disc with two concave troughs which serve as a stereo parabolic reflector. It can focus high-frequency sounds, particularly those between 3 and 9 kHz. The facial ruff, as it is known, is made up of rows of tightly packed feathers dividing the face into two ear-like depressions. The depressions function much like the external pinnae of human ears in channelling sounds to the ear proper. The ears of the owl are behind the eyes, at the focus of the two facial depressions.

Furthermore, the ears are not placed symmetrically on the head. The right ear is directed slightly upward, and is more sensitive to sounds coming from above, whereas the left ear is focused downwards and responds better to sounds from below. With this sophisticated sound-receiving system, the barn owl can compare timing and loudness differences at the two ears, not only from left to right, but also from above and below. So the owl is capable of detecting the faintest of sounds, like mouse rustlings, at long distances, and of pinpointing the sound source to within a degree (the equivalent of a little finger width at arm's length).

The way an owl uses its facial ruff to home in on a target has been observed in the long-eared owl. At rest, a long-eared owl collapses the ruff. If it is startled the ruff is expanded and the head turned to face the source of the disturbance.

(The 'ears' of horned or eared owls, incidentally, serve no auditory function. They are not sound receivers, but are thought to be part of an interspecies threat display. Owls are often confronted with mammalian predators. In Scandinavia, for instance, eagle owls have 'face-to-face' encounters with lynx and arctic foxes. Eagle owl nests are accessible to these hunters, but by adopting a lynx-like face, complete with ears, the owl is thought to deter these nervous enemies.)

The owl's auditory sophistication was first recognized when it was noticed that as an owl swoops down it orients itself with respect to the target, whichever way the prey runs. The owl aligns its talons with the body axis of the prey; a remarkable feat if you consider the unpredictable zig-zag running of, say, a fleeing mouse. The owl must change the alignment of its talons rapidly with every manoeuvre. Experiments in the laboratory have shown that the owl can do this in complete darkness; it must therefore rely on sound cues.

The tests consisted of a series of head orientation experiments. Observers noted that an owl, on locating a sound source, quickly turns its head towards the sound, thus bringing it directly in front of the face. This directs both eyes and ears on the target. The object of the tests was to find out how accurately the owl could do this.

The owl being tested was placed inside an electric field produced by induction coils. A small search coil was placed on the bird's head and the electrical changes that took place between the search coil and the large induction loops were measured. This gave an accurate measurement of the owl's head movements.

Two sound sources were used. The first, the zeroing loudspeaker, was placed directly in front of the owl. The second, a mobile loudspeaker on a track, could be moved around the subject. It could also be moved up and down. Tests were carried out in the dark. A sound was played through the zeroing loudspeaker and the owl turned its head to face it. This was considered to be 'straight ahead' and the point from which all other movements were measured and compared. Then, a sound was played through the mobile or target speaker, the owl rapidly turned its head to face it, and the time taken and accuracy of movement noted. The whole ingenious system was motorized and computer controlled.

The owl's reactions were so fast that its head oriented towards a sound source even if the signal was switched off before the head turn began. This showed that the bird had registered vertical and horizontal information and determined the location of the sound before even turning its head. To accomplish this, the owl makes a comparison of the timing, intensity and quality of the sounds reaching both its ears. Further tests have shown that it is primarily interested in the intensity and directional components of the signal. Because of the size of the owl's head and the separation of the ears, the phase delay of high frequencies only is registered – hence its ability to hear those whispy sounds associated with mouse rustles and even the ventriloquial alarm calls of small songbirds. Experiments in a large anechoic chamber which had loudspeakers hidden below the floor showed that the owl found high-pitched sounds easier to locate than low-pitched sounds.

But the story doesn't end at the ears. Sound signals arriving there are converted into nerve impulses which are relayed to the brain. Here, the owl has an amazing way of processing the information. It creates a sound map of the world about it.

Each neuron is excited only by sound signals coming from a particular point in space. The sound map is constructed in the midbrain – in fact, in the *mesencephalicus lateralis pars dorsalis* – and the information sent to an area of the cerebellum called Field L (equivalent to our own auditory cortex). The experiments continue to determine how neighbouring cells in the owl's midbrain are capable of responding to very subtle spatial differences in the sound source. In the meantime, the work has already shown how remarkable the owl's sound detection system really is.

BIRD SONG: THE BACKGROUND

No other aspect of animal behaviour, perhaps, has stimulated so much human interest as the songs sung by birds. These renditions, often sounding beautiful to the human ear, have prompted comment and speculation for centuries; and none more so than the song of the nightingale. Pliny, writing almost 2,000 years ago, described the nightingale's song with unfettered enthusiasm. 'There is not a pipe or instrument in the world,' he wrote, 'that can afford more music than this pretty bird does out of that little throat.' And Alfred, Lord Tennyson considered, 'The music of the moon sleeps in the plain eggs of the nightingale.' This human appreciation of the nightingale's song, however, gave rise to all sorts of theories about why birds sing. Even today, the non-evolutionists, non-selectionists and fundamentalists still contend that bird song has no function, and that birds make music for their own pleasure, or indeed, as some have proposed, for the pleasure of listening ornithologists. Romantic as it may seem, there is unfortunately no evidence that birds produce their songs for the sheer joy of it.

Song is difficult to produce, expensive in energy terms – as energy-consuming as flying, according to some estimates – and can be very dangerous in exposing the songster to predators. And the song can sometimes be out of all proportion to the size of the singer. The tiny wren, just a few grams of skin and feathers, lets rip with a song that can be heard over 500 metres away. Its entire body shakes and quivers as it delivers about 740 notes per minute. In Britain, it is probably the loudest singer for its size.

The yellowhammer, it has been estimated, sings its 'little bit of bread and no cheese' 3,000 times in a day and over half a million times during the breeding season, but the world record is held by a red-eyed vireo from North America which sang its 'see me – hear me' song 22,197 times in a day and therefore over a million times during the season. In nature, it is most unlikely that any creature would make such an effort, consume so much energy which requires so much food, if it did not have a valid reason for doing so.

The birds that sing songs are mainly the oscines or songbirds, a subgroup of the most recently evolved birds known as passerines or 'perching birds'. The passerines are represented by over 5,000 species of birds and, widely distributed, include such songsters as the warblers of Australia, the titmice of Eurasia, the sunbirds of Africa, and the honeycreepers of Hawaii.

Studies of proteins in bird tissues (the more types of proteins two species of birds share, the more closely related they are) have revealed that bird song most probably originated in Australia. About 60 million years ago, ancient tree-creepers, lyrebirds, honeyeaters, fairy wrens and Australian robins were evolving on the southern super-continent of Gondwanaland. These early songbirds gave rise to the birds that moved out of Australia and eventually colonized Eurasia. A second wave, evolving from a younger ancestral stock, began to emerge from Australia about 30–50 million years ago. This group included Australian flycatchers, magpies, cuckoo shrikes, babblers and bowerbirds.

Usually it is the male bird that sings. There are a few exceptions, like the duetting boubou shrike, but in about 95 per cent of cases the male is the songster. In temperate latitudes he does not sing all year round. In Europe, for example, most songs are sung in spring and they can be quite complex. Over the years naturalists have associated this more complex signal – more complex than, say, bird-calls – with the transmission of a more complicated message. In fact there is no clear evidence that birds' songs *are* more complex and contain more complex messages. There appears to be no compli-cated code or language which we might try to unravel. Bird song simply conveys whatever message a bird might want to transmit in an effective way.

STARTING UP

A bird must know when to start its performance; and having started must know when to stop.

If a male bird is isolated in a soundproof chamber so that it can hear nothing other than the sounds of its own movements, it will sing to a regular schedule. It will commence singing in the morning as if still living in the wild and still part of the dawn chorus. There is an endogenous circadian rhythm – an internal clock – that governs the time it sings and guides its singing programme through its repertoire of songs. Superimposed on this schedule, in the wild, are other stimuli that might trigger song production. If a rival male starts up, for instance, then a male will sing in reply.

If, however, a hand-reared male bird is isolated from any sounds it may learn and is placed in a soundproof chamber, it will try to sing its song at the right time, the time that its biological clock has determined is appropriate, but it is unable to sing the song properly – evidence that the song is learned.

It was thought at first that the build-up of the male sex hormone testosterone stimulated a young bird to learn its song. Indeed, singing in the spring and its cessation in late summer or autumn are paralleled by testicular growth and regression, so the hormone must have something to do with a bird's ability to sing. A castrated bird with little testosterone in its blood does not sing well, but it *does* sing, and it can tackle the early practice versions of song – subsong and plastic song. This led to the notion that testosterone is not the initial song trigger.

Castrated birds have significant levels of the female sex hormone estradiol in their blood during the early stages of song development, and it could be this hormone that pushes a young male bird to learn its song. Testosterone, it is thought, makes the whole thing possible – it is involved in the crystalization of song. It is also this hormone that binds to the nerve cells in the song centres in the bird's brain, stimulating brain cell activity and all the motor functions of song production.

SONG PRODUCTION AND CONTROL

Bird songs and calls are made when air from the lungs is forced over vibrating membranes – the syrinx – much as in our own larynx, but there the similarity ends, for the bird syrinx is a little more complicated.

Unlike the human larynx, which is at the top of the windpipe or trachea, the bird syrinx is at the bottom, where the two bronchi coming from the lungs meet. The syrinx sits astride the junction. In many birds there are separate vibrating membranes or chords on the two arms of the syrinx, and as a consequence they have the remarkable ability to produce two sounds at once. A bird can sing two quite distinct tunes at the same time.

Traditionally, it was thought that a bird's vocal production differed from human speech production in that much of the structure of human speech results not from variations in the voice-box but from the movements of the tongue, mouth and nose and the shape of the vocal tract. The movements change the resonant properties of the various cavities. But, more recently, analysis of bird songs recorded in a helium atmosphere (in which sound travels faster than in normal air) have shown that the bird's vocal tract colours a bird's utterances too. It acts as an acoustic filter and its movements are coordinated with the sound being generated by the syrinx, a little like human speech production and something that even other apes do not do.

Even more remarkable is the fact that the two parts of the syrinx can produce sounds independently. American thrushes and Eurasian warblers are fine examples of birds that can sing two songs simultaneously, but with a harmonious relationship between each rendition, producing some quite extraordinary tonal qualities which, some researchers feel, are not matched anywhere else in bird song.

The reed warbler and the American woodthrush, for example, can sing with different notes coming from each side of the syrinx. The woodthrush sings one component at 6 to 8 kHz and another at 5 kHz, each with different rhythms. The Gouldian finch of northern Australia maintains a constant drone at one frequency whilst chirping away at another. And the brown thrasher of North America goes two better, for at one point in its very elaborate song it sings four notes at the same time.

A mature song bird, then, has two sets of contributions to its song – one coming from the left side of the syrinx and the other from the right – and they are precisely coordinated. One of the problems a young bird must come to terms with, then, is how to achieve that remarkable level of coordination.

A study of the calls of nestling chaffinches revealed that it was relatively easy to distinguish between contributions from the right and left side. It was found that, in the young bird, the relationship between the two sides of the syrinx is controlled at first. The coordination varies, giving the song a harsh quality. It seems that the fledgling call is providing practice in syrinx coordination, which is a necessary prelude to the process of singing and of song learning.

Birds learn to sing by reference to auditory information. There is a set of built-in rules that specify the kinds of auditory information to be accepted, and a repertoire is developed by reference to these auditory expectations. Normally the song manifests itself in imitations of other adult models. How, then, is the brain handling all this?

In principle there should be a nervous pathway from the brain to the syrinx and an auditory feedback which at some point must integrate, so that when the song is matched to the auditory template, and learning completed, the pattern may be held and stored in long-term memory. In the USA, a New York research team wanted to find out which part of the brain carried out these tasks. They started by looking at the outgoing (motor) part of the auditory loop as this is more accessible. Attention was focused on the control of the syrinx.

The research team found three regions of nerve cells or nuclei in the brain which seemed to be devoted, almost exclusively, to the control of the muscles of the syrinx. It was assumed that these regions also control aspects of song learning related to the performance of the syrinx. These song nuclei are simple clusters of cells which are quite distinct, with discrete boundaries, and which can be easily identified with specific cell-staining techniques. Two are located in the forebrain, the telencephalon, and on in the hypoglossus. Put simply, the first forebrain centre, known as HVC, which originally stood for the tongue-twisting name *hyper-striatum ventrale pars caudalis*, is at the top of the forebrain. Now HVC stands more simply for 'High Vocal Center' since it was recently established that this song nucleus is not a part of the hyperstriatum. It, however, is linked to the second forebrain centre, known as the RA or *robustus archistriatum*, which in turn tells the neurones (brain nerve cells) of the hypoglossus to organize and trigger the muscles of the syrinx.

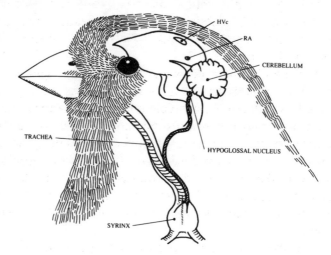

The song centres in a bird's brain and the nerve pathways to and from the bird's brain and syrinx.

The researchers carried out some simple surgery on the brains of canaries. If the top nucleus, the HVC, was put out of action, for instance, the birds continued to sing, but they did so in a virtually silent fashion. The dynamics of the song were expressed but not the sound itself. The throat quivered, the bill was held slightly open, the body feathers sleeked, and the silent singer turned around and directed its behaviour to a rival in another cage. All that was heard, though, was a faint clicking which corresponded to the temporal pattern of the song; there was no frequency modulation (tune), none of the sophisticated patterning characteristic of canary song. It was as if the motivation for singing was there, for much of the motor control for song was present, but the syrinx did not function. By knocking out one of the nuclei, the team had demonstrated that the three-nuclei auditory pathway is primarily concerned with song production.

The canary is a 'left-handed' bird – it is mainly the left half of the syrinx that is involved in singing. The right half does very little (and, indeed, in some species of birds it does not play any role at all). The nerves running from the brain to the syrinx and back again are said to be ipsilateral, that is, the song nuclei in the left side of the brain control the left side of the syrinx. This is unlike many other nerve pathways, which are crossed, so that one brain hemisphere controls the behaviour of the other half of the body. In humans, for example, the left hemisphere controls what the right hand is doing. But in canaries the left hemisphere controls the left side of the syrinx and the left side is dominant.

The team did eliminate the song nuclei on the right side of the brain and they found that song production was barely affected: some syllables tended to be unstable and a few disappeared, but the phrase structure and repetition of syllables typical of canary song persisted. There was, however, a surprise. If a canary that has had the left song nuclei destroyed is left for a few months, gradually the right side will take over. So, even though the bird has two parallel pathways for song control, and even though the left side is dominant, it has a right side which is underused, but can do the job just as well.

Left-hemisphere dominance seems to be the case in many bird species. Of those examined, the chaffinch, white-crowned sparrow, Java sparrow and white-throated sparrow have turned out to be left-handers. But not all birds are left-handers – zebra finches are right-handers.

The New York team went on to examine other aspects of brain control of song production and hit upon some intriguing results when they came to examine the canary's annual song cycle and the associated events taking place in the brain. They considered that if song-control nuclei in the brain control a bird's singing abilities, an activity taking place mainly in spring and early summer, it might be expected that the nuclei change with the seasons. So, they looked for evidence of change in the canary song nuclei throughout the year.

In spring, when canaries sing a lot, they discovered that the nuclei appeared large. In the autumn, five months later, the nuclei seemed half as large. Could the reduction in size be linked to a reduction in the amount of time devoted to the control of singing? Is the network partially dismantled? Were the neurons further apart at this time? Or was something else happening which the researchers could not see?

The researchers argued for many years that the song nuclei grow and shrink with the seasons, but the interpretations they put on these observations, although intriguing, were, in fact, wrong.

The team had used a tissue-staining technique known as the Nissl stain. When thin slices of brain tissue are soaked in the stain, the neurons show up in a particular colour and can be seen quite easily with a microscope. Using this technique the song-control centres do, indeed, appear to change size during the seasons. But another research team from Texas tried two other stains and they found that the HVC does not change its size, instead it remains the same all year round. The apparent size differences are due to the fact that the neurons of the song nuclei do not pick up Nissl stain in the autumn and winter. The reason is that this stain is taken up by organelles within the cell that are associated with cell activity. This means that although the cells are still present throughout the year, many simply shut down outside the breeding season when they are not needed.

Other experiments with the rufous-sided towhee – a bird that, unlike the canary, learns a once-only, one-off song repertoire when it has just fledged – have shown that the song centres in its brain also have seasonal variations, more evidence that changes in the activity of the song nuclei have few links with changing song repertoires each year, as in the canary.

There was, however, more to come. It might be expected that song nuclei in the brain would appear different in males and females. After all, males sing and most females do not. And indeed, examination of the brains of canaries and zebra finches has revealed that song nuclei, particularly those in the forebrain, appear several times larger in males than in females when stained using the Nissl technique. Traditionally, the view had been that the brains of males and females in any vertebrate species were virtually identical. Only small differences, requiring microdissection and electron microscopy to detect, were thought to occur. But in the canary the sexual dimorphism is so marked that a slice of brain tissue coloured with the Nissl stain, held up to the light, shows the difference clearly. The cells of the male bird's song centres are metabolically more active than those of the female's.

This seemed to make some kind of sense. The male canary spends a good deal of time learning to sing and then sings with gusto in the spring. The female does not sing at all. It seems like good brain economics that if the female does not indulge in a particular piece of behaviour then she should not devote much brain activity to its control, although she must be aware of its existence. The HVC nucleus, it has been speculated, is a link between a bird's hearing and its ability to produce songs. If hearing is involved then a female bird must have at least part of the HVC active to appreciate male song.

The research went further. Male canaries have considerable variability in their songs. Some appear to have song repertoires three times larger than others. Might repertoire size be linked to the number of active neurons in the song centre? The answer is yes. The researchers found that birds learning larger song repertoires appear to have larger forebrain song nuclei. Again, the Nissl staining showed an apparent difference in activity; birds with larger repertoires must operate with many more active song-centre neurons.

Interestingly, female canaries can be induced to sing with hormone treatment. Three weeks after injection females come into song, but the complexity of their song is that which would be expected from the number of active cells in their song nuclei. Instead of thirty to thirty-five different song syllables, they sing only five to ten.

There is speculation that the reduction in active song nuclei cells is linked to the moult, when all kinds of physiological changes take place.

STANDING OUT

A bird's world is often a noisy place. At the times when a bird might want to send its message all the other birds are sending their messages too. With a background of the songs and calls of other birds, gurgling streams and rustling leaves, waves and waterfalls, atmospheric noises and disturbances and other extraneous sounds, a bird might find it difficult to be heard. By repeating its message, however, a bird eventually gets its message to the intended recipient, with less risk of its being lost in the transmission process.

An almost pure-tone musical song will stand out from wide-band background noise. Give the notes a rhythm, a temporal pattern, and they differ sufficiently from non-animate sounds to be picked out loud and clear. Imagine a bird which is only capable of producing a simple whistle as its sole means of sound communication. There are several ways in which it could encode its signal in order to send a meaningful message, but only certain ways would be effective. If, for example, it encodes its signal by making the sounds alternately loud and soft it would find it hard to communicate over long distances, because, as the wind blows and the acoustic properties of the environment such as those caused by changes in pressure or temperature alter, the whistle pattern would be degraded and the signal garbled. Sometimes, when a signal was meant to be quiet it would come through loud, while at other times a loud signal might appear unpredictably soft. The listening bird – the intended receiver –would be utterly confused as the pattern it heard would be quite different from the one that was sent. If, on the other hand, the signal were sung long and loud, followed by a period of silence and then again short and loud, this pattern would be more likely to get through. If that pattern were repeated there would be an even better chance of its reaching its target. So an elaborately patterned song, with numerous stops and starts, is the means some birds have acquired in order to talk over long distances to other individuals of the same species.

Having established its coded signal, a bird must overcome particular environmental and acoustic constraints depending on where it lives. In a forest or wood, for example, the vegetation – leaves, branches, trunks of trees, fallen logs, epiphytes, blades of grass, flowers, bushes and leaf litter – can interfere with a bird's carefully composed song, making it difficult to transmit the message to any useful distance sufficiently unchanged to be meaningful to the receiver.

This is where we must consider a bit of physics and take account of one of nature's basic physical laws. In a hypothetical, homo-geneous and frictionless medium, sound will travel out from the sound source in the shape of an expanding sphere; that is, it will spread out equally in all directions. But the energy in the sound signal is more thinly spread as the sphere enlarges and the signal is said to attenuate – it becomes quieter the further it travels from the source. But in the real world, in air, a bird's song not only attenuates; the high, middle and low frequencies contained in the song attentuate at different rates. High frequencies lose their energy faster than low frequencies. A song made up of both high and low frequencies, therefore, will reach the receiver in a slightly modified form from the one in which it left the sender.

In the real world there are also things that get in the way. In addition to the air itself there are vegetation, temperature change, wind movement, eddies and currents, density gradients and interference from other creatures that are using the same channel of communication. A forest, for example, is a particularly complex environment compared, say, to a flat, grassy plain and birds adapt their songs and their singing positions to suit.

In the forest there is a narrow 'sound window' – between 1.5 and 2.5 kHz – in which a bird's song propagates best, but only if the bird is at least 1.5 metres above the ground. The song of a bird singing directly from the forest floor will be absorbed rapidly. If the singing bird and the bird hearing the song are more than 30 metres apart, the sounds are filtered or absorbed by trees and bushes, although some sounds are helped along by being reflected from the leafy canopy. This is particularly relevant in a coniferous forest, where cedar, pine and spruce leaves or needles actually enhance the transmission qualities of sounds between 1 and 3 kHz.

There is also reverberation – the way in which sounds bounce off objects in the environment and either 'resonate' in a particular way or repeat certain elements so that units of a song blur into each other. The pattern of the song can be lost and any bird listening might be hopelessly confused. And the problem with reverberation increases with frequency: the higher the frequency, the more likely it is to bounce around. In dealing with this constraint, songbirds have a fundamental problem – they are small. Ideally, a bird should sing at the lowest frequencies in its available sound window, but its sheer body size and the size of its syrinx dictate that it must sing at the higher frequencies.

In the grassland habitat there is no appreciable sound window and reflections from obstacles play very little role in distorting or attenuating sound transmissions. There is, however, the problem of wind: wind is stronger in the open. And there are changes of temperature throughout the day. The heating of an open plain by the sun, for instance, results in rising columns of warm air. Sounds travelling across such a turbulent plain are likely to be distorted.

In order to accommodate the constraints of local conditions, therefore, birds in the two habitats have developed very different songs, two important features being the song's dominant frequency and its quality – whether a buzz or a tonal whistle. In the forest, birds living at low levels beneath the canopy sing a song which consists of a tonal whistle with an average dominant frequency of 2.2 kHz (which fits the available sound window). They get their message through, however, by changing that frequency, thus producing a song which might be considered 'tuneful'. Birds in forests must avoid rapid repetitions of any one frequency component. The European blackbird and nightingale have this kind of song, as has the hooded warbler of North America.

In the open grassland, birds sing in the higher registers and their songs have a buzzy quality, like that of the lark. They rely more on a temporal pattern than a tune to send their message over long distances. They should not sing slow melodic acoustic patterns. Grassland birds must also avoid a curious 'sound shadow' near to the ground. This is due to temperature changes and air movements at that level. Their song would also be absorbed by the soil. They overcome these constraints by hovering or flitting above the ground at a height of 3–6 metres and by singing their buzzy kind of song from this elevated position.

There are exceptions; although even these oddities fit in with the general rule. The rufous-tailed hummingbird of Panama, for instance, is an unusual grassland bird in that it has a tuneful call, albeit at the higher frequencies. It overcomes the problems of wind, air turbulence and temperature gradients by singing between six and seven o'clock in the morning before the air has had time to warm up. Its neighbour, the fork-tailed emerald, on the other hand, buzzes away quite contentedly for the best part of the day. And there are two groups of wedge-tailed ground finches, living in the same area, that have adopted both methods depending on their daily schedule. One group rises early and sings tuneful songs before the sun rises, while the other sings later in the day with a buzzy song.

One bird, the great tit, lives both in forests and more open areas, and is widely distributed across Eurasia, from Japan in the east to Ireland in the west, and from Siberia in the north to Malaysia in the south. Those birds living in forests, whether in Britain, Poland,

Norway or Morocco, have simple songs, narrow in frequency range with a relatively low dominant frequency and a slow repetition rate of notes. In contrast, those in arid, sparse woodlands and parklands have a wide frequency range, higher dominant frequencies, and a higher repetition rate. Birds, it seems, adapt their songs and calls to suit the place in which they live.

But degradation is not all negative – it can be useful. If birdsongs are inevitably going to be degraded over distance, could it be that birds actually evolve song structures that permit some degradation for the express purpose of allowing receivers an easy mechanism for judging that distance? In evolutionary terms it might prove to be advantageous for birds in certain circumstances to be able to judge distances simply by the quality of the song. If a bird proclaiming its territory cannot easily locate and judge the distance of its singing neighbour, the only way to settle a boundary dispute would be by a short-range encounter which might be traumatic for both parties. How much better then to determine that distance by a long-range vocal avoidance mechanism.

In order to test this idea, North American researchers carried out some interesting field experiments with Carolina wrens. These obliging birds were chosen for the tests because they have a characteristic response to experimental song playbacks. If the song is played back inside the bird's territory it stops singing, makes aggressive utterances and may even attack the loudspeaker. As long as it judges the rival singer to be inside its territory it will not sing. If, on the other hand, the song is played outside its territory the resident responds by singing at the playback. Therefore, could a Carolina wren, asked the research team, tell whether a singer is inside or outside its territory solely by judging the distance on the basis of some predictable degradation in the song pattern as a result of propagation through the forest?

Carolina wrens in the wild were recorded at two distances, one at 10 metres and the other at 50 metres. The recordings were filtered to exclude frequencies above 3 kHz to minimize frequency-dependent attenuation as a cue for judging distance. The recordings differed mainly in the amount of reverberation. Those recorded close to a wren were relatively clean, while those at 50 metres had reverberation colouring the signal. The recordings were then played back to birds on their territories with the loudspeaker set at a standard distance of 25 metres from the resident bird. If a real interloper had sung from this distance it would have been close enough to be inside the resident bird's territory. This would normally have resulted in the termination of singing on the part of the resident and elicited an aggressive approach. The resident wrens, however, responded quite differently to the two recordings. They stopped singing and approached the loudspeakers playing the clean recordings, as expected, but the degraded recordings broadcast at the same volume and at the same distance evoked counter-singing. The conclusion is that Carolina wrens, at least, can use the degradation that naturally occurs in the transmission of their songs through the forest to judge the distance to a singing bird.

Another factor that intrigued the research team was the notion that birds do not have time to hang about and wait for a message to come from another bird. A bird has to live, to feed, to watch out for predators, and to attend to its mate or offspring. But it must be alert to potentially useful messages in the general background noise of the forest. Maybe, thought the scientists, birds have some kind of alerting component in their song. A receiver could then operate with a low level of vigilance, assured that this alerting component would warn it that a message was coming. This would have to be an easily detectable part of the song or call, which suffered low degradation and had high contrast with the background noise. Once the alerting component was detected, the receiver could switch its attention to a brief 'time window' that it knew would contain much more information, such as species, sex or individual identity. Many birdsongs, they noted, appear to be designed this way. They start with a simple tonal element, often a simple whistle or series of whistles repeated at a slow rate, then the acoustic structure becomes more complex with rapid trills and so on.

Again, an experiment was designed to test for alerting components. The subject on this occasion was the rufous-sided towhee (one of the New World buntings), which begins its 'drink-your-tea' song with one or two simple whistles and then follows with a complex trill. Towhee song played back within a resident's territory will evoke counter-singing.

The researchers 'doctored' the recordings of towhee song, isolating the suspected alerting component and the message part. Some recordings were degraded to simulate the passage of the sound through the forest. They then played back the entire song, followed by each of the two components alone, to a resident bird, and watched for its reaction.

If the degraded opening whistle or the degraded trill was played to the resident bird there was little or no response. A clean trill, with no reverberation, evoked a strong response. The key experiment came with playbacks of clean and degraded full song. A clean version of the entire song, not unexpectedly, received a strong response, but what was interesting was that so, too, did a degraded version. The researchers were able to conclude that an alerting component in towhee song *does* allow another towhee to recognize the signal as coming from a rival towhee, and permits the receiver to get the message in the face of high levels of degradation and noise. So, in that one species, at least, there is evidence that the acoustic pattern of a bird's song is adapted very nicely to improving signal detection.

This interpretation, though, may be too simplistic, for other bird species recognize others of the same species in different ways. The brown-headed cowbird and the ovenbird, for instance, rely on specific sequences of song parts for species identity. In redwinged blackbirds, the trill alerts males but all the song must be sung to grab the attention of females. Over long distances – say, the width of two territories – the opening trill of the North American redstart gets lost in the mish-mash of background noise, whereas the very last syllable of the song reaches a distant listener. Might it be that a bird picks out parts of the song or sequences of the song as conditions permit and that while the experiments are correct within the parameters they examine, in fact they only reveal a part of the story? The research goes on.

GREEN POSTSCRIPT

This bit of slightly esoteric science is not only relevant to those studying bird behaviour; it is also of practical importance in bird conservation. When a species gradually, over tens or maybe thousands of years, emigrates from, say, forest to field its old song becomes inappropriate and it evolves a new song to fit its new home. What then happens if habitats are lost more rapidly? Can birds adapt quickly enough to overcome the constraints of the environment imposed on them by man's activities today? With tropical forests, for example, disappearing at a rate of 20 hectares a minute and changing forest acoustics into those of a grassland, even a simple task like talking to others of the same species suddenly becomes a major problem, and may even become impossible.

5

SOLOS, DUETS
AND CHORUSES

BIRDSONG, PARTICULARLY THOSE MERRY NOTES HEARD AT DAYBREAK IN
the spring, has long been a part of a chocolate-box view of the
natural world but why should birds sing so enthusiastically at
dawn? The poet W. Davies thought he had the answer:

> I could not sleep again, for such wild cries,
> And went out early into their green world:
> And then I saw what set their little tongues
> To scream for joy – they saw the east in Gold.

But is birdsong, as the poets would have us believe, just a
comment on the sunrise, an expression of fun, an avian celebration
of the joy of being alive? Who are the birds singing for, and, more
importantly, why do wild song birds expend so much vital energy

186

and risk giving away their position to waiting predators in order to sing at all?

DAWN CHORUS

At break of day, and again at dusk, birdsong is more than evident in spring. In the tranquillity of the English countryside the matinal cacophony can be almost deafening. Not surprisingly, country folk are encouraged by the avian chorus to 'rise with the lark' or sleepily emerge from their beds at 'cockcrow', but why should these inconsiderate animals be singing or calling at this inconvenient hour? Would they not be better employed foraging for food or keeping watch for a wary fox? Singing, after all, is just one of a bird's daily activities, competing in its schedule with food gathering, drinking, spotting predators and the many other things it must do to stay alive. Why, then, should singing be the dominant activity for male birds during the early part of the day?

At Oxford University, researchers tried to find an answer to this fundamental question. Their study animal was the great tit, and they tried to work out how this bird apportions its time to different activities throughout the day. They reasoned that early in the morning, when the sun and air temperature has still to rise, is not the best time to gather food. Prey availability is generally fairly low. The insects on which great tits feed are inactive and difficult to locate in the half-light. With little food to collect, the motivation to feed is low. The researchers also noticed that birds still seeking living space were generally more active in the early morning, so that a territory-holder is under greater pressure from wandering birds. Also, territorial holders tend to be killed during the night, so a prospecting male is more likely to find himself a vacant possession in the early morning. Resident birds would therefore find it prudent to sing at this time of the day.

Other researchers, studying the way sounds travel through the air, had already shown that transmissions are more effective at dawn. Temperature gradients are favourable and air turbulence is usually at a minimum. But, the Oxford team thought, there was more to it than this.

To test their ideas they set up large aviaries and introduced great tits. The male birds immediately established territories. Next several factors, such as the availability of food and the pressure from rivals, were altered. A bird's internal clock, independent of food or rivals, was also taken into account for it might determine when a bird sings or when it feeds.

After many hours of careful observations, food availability was identified as the main factor influencing the timing of singing at dawn or at dusk. If a bird was given plenty of food it was less likely to give up feeding in order to sing or chase away a rival. When the food was reduced, there was a greater chance that it would sing.

Feeding efficiency under different conditions – at low light levels and low temperatures – was monitored, and it was discovered that birds were less successful at dawn than, say, three hours after sunrise. With time on their hands, therefore, birds without a territory have one thing on their mind – to go out and get one. A territory holder, then, is best employed in chasing out any would-be interloper, and a part of a bird's territorial proclamation is its song.

The quality of that dawn (and dusk) performance, however, is also important. Theory has it that the fitter a bird is the better it will sing, and the better it sings the greater its ability to deter rivals and to attract a mate. And it is only fit if it feeds well. Another team at Oxford tested this notion.

Each afternoon in early spring, the diets of selected blackbirds were supplemented with plums, mealworms, bread and pastries, while the diets of other birds were untouched. The morning after, their singing abilities were assessed. Those with the supplementary diet sang earlier, longer and with more vibrance than those that relied on normal foraging. The birds that had fed well were better able to advertise their health, and early in the breeding season the males' song rates depend on the food they have gathered the previous day.

This was also corroborated by a Swedish study of pied flycatchers. They arrive at their breeding sites in Sweden in late April and early May. The males sing long and loud from the moment they arrive, stopping only when they have paired. When the first egg is laid the male sings again, hoping to attract a second female to another territory. Whether he succeeds or not depends on how fast he can deliver his songs, for the song rate of male flycatchers is directly related to their food intake. So the rate at which a male bird sings can tell a prospective mate how good he is at obtaining food or how well stocked his territory is. This is particularly important at low temperatures, such as those experienced at dawn. Song rate has been observed to increase as the temperature increases, but at dawn, when the temperature is low, it is food availability only that affects song rate, and therefore it is a time when a female will get a true assessment of her prospective mate.

That, though, is not the end of it. Further research has shown that the female of the species can make even greater contributions to the dawn-chorus story.

A male blackbird's singing is influenced by the activities of the female. He will stop singing, for instance, when the female leaves the nest in the morning, her timing determined by the light intensity. The two forage together for part of the day. The male returns ahead of his mate, joining the dusk chorus until she returns later to the nest. Then he stops singing. As her peak fertility period approaches and there is the greatest danger that a rival male will move in and mate with her, the cock bird sings with more gusto. And each day he sings progressively earlier. When she has laid her eggs he stops singing.

Great tits have also been closely observed. At the peak of breeding activity, male great tits get up early and sing their hearts out for about a half an hour. When the female emerges from her separate roost hole, the male stops singing abruptly and they mate. Does the female cause the male to stop or would he stop, influenced by some environmental factor like increasing light level, at the same time each day anyway? The tits were tested.

After the female tits had gone to their roost holes in the evening, the entrances were blocked temporarily so that they couldn't get out in the morning. The blocks were removed and the birds released about a quarter of an hour after their normal time. The male birds went on singing until the females arrived. They had, indeed, influenced the males' dawn chorus. What could be happening?

Most songbirds, great tits included, lay their eggs at dawn and the females are most fertile just one hour after egg-laying. Mating at this time, therefore, would have the greatest chance of a successful fertilization. The female's partner must ensure that he is the only male great tit around, for females have been known to mate with the first male that comes along and would certainly mate with an interloper if a partner should disappear. The resident male, then, must sing at dawn both to discourage rival males from entering his territory and to stimulate the female to accept him to mate.

So dawn is the most effective time to sing; it is the time of day when a male bird will benefit most from that activity – the physiological and behavioural events being a far cry from what the poets and lyricists would have us believe.

THE MESSAGE – KEEP OUT!

Charles Darwin, writing in the nineteenth century, proposed that a male songbird's main interest is in charming a female to approach, share its territory, and be its mate, and that mate attraction is the principal function of birdsong. Eliot Howard, writing later in 1920, convinced many naturalists of his time that birdsong is mainly concerned with staking out and defending a territory. Who was right? Is birdsong used primarily to attract a mate or to repel rivals disputing a territory, or does it have a dual function, part of a complex ethological jigsaw?

One piece fell into place after the completion of some experiments carried out by population ecologists at Whytham Wood, near Oxford, England. Their interest in birdsong came from the population dynamics of birds and they were investigating whether the breeding density of birds in a particular habitat is limited by territorial behaviour. First they wanted to be sure that intruders are kept out by some kind of behaviour on the part of the territory holder. They suspected birdsong to be a long-range 'keep out' signal, a proclamation of ownership, but they wanted to know whether there might be other forms of signal that are just as important.

The study bird was the ubiquitous great tit. From January onwards in southern Britain the male great tit acquires a three-acre territory and defends it against all-comers. At about the same time he begins to sing his characteristic 'tee-cher, tee-cher' song. He may already have a mate but must wait until April or May before breeding starts. In the meantime, the Oxford team tested whether his simple song is a 'keep out' signal.

One spring they carried out some simple experiments which involved removing some territory holders from a breeding population of great tits. Immediately sites became vacant new birds flew in and filled up the empty spaces. The new arrivals came from poor habitats nearby, where breeding success was low. The birds had been waiting on the sidelines, ready to move house when a better living space became available. But how, thought the researchers, did the birds know that the territory had been vacated? The intriguing thing was that the birds came in very quickly after the removal of the territory holder. The obvious answer was that they listened for a resident's song, sound signals being more effective in a forest than, say, visual or olfactory cues.

190

Previous to these experiments there had been many studies showing that, when song is played back to a territory holder, it reacts by approaching and maybe attacking the loudspeaker, and this was taken as evidence that song acts as a territorial signal. But no-one had checked that, when a bird sings in its territory, it is actually saying 'keep out', and therefore defending its territory against the birds waiting in the wings.

In 1975, the Oxford team carried out their classic, yet simple, removal experiment. They took away territory holders, as before, leaving empty spaces in the wood. This time, however, they replaced some of them with loudspeakers playing the songs of the birds they'd taken away. In other territories they put loudspeakers playing a control sound – a tune played on a tin-whistle, which had the notes of about the right frequency and duration. Other territories were left empty. The researchers sat and watched.

Sure enough, in came the birds from outside the study area. The territories with playback of normal song were treated as if a bird were in residence and were avoided. Instead, the new arrivals went to the empty spaces playing nothing or those playing the tune on the tin-whistle. This seemed to show that the original idea was correct – male great tits waiting to enter and take over territories know whether a territory is occupied or not simply by listening for the resident bird's song.

Having established a territory, a bird must maintain and defend its borders. Further research on great tits in Oxfordshire has revealed the way these birds decide how to apportion their time during the day; after all, territorial defence and, say, foraging are two important activities and a bird cannot do both at the same time. The key is food availability. If a bird has a plentiful supply of food, like a well-stocked bird table, nearby, and it can eat its fill quickly, then it is more likely to react strongly to an intruder and chase it away. Those birds having a hard time seem to be preoccupied with searching for food and will pay only scant attention to an intruder, pausing from feeding momentarily to sing at it. But when rivals do sing at each other there seem to be set rules of engagement.

In some species, neighbours sing at each other across the line of demarcation. Often they sing the same song, a form of countersinging known as 'matching'. But which bird should sing first? And, as many birds have more than one song type, how does an individual, having started, know which song type to sing next?

The long-billed marsh wren is a North American bird with a large, rapidly sung, rattling, song repertoire. Male marsh wrens in neighbouring territories sing the same song repertoire back and forth to one another each day, sometimes flying up to 4.5 metres above the reeds and cattails only to flutter down at an angle back into the territory, singing all the way. Other species, with very simple songs, would have little scope for improvisation when matching with neighbours, but for marsh wrens the sky's the limit. A couple of males, with over a hundred song types to choose from, could sing their songs in a million different ways. So how do they decide in which order to sing?

In a pilot experiment, two wrens were taught nine song types from tape recordings. They were allowed to sing to each other quite freely and it soon became apparent that the physically larger male became dominant and led the singing. The smaller, submissive bird matched the other's song and followed the dominant bird's song-singing order. The researchers then interfered. Using a microphone, amplifier and loudspeaker, they increased the loudness of the submissive bird's singing. The dominant bird then began to follow the amplified bird's song and the previously submissive bird started to lead the proceedings.

In a parallel field project, the researchers placed a loudspeaker, playing long-billed marsh wren songs, in an established territory to simulate an intruding male. Normally a resident bird is dominant to an intruder, and the researchers found that, because the order of singing in marsh wrens is so stereotyped, the resident bird was able to anticipate the order of songs on the tape recordings and get in with matched songs first. In this way it actually led the tape recorder!

Why the submissive male should play this game is not clear, although the reseach team had some hunches. Territoriality might be viewed as an exploded dominance hierarchy. Males entering a breeding area must toe the line before they are able to establish themselves. By matching the songs of dominant residents they might gain a foothold. And perhaps females searching for a mate are more responsive to the bird in the leading role – the bird higher in the 'pecking order'.

MATCHING

If matching is taking place, to what standard are the songs being compared? Some of the people studying bird song feel that an individual's own song is important. Some of the imagery a bird has of its species song may develop around its experience of its own individual song. If a male memorizes its own singing, uses those memory traces as a basis for matching the songs of others, and only accepts as rivals those that are a close match to its mental picture, then playback of its own song should have interesting results, because it is going to be a perfect match to its image of what the species song should be like. In some experiments, however, a male's own song has turned out to have an intermediate rank as a stimulus, falling somewhere between the song of a familiar neighbour and the song of a stranger. Nevertheless, there is still evidence that a male's own song has some unique status as a sound heard, but just what its role may be in development is not clear. This unresolved issue is of interest at present because of the notion of 'self'. In human development, for instance, a child is considered to reach social maturity when it develops some sense of its own personal identity, and can use that as a basis for relating to others. The search is on for a similar phenomenon in other animals.

The Oxford researchers looked at matching in the great tits of Whytham Wood. They played to birds songs from their own repertoire and recorded whether or not they were matched. They found, not surprisingly, that great tits match their own songs. What they also found is that the reliability with which they matched varied according to circumstances, but it was not clear what those circumstances were. They looked in more detail.

In another experiment, birds were presented with different kinds of playback of song types from their own repertoires: firstly a neighbour's version; and secondly a version of that song type sung by a complete stranger. Typically, birds would approach the loudspeaker, fly about looking for an opponent, and then begin counter-singing. The intensity of the challenge was not always the same, though. A neighbour's version of the song resulted in a weak response. The resident bird approached slowly and sang little. A stranger's version evoked a full-bodied challenge which sometimes ended with the resident attacking the loudspeaker. The stranger, it seems, poses a greater threat than does the neighbour. The neighbour has a territory of its own and is recognized by the resident bird. The resident therefore doesn't get worked up upon hearing its song. This reduces the amount of unnecessary effort, time and risk spent in fighting and chasing, by allowing a bird to ignore, to a certain extent, the songs of immediate neighbours.

The accuracy of matching varies too. Birds most reliably matched their own songs; next most reliably matched the songs of neighbours, and least reliably matched the songs of strangers. This still did not establish what purpose matching serves; rather it showed that matching is based on a precise similarity between the song version played to the resident bird and the bird's own rendition of that particular type of song. The researchers looked at their data again and came up with a possible functional significance for matching.

They recalled the environmental degradation experiment with Carolina wrens – wrens are able to judge the distance to a rival bird which is singing, simply by listening to the way the signal is degraded by reverberations and so on. But how, wondered the Oxford team, can a bird actually tell if a song is degraded? It would need to compare the song it hears with a standard of what the song would be like if it were not degraded. They concluded that the standard is in its own repertoire.

When a resident hears a song, it is compared with its own rendition of the same song and the bird can assess whether the song is degraded or normal, thus discovering the distance of the rival. So, if two neighbours match each other's song types, the receiver can say 'I have the same song type as you, therefore I can judge exactly how far away you are, because I can measure the degradation of your song'. It is a mutual exchange of information about distance, and it is reliable too – the degradation depends solely on the properties of the habitat, preventing the birds from cheating on the system by pretending to be closer or further away than they really are. By matching its own song, a bird can tell exactly whether a neighbour is, say, 25 metres and not 20 metres away. The 5 metres difference could be important because a neighbour 25 metres away might be inside its own territory and no threat, but 20 metres away it might be inside the other's patch and attempting to steal a piece of ground. Neighbours save time and energy if they keep telling each other how far apart they are. If the song a bird hears is very different from its own version, it would be difficult to judge easily the amount of degradation; hence the more violent or alarmed reactions noted with intruding strangers.

SONGS AND DECEPTION

Another factor to be considered is the complexity of the song. If birdsong is simply saying 'keep out this is my territory' need it be an elaborate signal? Is there any advantage in male birds singing a more complicated keep-out song? In search of an answer the Oxford researchers returned to their removal experiments. This time the loudspeakers played back songs with different numbers of song types. In one territory a varied repertoire of song types was played, while in another a single song type was played over and over again. If song does play a role as a 'keep out' signal, then perhaps the repertoire in some way increases the effectiveness of song in repelling rivals.

When the resident birds were removed and the tapes played back, new birds arrived and scouted around to find empty spaces. The spaces with no playback were quickly reoccupied as before, but interestingly the spaces playing the single repetitive song were more prone to occupation than those with the varied repertoire. Larger repertoires make better 'keep out' signals. But why? Could it be something to do with boredom?

The mechanism may be a very simple biological property of animal nervous systems. When exposed to a repetitive stimulus an animal often habituates, that is, stops responding to the stimulus. If a territory holder sings the same song over and over again, rivals might gradually get used to it. If the resident bird changes its tune, the variety in its song reduces the chance that others will habituate to it. Why wandering birds should habituate to song is not clear. Perhaps it is simply a property of their brains; but scientists would prefer a functional explanation, and maybe cheating has something to do with it.

Territory holders with varied repertoires have an opportunity to deceive. Wandering birds will be on the look-out for suitable areas with few residents, places where there is less competition for partners and food resources. By singing a variety of songs, a resident bird might give the false impression of there being many other birds in the area. The deceit could be further enhanced by constantly moving about the territory singing from song-post to song-post, making it seem more profitable for an interloper to look elsewhere. This has been named the Beau Geste Hypothesis, after the novel by P.C. Wren in which the gallant legionnaire successfully defended a desert fort by propping up dead bodies around the ramparts to make it look as though there were many more defenders.

One bird that is seen to dash around its territory incessantly – often to the irritation of the wildlife sound recordist or film cameraperson – is Cetti's warbler. It may sing its first song in front of you, but it will disappear for a few seconds only to reappear at another song-post, a little further away, to sing its next song. Another is the red-winged blackbird of North America. Analysis of its song length and the frequency with which the songs are sung has shown that they are as variable within a single bird's repertoire as they are between repertoires of a group of different birds. Also, male red-winged blackbirds tend to change song types when they change song-posts.

The red-capped cardinal, in defending its patch, appears to go to exceptional ends – not to deceive, but to patrol its expansive territory. One population of this attractive New World songbird lives alongside lakes in the Manu National Park in Peru. Each male cardinal takes up a territory that straddles the lake, with a stretch of shoreline on each side. To defend the curious-shaped territory the bird flits from one shore to the other. In the dense foliage along the lakeside it is difficult to spot intruders on the same shore but the bird can spot them more easily from the opposite shore. An intruder spotted from the opposite shore is seen off with a simple vocalization and a short flight towards it. The eviction takes no longer than half-a-minute. But a hidden intruder on the same shore as the resident bird can only be shifted by force, and it takes over a minute. It may seem as if the red-capped cardinal is wasting energy during its frequent trans-lacustrine journeys, but in reality it could be saving time and energy by crossing the lake and spotting intruders at the earliest possible moment and using a vocal 'keep out' signal instead of having an energy-demanding fight.

THE MESSAGE – COURTSHIP

The mockingbird jumps around its territory, flying in looped flights from song perch to song perch and singing its complicated song. But if a rival male arrives it does not sing at it; instead it silently chases the intruder away. So, might the mockingbird's song have a function other than territorial proclamation?

Unmated male mockingbirds sing more than mated ones and

mated birds tend to sing into rather than out of the territory. Indeed, the sound of a singer is louder if the listener is in front than if hearing the song from behind, so wherever the bird is pointing seems to be the way that it wants its song to go. Unmated birds seem to vary their singing direction, a piece of behaviour designed, perhaps, to ensure that the unmated bird's net is cast wide, giving it the best chance of attracting a mate rather than seeing off a neighbouring male. The mated male sings just for his mate and points into the territory.

If the female of a mated pair is removed, the male increases his song rate and changes his direction of singing. During the breeding season, a pair might have several broods and the male's song cycle parallels events in the life cycle. Song peaks during nest building, copulation and egg-laying but subsides during incubation and disappears altogether while the nestlings are at home. When the youngsters have flown the coop, the male starts up again and follows a similar pattern of singing for the next brood, and maybe another after that one.

So, might another function of song be to attract a mate? Courtship is an important aspect of bird behaviour, for it creates the right conditions in which the male and the female of the species can meet in order to reproduce. The male songbird, sitting pretty in his territory, cannot chase about the countryside in search of a mate. If it left the territory would be invaded. So it must use some form of communication – whether visual or acoustic – to attract a passing female. Where visibility is restricted, such as in a forest, song is an effective channel of communication.

One problem, though, is that a song might not only attract a potential mate; it might also attract a predator. So a courtship display must be a compromise between attracting a member of the opposite sex and exposure to a predator. And, to complicate things still further, to avoid wasted effort, courtship must attract only females of the same species. Song must be recognizably distinct for each species.

Another problem is that a bird might be agitated about the close proximity of another individual of the same species – a potential mate could be confused with a marauding intruder or a competitor for food. A male's song, therefore, must not only attract the female, it must also suppress her natural tendency to flee.

Also, from a female's point of view, not all males are equally suitable for mating. She must have a means of selecting the fittest.

The strongest and healthiest males usually have the highest reproductive potential – they have the best territories with the most food and, if inclined, will look after the brood better. These are short-term benefits. In the long term the male offspring are likely to inherit their father's ability to maintain and defend the best available territories, so there is an obvious genetic advantage in selecting the best available male. A male's song may indicate to a female his suitability as a mate. So, might it be that the ultimate function of birdsong is sexual attraction?

Male flycatchers normally arrive at breeding sites, establish a territory and sing near the nest hole to attract a passing female. In order to prove that the song is used to attract females, female collared and pied flycatchers were fooled into taking part in a Swedish experiment with nest-box traps. Inside some of the nest boxes were loudspeakers playing male flycatcher song, while others were empty. Examination of the traps revealed that nine out of ten trapped females were in boxes containing loudspeakers – proof positive that flycatcher song attracts females.

In Britain, another research team has been watching the sexual antics of warblers that breed in Europe – the reed warbler, sedge warbler and marsh warbler. These *Acrocephalus* warblers are small, well-camouflaged birds which live in dense marshland vegetation. As they cannot see each other clearly, there has been an obvious premium on vocal, rather than visual, communication in their evolution. The first clue that song is important in sexual attraction for these species came from studies on their seasonal and daily rhythms of song production.

They are migratory birds, the males arriving in Europe during the spring to take up territories in which they sing for long periods of time, sometimes throughout the day and night. The females arrive a few days later, find a mate, and settle in for the breeding season. After pair formation, the male's routine changes – he reduces song production, and in the case of the sedge warbler, stops singing altogether. This, the researchers thought, indicated that the male is using his song to attract a female. Once he has found her there is no need to sing, so he stops.

This was confirmed by playback experiments. A loudspeaker was placed in a sedge warbler's territory and a rival's song played to him. The resident approached the source of the sound, hunted around, fluffed up in a threat display, but didn't sing. He defended his territory, but not with song.

Further evidence for sexual attraction lies in the warbler's elaborate song. The sedge warbler can have a hundred or more separate song syllables. The male selects from his repertoire several syllables which are composed into a long and elaborate song by repeating them, alternating them, and recombining them in a variety of patterns. The patterns are so variable that the researchers, having analysed miles and miles of recording tape, could find no instance of a sedge warbler repeating a song. Each song is a separate musical composition, a distinctive behavioural event. It is much like a peacock's tail in that it is a flamboyant and extravagant signal used for impressing and attracting females.

To test whether sedge warblers with more elaborate songs are more successful, the British researchers recorded wild sedge warblers as they arrived in England. Each bird's arrival time was noted, as was the time at which it attracted a mate and stopped singing. The date of arrival and the date on which a male attracted a female into his territory was filed away together with a recording of his song. The songs were then analysed and the complexity of the rendition assessed. The number of elements in a bird's repertoire was plotted against the pairing date and it was revealed that the birds with the most complicated songs attracted females first. Those with simple song repertoires had to wait. Birds with elaborate songs clearly had some advantage over their rivals.

Warblers vary in song complexity from species to species; some have even more complicated songs than the sedge warbler. By looking at each species in the study group the researchers sought some clue to the evolution of the songs. They looked at ecology and behaviour and found major differences.

Some *Acrocephalus* warblers are monogamous – one female per male – and others are polygamous – each male attracting several females. Many bird species are monogamous. Both parents are needed to bring food to the nestlings or the chicks may starve. In certain habitats, however, food can be so plentiful that one parent can do the job. In marshlands, for example, there is often a superabundance of insect food and a female bird can catch enough large insects near the nest to bring up the youngster by herself. The male, in that circumstance, might desert the female, confident that his genetic investment is safe, and polygamy evolves.

In the *Acrocephalus* warblers polygamy has evolved in two European species – the aquatic warbler and the great reed warbler. If sexual selection has driven the evolution of elaborate birdsong, reasoned the British team, then polygamous males will have evolved more elaborate songs. A 'showy' male, attractive to a bevy of females, would leave behind more offspring.

The prediction was tested by assessing the song syllable repertoire of each species of European warbler, but the study was to throw up a big surprise. It was, in fact, the polygamous species that have a song repertoire of only 10 to 20 syllables. The monogamous species – the reed, sedge, marsh and moustached warblers – have the most complicated songs with 35 to 100 song syllables. The polygamous birds sing short simple songs while the monogamous males produce long, continuous and variable bouts of song. For an explanation it was necessary to look more closely at the birds' ecology and behaviour.

In a polygamous species, a female is less concerned with the quality of the male, as she is likely to be deserted and must bring up the chicks on her own. To maximize her reproductive success she should be more concerned with territory and the food it will provide for her young. The female is not selecting her mate directly on his own attributes, but indirectly through the quality of the territory. Polygamous males defend large territories in rich marshland. So male song may have evolved primarily within the context of competition between males for territories, the result being short, simple songs; songs with gaps between them so that a male can listen for the song of a rival.

In monogamous species, with long elaborate songs, the male is important in helping to feed the young. The female chooses a good quality male rather than a good quality territory. Territories tend to be small, sometimes in drier areas, with most food obtained from outside the territorial boundaries. The birds make long flights in search of food supplies, so the male must be strong, physically capable of many arduous flights for foraging. The first indication a female may have of a male's suitability is his song, which she hears some distance away. She may or may not be attracted by what she hears. She can stand off and assess the available males, and the males with the most elaborate songs obtain their mates first. There may, in fact, be a mutual advantage – the male, by singing an elaborate song, reaches one of the more active, alert and discriminating females, while they get to choose from the cream of the males.

The British team considered that the ultimate function of birdsong is to obtain a mate, breed successfully and produce more offspring than other individuals. Even those birds singing to defend territories are selected for through the quality of the living space. The end result is that a male obtains a female by the indirect route of proclaiming a territory.

THE MESSAGE – DUAL FUNCTION

But the repulsion of males and the attraction of females are not mutually exclusive. A song may serve both functions, although in differing proportions. In the sedge warbler, which stops singing after pairing, it is clearly mate attraction that is more important. In the other species, which reduce their song output after pairing but retain it for use later, it may well be that there is some territorial function in the song.

The great reed warbler has two functional versions of its song. It is a simple song, but with a certain amount of variation. It starts with a number of short, clicking sounds and expands into more melodious notes towards the end. When the bird is setting up a territory and trying to attact a mate it sings a long, elaborate version of the song, each song lasting between 3 and 20 seconds. When a female has been attracted, the male stops singing the long, complicated song and instead sings just the clicking sounds.

This was confirmed with playback experiments. A loudspeaker was placed in the territories of birds which were singing the long, elaborate song. If the song of a rival was played the resident bird approached the speaker, at the same time shortening his song to the simple clicks.

Duality of function may be the real answer to the question of the ultimate purpose of birdsong. It could be that the same song or parts of a song have two quite different meanings, depending on which individual is receiving it. A resident male might sing to repel an intruding male, yet sing the same song to attract a passing female. Any sophisticated communication is coloured by the context in which it is given and received, so the way these two functions of song emerge depends on the life cycle of the bird.

In the temperate regions of Europe and North America, the male birds tend to arrive first at breeding areas. They then compete vigorously for territories, but after two weeks at the most they will have staked their claims and be sitting pretty on the basis of whatever agreement has been reached with the neighbours. Many do not then stop singing; there is simply a shift in function. Singing continues, but to attract and stimulate females. So, even though the same song may be used for both territorial proclamation and courtship advertisement, there is often a separation in time.

The male western meadowlark has a repertoire of between three and twelve songs. During the early part of the breeding season, he sings all the songs, switching from one to the other until he successfully attracts a mate. The larger his repertoire, the quicker he finds a partner. Having achieved this, he shuts down and sings a single repetitive song. But as soon as the female's back is turned and she is busy with nest building, the male starts to switch songs again in order to attract a second female.

Interestingly, the meadowlark also uses his songs for territorial proclamation and he similarly changes his singing strategy depending on who the intruder might be. Neighbouring males are greeted with a simple repetitive song, whereas strangers are given the full-blown treatment. This is, probably, another way to save energy. A simple, clear statement of identity and residency is all that is needed to remind the neighbour or the wife, but an impressive display is essential to win over a potential mate or scare off a stranger.

North American chestnut-sided warblers have a primary song and secondary songs, the former used to attract a mate and the latter to defend a territory. If the mate of a newly paired male warbler is unfortunate enough to be caught by a predator, the male bird immediately changes its singing from secondary songs to its primary song, belting it out at a rate of 250-plus times per hour until another partner is attracted to him. With the new partner in place the male warbler returns to secondary songs, delivered at a rate of 157 per hour, but still with the odd primary song popping up from time to time – about two in every hour.

Evidence that both males and females respond to birdsong and that it may have a dual function can be found in physiological studies of the chiffchaff. Hand-reared and wild birds, both males and females, have had electrode implants inserted into the neck and chest and their heart rates monitored. After exposure to the song of the local chiffchaff population (mid-European) all the tested birds showed an increase in heart rate of between 3 and 12 per cent. When a song was played the heart rates of both males and females went up. Even birds reared in isolation responded, indicating that some innate template of wild song is to be found somewhere in the brain of both male and female chiffchaffs. The songs of other species did not receive the same response, showing that the heart-rate change was not caused by a 'startle' factor. One curious result, though, was that the mid-European birds did not respond to chiffchaff song from Spanish or Canary Island birds.

Not all birds show this duality of song function. Song may be weighted more towards one than the other. Perhaps there is a continuum of species, from those in which mate attraction is the more important function, through to those which are more concerned with the repulsion of rivals, with all shades of grey in between. But whichever emphasis song function has, this also has some influence on song structure.

GAPS OR NO GAPS?

In the 1950s, the naturalist Charles Hartshorne recognized that some birds are 'continuous' singers – males produce a string of song with no gaps – and others are 'discontinuous' singers – they sing for a few seconds, pause, sing again, and so on. Hartshorne interpreted his finding in his 'monotony threshold hypothesis' – put simply, the more continuously a bird sings, and the greater the repertoire, the less 'bored' a listener is likely to be.

More recently, scientists studying bird behaviour have suggested a different interpretation. They propose that Hartshorne's discontinuous singer is more interested in chasing off rival males. Its song is simple, is spaced out in order to listen for a reply, and is sung as long as there are rivals on the loose. It also tends to copy other songs accurately in order to match the neighbours, for their language has to be shared. And discontinuous singing has the advantage that gaps between or within songs allow the bird to keep an eye and an ear open for predators, especially as it is drawing so much attention to itself. The great tit, chaffinch and white-crowned sparrow are discontinuous singers.

If the emphasis is to attract a female, however, a male's song can be varied, with no breaks, and terminated after a successful mating. It need not wait for a reply. And continuous singing is likely to result in more improvisation, to offer a more attractive song than the next bird's, and to involve less copying; copying after all, allows a female to make a closer comparison between the rendition of the same or similar songs. The nightingale, sedge warbler, grasshopper warbler and brown thrasher are continuous singers, and each sings a song that is simply a continuous announcement that an unmated male is here, ready and waiting.

In Britain, researchers have investigated continuous and discontinuous singing in thrushes. They found that woodland thrushes like the blackbird and song thrush have elaborate songs that go on and on without a break, whereas the ring ouzel and redwing, living in more open terrain, sing simpler songs with breaks in them. The link between habitat type and song type has not been explained.

STIMULATING SONG

There are also other functions of song. It is vital that a receptive female is raised to the same state of readiness to mate as the male if mating is to be successful and fertilization to take place. In the USA, researchers tested for this function with white-crowned sparrows. During the winter they created artificial spring and summer conditions in the laboratory. Because it was really winter and out of the normal breeding season, the females were not physiologically ready to mate: their ovaries were small and they were not receptive to males. By extending the day length artificially, however, the research team were able to create spring in winter and, in doing so, caused the ovaries in the female sparrows to grow. They then exposed one group of birds to tape-recordings of male song and their ovarian growth rates were found to be considerably higher than in those that heard nothing.

REPERTOIRES

Some birds sing more elaborate songs than others. The cock blackbird, for example, sings a complicated song with a variety of song types, repetition of phrases and variations on song themes. But other birds achieve the same results, whether it be territorial defence or mate attraction and stimulation, with a much less complex signal. So why the elaboration? Is it that the basic information is transmitted more effectively in a complicated song, or is there more information within a song than we have so far been able to identify?

Clearly repetition and some form of frequency modulation (tune) will get a message through the woody habitat in which a blackbird lives, but this still does not account for the beautiful complexity of the melody of a blackbird's song. To find an answer we have to turn to Charles Darwin and his theory of evolution. If the ultimate function of birdsong, whether through territorial acquisition or courtship, is to facilitate successful breeding, then sexual selection will operate when there is intensive competition for mates. Song elaboration may be an example of this kind of competition.

Why then should a male bird have more than one song type? In an experiment, twenty-four unmated, virgin canaries were divided into two groups. To one group, normal complex songs with thirty-five song types were played. To the other were played modified recordings, in which songs were edited and pieces removed until there were, at the most, five song types remaining. It turned out that the female canaries exposed to the more complex songs were turned on physiologically to breed more quickly than were the females that heard the simple songs.

The experiment was monitored using a technique developed in Cambridge, England. Bundles of 10-centimetre-long strings were placed in the cages, and each female placed the strings into a nest cup as if building a nest. The researchers simply had to count daily the number of strings being used. Those birds hearing the complex songs built their nests faster. They also tended to lay more eggs, although without a male present they were infertile. These results suggested that males with larger repertoires, within a species, might have some kind of advantage when the females choose their mates. If the male can 'impress' the female with a more complex song and larger repertoire, then that might say something about the quality of his breeding potential. Also, for a male songbird to learn and de-velop a large song repertoire must mean a considerable investment in energy terms. Perhaps the female recognizes this investment.

In canaries, the males tend to learn more songs and develop larger repertoires as they get older. Maybe the female sees some advantage in going for a more mature and obviously successful male bird, and recognizes that there is some link between the number of songs a male bird sings and its age. It is known, for instance, that older red-winged blackbirds are more successful breeders than younger, less experienced birds.

In another study, this time in the wild and in Oregon, the movements and activities of Bewick's wrens were followed. The wren population in Oregon sings throughout the year. Each bird was identified by a coloured band on its leg. Seven individuals were followed and their songs recorded. The birds sang from about one or two o'clock in the morning until way after dawn, usually about eleven o'clock. When the number of songs each male sang was plotted against the date it had hatched the previous year, it was found that there was an interesting link: the earlier the male had hatched, the larger the number of songs in its repertoire the following year. Perhaps female wrens can recognize this; after all, a male hatched earlier in the year might have a better choice of territories than a male hatched later, and a better territory would give a female a better chance of raising a family.

So the sooner a male bird starts to learn its songs, gains a territory, attracts a mate and begins to breed, the greater chance it has of gaining an advantage over its rivals, and this may be reflected in the quality of its song. For some species, therefore, a large repertoire appears to be desirable. By having a rich and varied repertoire, a bird is thought to gain some evolutionary advantage.

It came, then, as a great surprise to discover that birds of the same species in different habitats might not have the same aspirations in repertoire size. There are, for example, east–west differences in the songs of winter wrens. In Oregon, males may have up to thirty different songs, while those in New England have only two. European wrens have four song types. Similarly, male long-billed marsh wrens have 150 song types in the west of North America, and only fifty in the east. Is the difference inherited in the genes or triggered by factors in the environment? Is it nature or nurture?

What is clear is that there is some link between the song repertoires of wrens and the places in which they live. The male marsh wren has a small territory to defend and those with the smallest territories have the largest repertoires. Where there is considerable pressure on a territory due to a large and concentrated wren population, the cock birds have a hard time. Neighbours raid each other's nests and destroy eggs in attempts to get a larger slice of territory. A successful male may mate with several partners during the season, and so there is considerable competition to gain the best nest sites and attract the females. In this frantic environment, birds have developed large repertoires, delivered at a fast rate with a variety of songs sung in rapid succession.

North American wrens – like the house, winter, Carolina and Bewick's wren – living in less troublesome circumstances, have a slightly easier time with neighbours of the same species, as population densities are comparatively low, but they have a problem being heard over the noise made by other species. Therefore, their songs are simple, and each song type is sung over and over again in order to get the message through.

There is also a genetic component. Marsh wrens from the repertoire-rich west and the repertoire-poor east were taught a variety of song types. On average, the western birds learned 2.4 times as many songs as their eastern cousins.

The great tits of Oxford's Whytham Wood also contributed to the debate, and they too threw up some more intriguing surprises. If a song repertoire is important, then there should be a link between repertoire size and reproductive success. Male great tits breeding in the choice territories should have mates laying the largest clutches of eggs and therefore producing the greatest number of surviving young to breed the following year. In Whytham, the songs of male great tits were recorded and individual song repertoires were compared with the ability to rear successful families. As part of a long-term population study of the great tit, the number of eggs laid by each pair of birds is counted; also, how many hatch out to produce young and the number of young that survive through the winter to breed the next season is established.

At the end of the season it was shown that there was indeed a relationship between the size of song repertoire and breeding success, although the result was not the one expected. Males with poor repertoires containing one or two song types did not fare so well as those with repertoires containing three to four song types. So far so good. But what came as a surprise was that males with larger repertoires containing seven or eight song types also did not do well. There seems to be, in great tits at least, an advantage in having a certain number of variants but a disadvantage in having too many. Why this should be so is at present not clearly understood.

SONG LEARNING

Early work on birdsong learning was carried out by the English scholar Daines Barrington (1727–1800). Nowadays he is probably better known for his legal treatise *Observations on the More Ancient Statutes*, or his observations on polar travel, card playing, Mozart and the great flood at the time of Noah. But Barrington was also an amateur naturalist, a common activity amongst the gentry of his day. Unlike his contemporaries, however, Barrington carried out experiments. His subject was the linnet, a European songbird that became popular as a pet in the nineteenth century. Careful observations of this small bird, which takes readily to captivity and has a pleasant and melodious song, enabled Barrington to reach conclusions about song-learning behaviour that are still supported today.

He noted, for instance, that a baby linnet must hear the song of the adult male before it can sing a linnet song itself. He recognized that song is not innate but learned; that there are regional dialects; that birdsong is mainly in the male's domain but that females recognize the song; and that different species of birds have vastly different vocal repertoires – and all this he revealed without the benefit of modern sound analysis technology, using only his ears, his eyes and his considerable brain.

Over 200 years later, a pioneer of the modern approach to the study of bird behaviour was Professor W.H. Thorpe of Cambridge University, England, one of the first ethologists to use the sound spectrograph, which had been developed for analysing human speech. It was with the advent of this machine that a whole new window was opened on the study of birdsong. No longer did naturalists have to dream up weird and wonderful ways in which to describe the sounds they heard. The spectrograph turns sounds into an accurate visual pattern that we, as mainly visual animals, can interpret and analyse.

Thorpe's pioneering work was with chaffinches. He found that birds kept in soundproof boxes were unable to sing properly. They attempted to sing, but unless brought up in the company of other birds they could only attempt rather raucous noises quite unlike normal song. Male songbirds sang abnormal songs if deprived of an opportunity to hear adult song during the first nine months of life. But if played recorded tapes of chaffinch song, they would learn to sing accurately as early as ten days after hatching. It became clear to Thorpe that songs are learned. At first he thought that the learning process was progressive throughout the first year of a bird's life. It was not until later that other researchers demonstrated that fledglings could learn whole songs, thereby narrowing down the likely learning period.

Other scientists in California have repeated Thorpe's experiments, but this time with the local white-crowned sparrow, an especially common species in the San Francisco Bay area, which shows very distinct local dialects. The white-crowned sparrow has just one song type, consisting of two parts. There are one or more introductory whistles followed by some brief, rapidly repeated syllables – the trill. Sometimes there is a whistle or a buzz at the end. The trill portion contains the dialect differences, and with a little practice you can tell where you are in the Bay area just by stopping for a moment and listening to the nearest white-crowned sparrow.

The Californian sparrow work confirmed Thorpe's chaffinch findings – white-crowned sparrows in social isolation developed abnormal songs. The song had the whistle sections present but the trill was absent. It did, however, have some normal qualities; ornithologists who were played the abnormal songs could at least identify them as coming from some new species of sparrow. Where had those normal bits come from?

To find out, in an experiment that, perhaps, would be frowned upon today, the songs of deafened white-crowned sparrows were recorded and analysed. The deafened birds developed songs that were even more remote from normality. They were a raucous buzz, reminiscent of an insect rather than a bird. The result, though, allowed the researchers to suggest a mechanism for song learning. They called it the auditory template theory.

Each songbird studied, they concluded, has some innate capacity to develop at least some of the normal features of the song as heard in the wild, and that capacity rests on a mechanism associated with the sense of hearing. When a young male sparrow begins to sing, in the normal course of events, he listens to his own voice. He has an image of what the song should sound like and he proceeds to match his singing to this expectation, template fashion. He gradually achieves a more perfect match with the template until he is able to sing a song with some of the normal features.

In a bird hearing normal song, the template is modified, overridden by the learned information, until the song includes features of the local dialect. The male now has a new template which is more advanced than the innate version. Thus he proceeds through a continuous matching process. First he sings a sub-song, which is an immature form of the song with long phrases containing impure notes delivered more quietly than in full song. Next comes plastic song. This is the pre-adult song: the phrases are shortened and the notes perfected. Finally, the song crystalizes into an imitation of the local dialect to which the male is exposed when he is young.

Another observation coming from these and other song-learning experiments has been that songbirds seem to have a sensitive period for song learning, typically when they are quite young. In zebra finches the sensitive period is considered to be between twenty-five and eighty days old. It was thought that when the song was learned during that time window it was firmly memorized and then sung unchanged. But recent work has shown that the rigidity of the sensitive period may not be real. Normally, zebra finches do learn their song during the period between leaving parents and sexual maturity, but if there is no bird available from which they can learn their song they will delay the sensitive period. A sexually mature male deprived of a song model can still learn his song, long after the traditional sensitive period is over, and then make up for lost time. The innate switching system can be modified by environmental factors. In other words, experience or lack of experience can determine when a bird is receptive to learning.

The normal sensitive period for the white-crowned sparrow is somewhere between ten and fifty days, at a time usually when the bird has left the nest but is either dependent on or associated with its parents. A young male white-crowned sparrow tends to move away from the nest area at around two months of age, so it must be doing its song learning at home, although it does not actually start to sing itself until some time later.

When it does start to sing the following spring it generates an imitation of the local dialect. The imitation, though, is not completely faithful to the models heard. A young male extracts certain features from those heard in infancy and keeps them intact, while allowing itself the freedom to improvise or invent other portions of the song. In the white-crowned sparrow the song is relatively simple so there is a strong tendency to conform to local fashion, although each male includes individual, personalized features.

So each male has a set of structural features in his song that label him 'white-crowned sparrow'. They identify him as a member of a particular species. There are also features of local dialect which tell about the area in which he was brought up. And there are portions, usually in the whistle section, which are his personal marks. These sound cues are employed in different ways in a bird's social life: he is able to recognize his immediate neighbours; he can distinguish neighbours from more distant members of the community; he can discriminate between dialects; and he can distinguish members of his own species. So there is a hierarchy of song features, containing a lot of information, which is present even in the relatively simple song of the white-crowned sparrow.

But what might be true for a white-crowned sparrow may not necessarily be the case for other birds. Sensitive periods for song learning are by no means universal. Those birds with well-defined dialects tend to have narrowly defined periods for learning; others have different learning patterns.

The learning pattern can also be changed according to the conditions to which a learner is exposed. By presenting a caged bird, like a zebra finch, with a visible rather than a tape tutor, the learning period can be extended and the songs of other species can be taught. So social interaction with the teacher can influence what is taught. In addition, a young bird will learn more song elements from an aggressive teacher. And if the tutor has a song resembling that sung by the young bird's proper father, the youngster will tend to prefer to learn that song too.

It is possible that a female can also influence things. In captivity female cowbirds appear to respond to certain sounds their male companions are practising more than others. At certain points in the song they flick their wings. The result is that the male sings songs that a female prefers. In turn, she responds to the song elements she likes by adopting copulatory postures. The influences, then, on a young bird learning his song may include both the experience of exposure to the sounds of a male teacher and the visual consequences of singing to a female recipient.

In some species the programme of song learning remains throughout life. The red-winged blackbird continues to add to its repertoire as it matures, and the domestic form of the canary discards quite a large proportion of its song from one year to the next, adding new phrases to replace old ones. In both these species the size of the song repertoire increases annually as the male gets older and more mature. Females tend to choose the older, fitter males, which have survived several breeding seasons, in preference to the young untested juveniles.

The song-learning period of the great tits of Whytham Wood did not escape scrutiny. Not only was the time of the year the young male great tits learn their songs determined but also from whom. Studies of zebra finches and bullfinches had shown that caged birds sing songs like their fathers, and traditionally it was thought that this was true for birds in general.

Using the ringed and well-studied birds of this Oxfordshire wood, the songs of fathers and the songs of their offspring the following year were analysed. A field study rather than a laboratory experiment was preferred so that the birds were offered a choice of song models from which to learn. A bird in a cage only hears the tutor or a tape; a bird in the wild sits in its nest or flies about tentatively after fledging and hears a variety of songs and other sounds. So does the wild bird know which song is his father's, and, having identified it, learn specifically his father's song, or does he just pick up whatever he hears?

Looking at the songs of known fathers and sons, it was demonstrated that there is no tendency at all for male great tits to learn songs from their fathers. Songs, in this species at least, are not passed from generation to generation within the same family. So from whom does the male great tit learn his song?

The young male shares the highest proportion of his songs with his neighbours in the year that he sets up his first territory, that is, usually when he is about nine months old. If the bird is hatched in June he will beome a territorial male in March the following year. This suggests that a great deal of great tit song learning occurs in the first spring of life rather than in the first few weeks, as laboratory studies of other species had implied.

It is likely that a resident bird will remember the voice of his neighbour from year to year. Male hooded warblers in North Carolina migrate away from their breeding quarters for about eight months. Like great tits they learn the songs of their neighbours and a peaceful neighbourhood is maintained because each recognizes the others' calls. In the winter they all head off to Central America and spend the next eight months or so in the sun. In spring they return to the exact same territory, and it has been shown by playback experiments that they are able to remember and recognize the calls of their neighbours from the previous breeding season. The advantage to the resident is that on returning each spring to the same nest site with the same neighbours it does not need to spend an inordinate amount of time squabbling with them to establish territorial boundaries. The time can be better spent courting a female and breeding as early as possible. The hooded warbler is the first non-human to show long-term memory of individual neighbours and it is likely that other migratory birds have the same memory capability.

But not *all* the song elements in an individual great tit's repertoire are learned from the neighbours. In Whytham Wood, some birds are 'resident', having been hatched in the wood and having known parents. Others are 'immigrants', having been raised outside the wood and having wandered in from several miles away. The elements of song repertoires are derived, seemingly, from the two sources. There are 'common elements' which many different males in the wood include in their song repertoires, and 'rare elements' which are sung by a few individuals in the population. Closer inspection of the genealogy of these birds revealed that the rare elements are sung by immigrant birds which arrived in the wood as first-year males. Since these birds have predominantly 'Whytham Wood' songs but with the occasional song element from elsewhere, the Oxford team was able to conclude that the local common song elements were learned on arrival at the wood and the rare elements were learned before they dispersed from their home nest area.

So from these field studies on great tits, two periods of song learning have been identified: some time early in life at the age of two to three months before they disperse, and some time later at six to nine months when they first set up territory. After the first year their repertoire is not modified. Individuals followed for several years kept exactly the same song repertoire after their first spring.

Studies with captive chaffinches showed similar results. Hand-raised birds learn songs both in their first few months of life, which corresponds to the pre-dispersal learning period of wild birds, and in their first spring, corresponding to post-dispersal learning.

The female great tit's response to male song was also the focus of study. Using the data of songs of known individuals, researchers investigated whether the song a female hears during her early life influences her beheaviour later, when she chooses a mate. Female great tits, like many female songbirds, don't sing very much, but that is not to say they do not know something about the characteristics of the song. In some species of songbirds a female bird injected with male hormones sings a normal male song. The song is tucked away in the brain even if it is not normally sung.

So do female great tits also learn songs while still very young, particularly their father's song, and then use this information later in life, when they pair with a male, to avoid an incestuous mating with the father? In-breeding in great tits, it has been found, is disadvantageous. Birds mating with close relatives are less successful in breeding than individuals mating with distant relatives or individuals from outside the population. Do females, then, choose males with different songs from their father's?

In the field study, data was collected for females where the song repertoires of the female's father and the female's mate were known. Then the amount of sharing of songs between the two was noted and a comparison made between the result and the chance expectation based on the rate of sharing of songs in the population as a whole. It was found that females are less likely than expected by chance to mate with males which share most of their repertoire with the female's father. In addition, however, it was found that females are likely to turn down suitors whose song is too different from that of the father. Female great tits, it seems, prefer to mate with males with song repertoires slightly different from the female's father, but not very different.

This discovery fits with the notion that females, in choosing a male with which to mate, avoid close genetic relatives and incest, but at the same time avoid out-breeding with genetically too distant males. Genetically very distant males may be adapted to different environmental conditions. So, if there is any local population adaptation to different habitats, it is advantageous for females to mate within their own population. The same is true for local dialects – different dialect groups might be adapted to different habitat conditions (see pages 220–1).

PRACTICE MAKES PERFECT

Interest in song learning is not confined to the periods described above. The period between learning and the appearance of the fully mature song is the focus of more bird behaviour studies. This is the time when the learned song may change by identifiable stages – through sub-song to plastic song and finally adult song.

Sub-song is rather like the babbling of a baby before it begins to talk, and, as many mothers know, it is a fascinating stage of development. But for researchers it is also an impossible stage to understand and even document because the sounds are so variable. Nevertheless, scientists have tried, and a team in New York undertook the daunting task of analysing the sub-song of North American song sparrows and swamp sparrows.

Like the white-crowned sparrow of California, the male swamp sparrow learns from memory. He learns his song when quite young; the learning process is all over by sixty to seventy days of age. He doesn't come into full song until, perhaps, 200 days. Sub-song begins earlier, sometimes when song learning itself is taking place at two months. It was thought, traditionally, that sub-song is a period of rehearsal, when songs are committed to memory as they are heard, so that when the bird comes into full song the following spring the information is already firmly stored. The New York team thought, however, that sub-song was so unstructured that it was unlikely that rehearsal was taking place.

A group of sixteen birds was recorded once a week for a year and the tremendous amount of material representing the transitions from sub-song to plastic song to adult song was analysed. The birds were exposed only to playbacks of recorded songs, so the researchers knew everything the birds had heard during infancy. Thus in looking for evidence of rehearsal, the research team could examine the record for the very first appearance of anything that was remotely like the structure of the playback recordings the birds had learned when they were very young.

Rehearsal, it turned out, did not begin until the birds were between 230 and 250 days old. The male swamp sparrows had learned the tape-recorded songs when they were young, committed them to memory by ear without rehearsal, and stored them for up to 250 days before they began to produce anything remotely resembling the original recordings – a quite extraordinary feat. In what form they commit the songs to memory is the subject of current research.

Birds, it is thought, have an ability to memorize a model when young, and break it into sections or syallables which can be re-arranged to create new songs. They have the capacity to retain phonetic units that conform to the local fashion and yet can be recombined in new ways, allowing each male to place his personal mark on the song. They do this so freely that it is tempting to think that, when the song is committed to memory, it may well be done in a segmented form. By breaking the songs down into sub-units a bird could easily combine them later when it starts to sing in earnest. The units, however, are not the smallest units of song.

Birds, it is being revealed, have a remarkable capacity to make use of something which is very much like the syntax of language. This is not the lexical syntax of human language; the components of birdsong do not have the same independent meanings in the same way as human words do. The song is a message as a whole. In the case of birdsong, there is another and more relevant level of syntax called phonological syntax. The combinations of consonants and vowels or 'phonemes' from which words are constructed in human speech are analogous to the syllables of birdsong. For humans, every language has a limited set of phonemes and an infinite number of ways in which they can be combined, giving an endless capacity to generate new words. Perhaps the phoneme in human speech or the sound syllable – not the individual notes – in birdsong is the natural unit for the production of sound and the unit which young birds remember.

In addition to memorizing syllables and building them into songs, birds also invent new syllables. In the New York experiment, the researchers had such a complete record of everything the birds had heard that they were able to detect any subtle variations. When the birds sang their full song the researchers went through the spectrogram item by item, first looking for events attributable to learning in infancy, but found that some of the song components produced in adulthood did not match any of the components in the tape recordings. The components were identified as copies at an intermediate stage of development but later they were changed. The bird had engaged in a kind of vocal play, imposing small transformations, and so getting further and further away from the original model. By the time the bird produced adult song the end product could not be related easily to the starting point. The bird had invented a part of the song. So, along with imitation, there is also improvisation and invention going on. Birds are constantly generating new patterns of sound in nature.

The New York study revealed even more. When the team analysed sub-song and plastic song, they discovered that each bird generates far more song material in the course of development than is needed for normal adult song production. A male swamp sparrow has, typically, three song types. Analysing plastic song a week before it had crystallized to adult song, it was found that the bird had been using six syllables and not three. A couple of weeks before that, it had been using twelve (in one case as many as nineteen). So, in swamp sparrows, it was determined that as a bird approaches the moment of song crystallization the components get winnowed down rapidly until the mature repertoire is left.

Analysing the twelve syllables, it was found that five or six were obvious imitations, one or two were improvised variations of an imitation, and four or five seemed to have been invented. The New York team concluded that songbirds have the capacity for truly creative processes, and that conclusion was based on the song of a bird with one of the simplest songs. It is exciting to contemplate the degree of inventiveness to be discovered in the songs of the mockingbird or blackbird.

LEARNING THE RIGHT SONG

If all songbirds are learning songs at roughly the same time, why don't some of them learn the wrong songs? In some of the early Cambridge research with chaffinches, isolated birds presented with tree pipit song actually learned and sang it. Later, in California, white-crowned sparrows were given a natural choice of songs to learn.

In the coastal chaparral in which white-crowned sparrows live, another very common species is the song sparrow. The two species live closely together. As far as field research could show, white-crowned sparrows never learned song sparrow and vice versa. Birds were brought into the laboratory. White-crowned sparrows were given a choice of recordings of white-crowned sparrow and song sparrows and unerringly imitated white-crown. If presented with song sparrow song alone, the white-crowned sparrows rejected it and reverted to their innate song.

This was an intriguing discovery. Here was one of the most elaborate learning processes known in animals, and yet there appeared to be innate instructions or guidelines as to what the bird should be learning, an interesting interplay between nature and nurture. A bird cannot develop normal song without the opportunity to learn and yet it inherits some capacity to identify what it ought to be learning.

The experiments were repeated in New York with swamp sparrows and song sparrows, two species that also live closely together in the same habitat within earshot of each other. In this study, however, the birds were not played normal songs but songs that had been 'doctored' in some way. Syllables were edited out and recombined in different patterns – some swamp sparrow-like, others song sparrow-like. For every pattern devised, two versions were created – one composed of mainly swamp sparrow and the other mainly song sparrow. The birds were trained on these songs at about twenty to sixty days of age, the period when their readiness to learn is at its maximum. The results were interesting.

The swamp sparrows, for example, were highly selective in what they learned, the selectivity being based on the syllable rather than the pattern. Swamp sparrows learned any swamp sparrow syllable irrespective of the pattern in which it was presented. The team concluded that selective learning is an all-or-nothing phenomenon and that at its heart is an innate perceptual process. Birds, from the age of a few weeks, have an innate perceptual filter in the brain which accepts or discards incoming auditory information.

Other researchers are not so sure about this conclusion. Another study with white-crowned sparrows in California casts some doubt on the universality of any innate filtering mechanism. The birds were taught all sorts of alien songs which, if a perceptual filter was working in their brains, they would be unable to learn. The trick apparently was to put the tutor and the pupil in visual contact. Birds, it seems, are fussy about what they learn from recorded tapes and are more prepared to learn from individuals with which they can interact.

In the real world there is a plethora of environmental stimuli affecting young birds and they must be provided with some innate instructions about how to sift the barrage of incoming information if their nervous systems are not to be reduced to chaos. To which stimuli should the bird attend and which should it ignore? At which point should it be ready to accept less favourable stimuli if the optimum circumstances do not arise? There must be innate instructions about timing, periods of life when a bird must go through certain processes of behavioural development to provide the skeleton on which later stages of development depend.

And they must get it right, for if they learn the wrong song or even, in some cases, part of a song they could be in trouble. It has been shown that female red-winged blackbirds, for instance, ignore singers performing abnormal songs, even though males accept them and challenge the singer.

In tests, male and female red-winged blackbirds were presented with normal male song and an imitation sung by a mockingbird. The males responded to both songs, the females preferring the normal rendition. This difference in response is not unexpected. Male birds need to respond quickly to intruding males and are unlikely to be so fussy about the detail of the rival's song, whereas females must be very particular that they accept a partner of the right species, coming from the right environment, singing the right song with the right dialect.

DIALECTS

A consequence of birds' having learned their songs, rather than having inherited them, is that individuals of the same species, living in different areas, will sing songs which are not identical. The early naturalists noticed this. Baron von Pernaus (1660–1731) and a little later Daines Barrington (1727–1800) (see pages 207–8) noted that just as local variation in human speech occurs from place to place within a country sharing the same language, so too do some birds have small pockets of song variation – local dialects.

Ornithologists in the San Francisco Bay area can place a white-crowned sparrow to within a couple of miles of its home range simply by hearing its song. The birds have an alerting buzz, followed by a trill, and finishing with a buzz. Around the bay there is, however, considerable variation on this simple song. At the Berkeley campus of the University of California the birds sing a simple series of three whistles and end with a trill. Main district birds at Inverness to the north of the city have an opening whistle, then a trill, and end with a trill. Individuals from Sunset Beach at Watsonville to the south have a double whistle followed by a buzz and terminating in a trill. The same sort of variation has been found in redwings and corn buntings in Europe.

In one study of San Francisco's white-crowned sparrows, re-searchers tested the birds for evidence that dialects were indeed a result of cultural transmission during song learning. Hatchlings that had not heard adult song and young birds that had were brought into the laboratory and reared in social isolation. The hatchlings deprived of adult example sang songs quite unlike their home dialect, whereas the birds that had heard the songs of their adult neighbours eventually sang good copies of the local dialect. Tutoring studies later showed that sparrows would learn, during the critical learning period, the home dialect or even dialects from other areas. This was evidence that dialects are learned; but what of their function?

Could it be that dialects are just accidental occurrences as a result of learning and have no biological value? The California team speculated that female sparrows might use song dialect for selecting a mate. The dialect might represent a local population indulging in some degree of inbreeding, and therefore, in a sense, could be considered as some form of incipient speciation, with the advantage that, as it is a learned behaviour, it could be reversed during the

219

course of a generation. Unfortunately studies elsewhere confused the picture. Female white-crowned sparrows, given testosterone to encourage them to sing like males, surprisingly sang with a different dialect from the one in which they were brought up.

The question of whether dialect has a function was taken up by another US research team. In one experiment it was found that female white-crowned sparrows only responded to the calls of male birds from their own dialect region. In another experiment they wanted to see if any genetic variations coincided with a boundary between two dialects. Using biochemical analyses to detect differences in the blood, they examined the genetic make-up of birds across a dialect boundary. They discovered genetic discontinuities which, they argued, are a consequence of males and females settling in an area where their home dialect is sung.

This line of thought was pursued further. Birds living along a transect from one dialect area to another were banded and their patterns of dispersal followed. Birds in the heart of a dialect area, they found, disperse more or less radially to establish territories and breed, whereas those birds at the boundaries dispersed asymmetrically, veering away from the boundary into the focus of the home dialect. The dialects of the study group of several sub-species of white-crowned sparrows form a kind of genetic mosaic. The birds are all members of the same species yet there is enough differentiation for each dialect area to constitute a 'deme' or selective unit. This means that all birds living close together tend to be kin, a situation that favours some of the elaborations of social behaviour, such as reciprocal altruism (mutual unselfishness), emerging.

In the light of these findings it is suggested that dialects *do* have a function, a notion investigated in Argentina with the rufous-collared sparrow. This bird has a wide distribution in a variety of climates and habitats, from cold tundra to hot desert. A female faced with choosing a mate might benefit from mating with a male from her own dialect group. A bird adapted to the desert would best pair with another desert bird of the same species. Mating with a bird from a polar area, for instance, would dilute the gene pool, possibly introducing inappropriate characteristics, and might make the offspring less likely to surive the rigours of the desert. Analysis of rufous-collared sparrows living on the Pampas revealed that dialects are indeed related to local conditions. On the plains, where the vegetation is uniform and conditions are similar across vast tracts of the countryside, birds many hundreds of miles apart sing in a similar dialect. In the hills nearby, however, where the climate and vegetation are different, the birds sing a different dialect from those on the plains.

In Europe, yellowhammers have two distinct dialects and each is linked to a particular nest site. Those birds living in eastern parts of Germany, Austria, the former Soviet Union, Finland and Denmark have one regional dialect and nest mainly on the ground, while those in other parts of Scandinavia, the British Isles, France and western Germany have another dialect and nest low in bushes. Female yellowhammers only respond favourably to males singing their regional dialect. Males who find themselves in both dialect areas play safe and sing both dialects.

Many birds are highly mobile. Where there are no obvious habitat boundaries they can flit from one area to another, yet they still show regional dialects. Male brown-headed cowbirds in the Sierra Nevada, for instance, have three-syllable songs in one area and four-syllable songs little more than a mile away. The function of dialect here seems to be to select for the most sociably acceptable partners.

Cowbirds are nest parasites, therefore the young males do not learn their songs from their father or the neighbours. They are only exposed directly to cowbird song when they begin to meet other cowbirds during their first breeding season. One way in which a female can tell if a male is older, experienced and therefore of superior status is to listen to his song. If he has picked up the local dialect, which may take him several seasons to learn, then his status is raised and he is deemed suitable as a mate. Young males or newcomers to the area will not have had sufficient time to learn the local dialect and have a lower social status.

That dialect has a function, though, is not universally accepted. Studies with chaffinches in Orkney suggest that dialect serves no function whatsoever in this species but are an accidental by-product of song learning. A young bird, within the first year of life, hears other chaffinches singing. He listens and learns, memorizing the exact details heard. The following spring, when his testosterone levels begin to rise, he starts to sing himself, matching his own output to the memory of what he has previously heard. The problem is that birds make mistakes, and mistakes in learned patterns are much more common than mutations in genetic transmission. As a result, song is almost certain to change.

Some individuals copy accurately, others not so accurately. Some song types may be copied less than others and become extinct; others are miscopied, thus creating new songs. If populations are distinct from each other, then birds will learn primarily within their own population, and as a result the song and their mistakes will be different from those of the population some distance away.

In the wind-swept Orkney Isles, off the north of the Scottish mainland, the chaffinch study involved the search for local song variations. There are few trees on the Orkneys, and consequently few chaffinches, so the researchers were able to record a very high proportion of all the birds in the area. They found that, not only was there more than one song type for the whole of Orkney and several song types for each major wood, but there were also individual variations.

Each chaffinch has between one and five song types. There are song types shared by many birds and other song types particular to an individual bird. In one wood with fifteen male chaffinches, for example, ten individuals were identified singing song type B; the phrases within the song were almost identical with few variations. Another bird in the wood might have a type very similar to B, but not quite the same. It was suggested that the bird had copied song type B but had made a mistake.

From the forty male chaffinches in the Orkney study area, seventeen song types were recognized. If every bird had had its own songs the number should have been nearer a hundred, but this was not the case. There was obviously a degree of overlap of the song types. The grouping, though, is not strictly into dialects. If it were, one stand of trees would have a particular collection of song types, while the next wood would have a quite distinct set. This is not what happens. It was found that songs tend to have foci. When the song is common, about half the population are singing it. Further from the focus, fewer birds are singing that particular song and another song type takes over. Travel a little further and the focus of another song type is reached. In chaffinches there seem to be no distinct dialect boundaries. Rather, there is a patchwork of overlapping song types where some song foci interact with others, and where song types are common to all areas. The song simply carried geographically from one area to another. The word 'dialect' then must be reserved for those species where there are areas in which a particular song type is sung, marked by border lines beyond which the song is not sung and another song is sung instead.

IMITATION

Whatever the explanation and whatever their function, dialects are the direct result of vocal imitation, one of several recognized aspects of bird behaviour known as vocal copying.

Researchers in California thought it appropriate that some semblance of order should be brought to the way in which different aspects of vocal copying, whether they be imitation, copying or mimicry, are described so that scientists are talking about the same piece of behaviour.

Their starting point, however, was an interest in the problem of two related species living in the same area. If they are breeding within earshot of one another, using songs to keep out rivals of their own species and to attract females of the right species, what are the implications for the kinds of signals being transmitted? The birds, after all, are close competitors, particularly if they are similar in size and shape and are competing for the same nest sites and food supplies.

Species A needs not only to keep out other species A males, but also to see off species B males. But this raises more problems of unambiguous recognition of signals on the part of each species. If species A songs are similar to species B songs, then species A males are likely to attract species B females, resulting in no offspring, or, at the least, infertile hybrids. Clearly this is not advantageous for the individual, so there should be some selection in its song for species specificity. But, at the same time, if a bird is in a situation where it may increase its own nesting success by excluding potential competition from other species, then there is the opposite selection pressure in the form of its song for some similarity of signal. This category of vocal copying is called 'vocal convergence' and it occurs when ecological competitors or close relatives have similar songs or calls.

Another type of vocal copying is 'vocal appropriation'. It refers to a bird copying the sounds made by members of another unrelated species. It is often accidental. A bird might incorporate into its song elements of another species' song simply because it lives in the same acoustic environment. It might also occur in an impoverished environment. If a bird is nesting in an area where the population is at a very low density and there are not very many role models around from which a young bird might learn, then a youngster might pick up the song elements of a close neighbour of a different species.

The starling is a great appropriator. It is known to pick up biological and mechanical sounds, including the songs and calls of other bird species. But, in a study on Fair Isle, it was found that starlings are actually quite fussy about what they mimic. The calls of oystercatchers and curlews are popular, but the starlings avoid complicated sounds, like trills and buzzes, in favour of simple whistles. It is unlikely that the starling is mimicking waders in order to extend the starling's territorial 'keep out' song to other species. Waders, after all, are not competing for nesting sites and food with starlings. The more likely explanation for the appropriation is that the bird has found a simple way of enriching its song repertoire.

That the starling collected the sounds of other species, including segments of human speech, was known in ancient times. Pliny wrote of some avian classics scholars of his acquaintance imitating Greek and Latin. These starlings, he wrote, 'practised diligently and spoke new phrases every day.'

Shakespeare thought the starling might be used to upset the sleep of King Henry IV. Hotspur suggested that a starling might be taught the name 'Mortimer', a nobleman the king mistrusted.

Schubert brought the starling into his song cycle *Die schone Mullerin*:

> I'd teach a starling how to speak and sing,
> Till every word and note with truth should ring,
> With all the skill my lips and tongue impart,
> With all the warmth and passion of my heart.

And on 27 May 1784 Mozart bought a starling, which, to the great surprise of his friends, he buried with all due pomp and ceremony some three years later. At the graveside, mourners heard him read a poem which he had written especially for the event, and modern historians wonder whether it was the starling for which Mozart grieved or for his recently deceased father.

Mozart was intrigued by the starling from the first moment he saw and heard it. The date can be precise because he recorded the purchase in a notebook documenting his expenses. Beneath the expense he noted the tune the starling was singing and it bears a remarkable similarity to the beginning of the final movement of his Piano Concerto in G Major, K.453, which was completed on 12 April 1784, but not performed until 13 June. It seems the bird had somehow learned the piece, but how? There is speculation that

Long and powerful legs enable the African ostrich, the world's largest living bird, to reach running speeds of up to 45 mph. It can outrun pursuers, such as lions and hyenas, but if cornered it can lash out with its feet and disembowel a careless predator.

A turkey vulture at Baja California, Mexico, takes advantage of the early morning sun. It perches with wings outstretched on top of a prickly cardon cactus.

Bird-watching can be dangerous. An aggressive Arctic tern attacks an intruder who ventured too close to a nest site. An attack can be so intense that a bird can draw blood from an unprotected scalp.

A mixed flock of dunlin and knot on the shores of the Waddensea, in the Netherlands, twist and turn in the air as one. The birds co-ordinate their flight movements much as a chorus-line of dancers perform a routine.

Thousands of northern gannets gather each spring on the Bass Rock in the Firth of Forth, Scotland. All the birds in the breeding colony prepare their nests, lay eggs, and bring up their young at the same time. It is a synchronized strategy for survival.

Red-billed quelea congregate into the largest bird flocks in the world. The flocks are so dense that they can blot out the sun. At sunset in the Etosha National Park, Namibia, an enormous flock flies down to a waterhole to drink.

Sandhill cranes stop over at the Platte River, Nebraska, during their migration north. They roost by night and feed by day until conditions are right to continue their journey.

A flock of snow geese are disturbed at their wintering site at the Bosque del Apache National Wildlife Refuge, New Mexico. In spring they head for the Arctic.

This group of Bewick's swans increases its flying efficiency by travelling in an echelon formation during its long migration from summer breeding grounds in Siberia to wintering sites in north-western Europe.

The poorwill of North America is the only bird known to truly hibernate. This bird is sitting on its nest.

The cock capercaillie performs an extraordinary strutting-and-calling display in order to attract the attention of a prospective mate. The greater part of its guttural call, however, is at a very low frequency and is inaudible to our ears.

The American bittern is a 'boomer'. Its very loud, low-frequency call can be heard up to three miles away.

The redshank is the 'sentinel of the saltmarsh'. Its shriek of alarm is the first bird-call to alert other shorebirds to approaching danger.

D'Arnauds's barbets, from East Africa, sing in duets and choruses. The choristers emit a simple doo-do-dee-dok song over and over and over again.

A female great bowerbird in northern Australia has been attracted to a male's elaborate avenue-like bower. The structure, consisting mainly of twigs, is decorated with discarded rubbish, predominantly in the cock bird's preferred colours.

The tawny frogmouth of Queensland, Australia, is a master of disguise. Its plumage resembles the colour and texture of wood, and by remaining absolutely motionless the bird looks to all the world like a branch.

The 'rushing' display of the western grebe of North America can be performed by a male and female, two males or even a group of males eliciting the attentions of a solitary female. They are birds that can walk on water.

Two colourful male long-tailed manakins from the tropical rainforests of South and Central America perform an acrobatic courtship display to impress the comparatively drab female who is looking on. Only one of the males will win her favour, although the other subordinate male may mate with other females who have been attracted to the performance.

The willow ptarmigan of northern lands changes its plumage with the seasons. In winter it blends in with its snowy background (left), but in summer it is camouflaged amongst the mosses and heathers with a coat of mottled brown feathers (right).

Forsaking flying for running, the greater roadrunner of the chaparral of south-western North America pursues its prey on the ground. It has caught a fast-moving lizard.

These red-billed oxpeckers will be displaced from their hippopotamus host's back when it enters the water. The birds feed on ticks and other insects that cling to the hides of large animals, such as buffalo, zebras and hippos. When the hippo re-emerges to feed on land, the birds will be there to peck away at the parasites.

A simple sugar solution of passion flower nectar is sufficient to fuel the rapidly beating wings of the bronzy hermit, one of the hummingbirds of Costa Rica's tropical rainforest.

A North American bald eagle feasts on a freshly caught salmon which it plucked from the river using its sharp and powerful talons.

In the absence of suitable real trees in a city, a telegraph pole serves as a winter larder for an acorn woodpecker. Each hole, neatly chiselled by the bird's tough bill, provides storage for a single acorn.

Roosting on rack ledges behind the waters of the Iguazu Falls in northern Argentina, a huddle of great dusky swifts has found a safe and secure refuge.

A pair of mallee fowl, having laboured for many weeks to build their enormous nest, open the mound in order to deposit a clutch of eggs. Having completed her task the female retires to the scrub, leaving the male to defend the nest and ensure that the eggs incubate at a constant temperature of 34°C no matter what the temperature is outside.

Pairs of cliff swallows gather beak-sized dollops of soft mud from the banks of nearby ponds and lakes and sculpt it into rounded, hollow mud-nests which are attached to rocky underhangs high on the sides of sheer cliffs. Here the nests are safe from all but the most intrepid of predators.

Weaver birds construct their elaborate nests of woven grass in places safe from predators. These Cape weavers have chosen to hang their nests over water.

King penguins take up to a year to raise their chicks, so at any one time a colony contains birds at different stages of development. Youngsters can be identified by their thick, warm, brown, fur-like down.

The world for a young fairy tern is no wider than a branch. In its eagerness to feed, the single chick, which emerged from an egg laid in the same seemingly precarious position on the branch, must be careful not to fall.

The male is mother. Having incubated the eggs from several females, male Darwin's rheas must continue to look after the family of half-brothers and half-sisters.

The main hazard on the golf course at a US airforce base on Midway Island in the Pacific Ocean is a breeding colony of albatrosses. The birds used the island long before the human aviators arrived, but birds and man are now in conflict. Birds flying to and from their nests represent a danger to aircraft flying to and from the airbase.

The long Islamic tradition of falconry resulted in Eastern techniques being introduced into Europe after the Crusades. As then, falconry today is a sport enjoyed by people from all walks of life. But there is a danger that populations of rare birds of prey are at risk from the taking of individuals from the wild.

A collection of rubbish, swallowed at sea by an adult Laysan albatross,
has been regurgitated when the bird returns to feed the young.
If fed to chicks these objects could kill.

Mozart himself visited the shop and either deliberately or inadvertently taught the bird his tune. He was so impressed that he bought the bird.

After its death, Mozart completed 'A Musical Joke' (K.522) which some ornithologists feel has some of the qualities of starling song, particularly in the way it jumps about awkwardly and comes to an abrupt end. Mozart, it is felt, 'collaborated' with the starling during the three years of its captive life and K.522 was a kind of requiem for his musical companion.

Mozart and his starling apart, the champion appropriator must be the marsh warbler. It may imitate over 200 species, drawing upon the songs or calls of seventy-six or more species in an hour. The marsh warbler migrates from Africa to Europe to breed and everywhere it goes it picks up contributions to its amazing song – thirty-one from Europe and forty-five from Africa. So for about two to three days in spring the bird sings non-stop, day and night, delivering sequences of skylark, thrush and swallow interspersed with drongo, bee-eater and weaver bird. By analysing its song, the route that it takes to and from the dark continent can be discovered. An element from the song of the boran cisticola, for instance, a bird with a limited distribution, tells that the warbler has been to an area covering southern Ethiopia and northern Kenya.

During the northern winter, marsh warblers live in Africa, and it has been discovered that they sing here too, not all day and night, but only during daylight hours. Just as they defend 100-square-metre sized territories on the breeding grounds in spring – at least for the period before the arrival of their mates and the time in which they are still fertile – they also defend feeding territories in the tropics. Although food is abundant, warblers have problems flying far to forage during the moult, so a small, well-guarded patch of food helps them through this vulnerable period – and they guard the same patch of food every year, despite having travelled 4,800 miles from Europe, via the Middle East, the Arabian Peninsula, the Red Sea and Sudan to eastern Kenya and wintering sites to the south.

Vocal appropriation is a form of 'vocal mimicry', but this label is reserved for a category of vocal copying where some kind of deception is taking place.

At the time of writing, there is only one well-documented study in which vocal mimicry takes place. The mimic is the thick-billed euphonia, a member of the tanager family. If a predator approaches the nest, the resident pair give the alarm and mobbing calls of other species which are then attracted to the nest site and mob the predator. The euphonia, meanwhile, waits on the sidelines and watches the action from a safe place in the bushes.

There are, however, other examples which have not yet been studied. European jays and Cape robin chats, for example, are also known to copy the alarm calls of other species and may well behave in the same way as the euphonia. And forest falcons in Panama rainforests are thought to mimic the distress calls of prey. They lurk in the undergrowth waiting to pounce on any unsuspecting bird that rallies to the call. Similarly, African crowned eagles have been reported to mimic monkey calls in order to attract them out into the open. Whether these are cases of true mimicry has yet to be investigated.

The fork-tailed drongo, however, might be taking this kind of mimicry to interesting lengths. This bird has been heard to mimic the whistle of local shepherds. Birds of prey and other animals dangerous to drongos tend to avoid humans and might be deterred by the recognizable sounds they make. So has the drongo learned the shepherd's whistle in order to reduce risk from aerial predators?

No matter what the copying category, some birds appear to copy the most bizarre sounds. European song thrushes, blackbirds and starlings have been heard to copy 'whistling' telephones and pedestrian crossing bleepers. Starlings were heard in the Second World War to copy the sounds made by the rocket motors of V1 flying bombs, and one bird apparently imitated a referee's whistle and disrupted an entire football match.

Why they should get up to this mischief is a mystery, for they certainly do not live in impoverished environments with a paucity of role models. It could be the rhythm of the ringing tone which stimulates imitation. A song thrush repeats each song phrase several times, like a warbling telephone, and a singer might be mistaking the sound of the telephone for another thrush with which it is trying to match song for song. On an old recording by Ludwig Koch (the pioneer of wildlife sound recording) made in 1910, a celebrated Prussian blackbird even imitated the distinctive sound of the Kaiser's motor klaxon.

In Australia the superb lyrebird seems to incorporate farm machinery noises into its courtship display. On the Indian sub-continent an even more puzzling form of appropriation to a bird-call occurs when wild hill mynahs copy the sounds of local tree frogs and captive birds accurately copy human speech. In 1664, diarist

Samuel Pepys encountered one in the Duke of York's drawing room at St James's Palace. It neighed like a horse and talked.

In 1988 this ability to imitate human speech and other sounds got a lot of birds, and their owners, into a lot of trouble. The occasion was the 45th National Exhibition of Cage and Aviary Birds at the Birmingham Exhibition Centre. Tempers began to flare when Basil, a parrot from the Amazon, ousted another parrot by the name of Oliver Cromwell for the world talking-bird championship. Basil's trumpet-styled rendition of the 'Charge of the Light Brigade' contributed to his victory over Oliver who, amongst other things, cried like a baby and laughed hysterically. Another bird who could manage a parrot-styled rip-off of the pop group Queen's 'I Want to Break Free' wasn't even in the final frame. Basil's victory, though, was not universally accepted and he was considered by rival owners as anything but a 'pretty boy'.

I doubt, though, whether Basil and his contemporaries could match the British champion of talkers, one Sparkie Williams from Newcastle. In the late 1950s Sparkie regaled the nation with his 550-word vocabulary and his ability to recite several nursery rhymes. His nearest rival was probably Moscow's Gosha, who in 1980 featured on a recording containing fifteen-word sentences, various songs, and the poetry of Kornei Ivanovich Chukovsky.

Talking birds are not a new phenomenon. In 29 BC the Emperor Augustus acquired not only a speaking parrot but also a raven who was taught to say 'Ave Caesar Victor Imperator.' History records that it was not the only raven trained that year. Augustus was just back from defeating Mark Anthony in Egypt. To play safe, the bird trainer had another raven ready to proclaim 'Ave Antonius Victor Imperator.'

But perhaps the most intriguing story from history involves the great explorer Alexander von Humboldt. He was journeying through South America when he was introduced to a parrot that spoke in a tongue which could not be recognized. It turned out that the bird had been reared by members of a tribe that had been exterminated and that the language was, in effect, a dead one.

DUETTING

A richer song repertoire can be achieved in other ways. In some species, for example tropical boubou shrikes, an elaborate song is built up from the contributions of two birds. Instead of the male singing alone, the female joins in too. The coordination and integration of the two songs is so well achieved that it often sounds like the song of just one bird. How the coordination is achieved nobody knows; but we can guess at the reason for combining songs in this fashion.

A clue lies in the habitat of most duetting birds, for they live almost exclusively in tropical forests or other places with dense vegetation. They also tend to be monogamous – pairing for life – and to retain territories throughout the year, for many years. Duetting, it is thought, maintains and reinforces the pair bond. In dense vegetation, with birds constantly out of sight of each other, a sound reinforcer is important.

Duetting birds are often seen singing at other duetting birds across a territorial boundary. Duetting, then, like solo song, may have a dual function both of establishing and reinforcing the relationship between a pair and of territorial proclamation.

VOCAL POSTSCRIPT

If you were beginning to feel that birds are remarkable automatons, accurately learning, practising, singing, matching, and repeating songs at amazing superhuman rates, then perhaps it is comforting to find that they, like us, are fallible. Seven Cambridge blackbirds were recorded daily for three months and it was found that in 8,620 song phrases recorded from one individual forty errors had crept in. The bird's attention was distracted by neighbours and as a consequence it made any of three basic mistakes. Sometimes it hesitated after it had just started a phrase and then, having realized it was making a mistake, went back to the beginning of the phrase and started again. It might also be distracted in mid-phrase, after which it repeated the preceding note and then completed the phrase. And thirdly, it got so confused that it could not complete the phrase at all and finished its rendition with any sounds that it could muster. On several occasions the bird mistimed its song and simply ran out of breath.

6

A BIRD'S EYE VIEW

BIRDS, LIKE OURSELVES, RELY LARGELY UPON SIGHT TO INVESTIGATE their world. Both birds and people have excellent eyes compared with most other animals, but the eyes of birds are far superior. Indeed, birds probably have the most highly developed sense of vision in the animal kingdom.

Like us, they can see colours, but they go that little bit further: birds can detect and appreciate an infinite range of colours and subtle hues some of which we can barely distinguish and some of which we cannot see at all. Birds have evolved such a range of uniquely modified eyes they are able to lead extremely specialized lifestyles. The development of colour in birds has progressed inseparably from their increasingly sophisticated powers of vision. This dual evolution has often resulted in slavish dedication to or conflict between the primary needs to attract and appease a partner during courtship, to find safe and palatable food, and to make themselves invisible to and therefore safe from predators.

THE BIRD'S EYE

Whilst eyes are made of living tissue, their performance is still governed by the same laws of physics as any camera or telescope. In order to understand how birds see a world very different from our own, it is perhaps useful to know a little of how an eye works. Its basic construction is not so different from that of a modern camera. The touchable transparent surface of the eye is the cornea and it acts like a protective neutral filter in front of the lens. In the same way that we alter the shape of a camera lens when focusing, so the shape of an eye's lens is altered by rings of circular muscles extending out from its edge. At rest the lens is rounded and it is focused by pulling it flatter. As the lens changes in shape, so the amount of light needed inside the eye changes. This is exactly what happens in photography. Too much light and the picture is bleached and overexposed. Too little light and the image is unusably dark. To overcome this, eyes, like many modern cameras, have automatic exposure control. The coloured part of the eye, the iris, is really a light-blocking diaphragm. It can close down to let in only a pinpoint of light, or at night open wide to gather as much as possible. It is because the iris changes with focusing that we can diagnose blindness (by failure to focus on moving objects) in babies.

By changing the shape of the lens the image is brought into sharp focus onto light-sensitive tissue, the retina, at the back of the eye. The retina converts the incoming light energy of the image to electrical energy that can be sent to the brain.

In the retina, light falls on two sorts of light-sensitive cells – the rods and the cones. In most animals and in nocturnal birds rods are the more numerous. They are like bottles filled with ink and they can only produce black-and-white vision. Light hitting the pigment bleaches it white. So, if an animal looked at a chessboard, it would immediately produce an exact copy, consisting of bleached white and unbleached black squares, on the retina at the back of its eye. A fraction of a second later all the cells would return to normal and would be immediately ready to respond to the next image.

As with a newspaper photograph, the image the brain receives from the eyes is composed of dots. Each dot corresponds to a rod or a group of rods. The more rods there are, as with the number of dots in a photograph or lines on a TV screen, the greater the resolution. The human eye has 100,000 rods in each square millimetre of retina. But this is where the birds show their visual superiority. Even the humble sparrow has four times this resolution with 400,000 rods per square millimetre. And birds such as the peregrine which are dependent on superlative visual accuity for their supper can have over 1 million rods per square millimetre. Birds, it seems, not only hear better than we do, they also have a far more sophisticated and powerful sense of seeing.

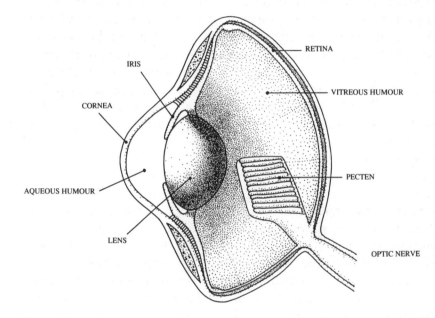

Birds' eyes can be divided into three main groups according to shape and function. Most birds have flattened eyes which gives them a large field of view but with reduced resolution. Globose eyes are common in birds of prey that hunt during the day. The longer optical axis enlarges the image on the retina giving these hunters sharper eyesight. Tubular eyes are common in nocturnal birds, such as owls. The long optical axis and extreme curvature of the cornea increase the amount of light entering the eye and enable the birds to see at very low light levels.

The cones in the retina enable animals to see colour. The retina of most diurnal birds contains a high proportion of cones and fewer rods. This helps explain why diurnal birds are reluctant to fly at night. Rods function in dimmer light than cones – that's why we tend to see mainly in black and white at night – so, with fewer rods, diurnal birds have less good nocturnal vision. They make up for it, however, with a retina filled with colour-discriminating cones.

Cones work basically like rods, but usually contain not one single dark ink-like compound, but yellow, green and blue pigments, each of which is sensitive to light at a different wavelength or colour. The reason why many animals see only in black and white is that they lack these cone cells. Diurnal birds, with their profusion of cones, have advanced colour vision, probably the most sophisticated amongst all animals.

Colours are just wavelengths of light energy at different frequencies within the electromagnetic spectrum. At the lower end of the spectrum is red light, which extends way beyond what we humans can see as infra-red light; we only feel that it has heat. Special infra-red night-scopes can 'see' these wavelengths and can be used to let us see heat-emitting living things in the dark. At the upper end of the spectrum is blue and beyond that ultra-violet light. Whilst we have pigments which see blue, this represents the limit of our range. But many birds have a fourth colour receptor which extends their visual capability: they can see in the ultra-violet frequency, an ability they share with insects. With an extra colour capability, the world looks very much more detailed and distinct to these birds. They can see the invisible guides with which plants mark their flowers. Insects use the markings, like the runway landing lights at an airport, to guide them to the nectar at the base of the flower. Similarly, many tropical plants use these hidden signals to guide hummingbirds to drink from their nectaries and pollinate their flowers.

Each rod or cone has a nerve running from it. These gather together to form the optic nerve that transmits visual information to the brain. In most animals, information from ten or more cells is pooled in a common nerve before being sent to the brain. Animal eyes, therefore, produce a relatively grainy image like those of a newspaper photograph. Birds go one better. Image quality is maximized, with almost every rod and cone wired directly to the brain, giving birds a greater visual resolution than any other animal, including ourselves.

COLOUR-CODED FOOD

Colour is of paramount importance to birds. They use it to attract mates, to spot prey and to discriminate between acceptable and unpalatable foods. They can, for example, distinguish differences in fruit ripeness, differences that are quite invisible to our eyes. To do this most diurnal birds have brightly coloured oil droplets in their cone cells. These fine tune the cones by filtering out all but a narrow band of light or colour wavelengths. By varying the arrangement or amount of oil in a cone, an infinite range of shades can be distinguished. Five different types of oil droplets have so far been found. When these are coupled with rods and the four cone colours, birds can discern hues of colours many times more subtle than those we can distinguish. But that's not all: they can also be used to amplify the image of a fish hidden in its murky water or to see through clouds by filtering out the light scattered by water droplets.

Colour discrimination is also vital if the food a bird eats might be poisonous enough to kill it. Many birds, for instance, eat butterflies. These colourful insects, in turn, attempt to warn off or fool the predators. The false eye spots of a peacock butterfly are probably designed to draw attention away from its vulnerable head. They might even be there to fool a predator into believing that what it is seeing is the head of a dangerous snake. Some hairstreak butterflies are designed with beaks in mind. They have a false head to draw the bird's pecks to a line of weakness on the wings. As the wing tears, the bird is left with the disposable wing fragment whilst the insect makes good its escape.

Some birds will not risk feeding on harmless hoverflies whose appearance mimics wasps and bees. Others are not fooled so easily. Visual specialists, like bee-eaters, can determine whether or not an insect is a mimic from some distance away. They are able to identify and remember minute details about a large range of insect colours and patterns and thereby eat the right, tasty morsel rather than the evil-tasting look-alike. Rufous-tailed jacamars are thrush-sized, glitteringly iridescent insect-eaters from South America. They are so sure that their eyes will not fail them that they readily distinguish between foul-tasting butterflies bearing warning colours and their identical edible mimics and devour the latter.

Monarch butterflies migrate annually from the southern USA and Mexico to central-southern Canada and must pass through the ranges of hundreds of different bird species, but no bird will reach out to take one. Monarchs are protected by foul-tasting poisons they pick up from milkweed when caterpillars and, when adults, advertise their unpalatability with bright colours. But, at their wintering grounds in Mexico and the southern USA, they encounter the black-headed grosbeak and the remarkably talented black-headed oriole. The grosbeaks, with little *savoir-faire* to speak of, have developed an immunity to the butterflies' chili-hot poison and scoff them whole with little ill effect. The discriminating oriole, however, uses its uniquely specialized sight to improve the odds. The bird can tell how poisonous a butterfly is just by looking. To our eyes the attractively coloured insects look identical, but some have larvae which have fed on poisonous plants and others have not. The latter are available to eat, if only the insect-eater can work out which is which. Only the black-headed oriole has the ability to tell which ones are safe to eat and can exploit the annual bounty to the full.

SHARP SIGHT

Birds have a range of other modifications to the eye's basic design. As you read, only one word at a time is properly in focus. This is because our cornea is round. In the same way that a point of light is made by a focused magnifying glass, so our curved cornea also produces only a small centrally focused spot. Birds improve their vision considerably simply by having a flattened cornea. This enables them to have their entire visual field in focus, making for the very efficient spotting of hidden prey and the potential for very fast reading!

Birds have a few more tricks up their sleeve: they have unique bones and muscles to more powerfully alter the shape of the lens, giving a much greater depth of focus. So, whilst a man could only see clearly somebody walking towards him, a parrot on his shoulder could at the same time see in detail another person carrying a bag of sunflower seeds trailing well behind.

The point of sharpest vision is called the fovea. It is the spot which sees the exact word we are reading. Whilst 95 per cent of all birds have foveas, half of them have two. Hummingbirds, for instance, have two foveas so that they can simultaneously concentrate not only on the flower on which they are feeding, but also on potential predators swooping in from the other side.

Other birds have different-shaped foveas to suit different jobs. Unlike our own typical round fovea, most bird foveas are elongated.

This helps to disturb the image dramatically if any part of it moves. This is part of the secret of the kestrel's success. When it is looking down on a field, the tiniest movement of a mouse sets off huge alarm bells in the signal sent from the eye. This allows the bird to use its other (round) fovea for binocular vision so that it can zoom in on the moving tail in the grass many metres below.

Kingfishers also have two foveas in each eye. The fovea at the back is sensitive to light coming from directly ahead giving the bird particularly sensitive binocular vision to spot small fish in the water. But light behaves differently in water than in air and so eyes adapted to air are no use underwater. In air the curved cornea, not the lens, does most of the actual focusing. The lens simply does the fine adjustment. Underwater, the focusing ability of the cornea does not work and so a bird diving below would not see very well. And for plungers, like the kingfisher, the impact of entry could damage an eye. So the kingfisher dispenses with sight altogether. As it enters the water, it protects the eye with a nictitating membrane and dives blind. It has ensured it has the correct trajectory before entry, and reduces the air-water problem by flying in at an angle of 45°. Cormorants do it differently. They do not plunge, but they need to see the fish they chase underwater. To do this they have a special soft lens which is squeezed into a more bulbous shape for underwater vision.

Other hunters have a set pattern of deliberate blind spots. This may help produce a stroboscopic effect as light hits the retina. Under normal conditions, slowly moving objects are hard to spot. Under stroboscopic light we notice them moving because they reappear in a slightly different place in each flash. These blind spots in hunting birds probably have the same effect and help to draw the birds' attention to slight movements.

The most obvious adaptation birds have made is to drastically increase the size of their eyes. Whereas a mammal skull is largely filled by the brain, bird skulls are largely there to accommodate the eyes, a feature recognized even in the earliest of birds. The brain is a fairly small organ sandwiched between two massive eyes. Ostriches have the largest eyes of any land animal at over 5 centimetres in diameter. The eyes of a 500-gram hawk or owl may actually be larger than those of a person 140 times bigger! Whilst birds' eyes generally are not quite round, the eyes of raptors take this to an extreme. In effect, having used all the skull space available to a normal eye, they continue to improve their distance vision by elongating the eye back down the eye socket. The eyes of many hunters are so enlarged that they are actually tubular. This is the case in owls, whose eyes are too large and elongated to allow them to be moved. To compensate these birds have developed the ability to swivel their heads round virtually through 360 degrees. They also tend to move their eyes by comical bobbing movements when something of interest is spotted. This helps them to judge their distance from prey.

Hunters like hawks and owls need good stereoscopic vision for detecting and pursuing prey. Their eyes are therefore not only very large but are also mounted facing forward. Potential prey species, on the other hand, tend to feed on foods which are more easily found and instead have side-mounted eyes to provide wraparound vision. The eyes of mallards, for instance, can see in front, below and to each side, and more importantly can still see a falcon swooping down above and behind them. Not only this but their eyes overlap to produce a binocular strip 20-degrees wide. This gives them a band of stereoscopic vision above and below, running from in front of their beak to behind their tail. Mallards seem to have the best of both worlds. They can not only see everything anywhere around them, but can assess how far away a predator or a meal is just by looking straight at it.

The eyes of woodcock are mounted to give them 360-degree vision above and in all directions around them. Their eyes are mounted at the sides of the head but are actually positioned so high that they bend towards each other across the scalp. This device means that a woodcock need never expose itself by moving its head to get a better view of a predator. These bug-eyed birds have the ultimate 'sit tight and see' defence. They rely on camouflage to make themselves merge with ground cover and use their 360-degree, high-mounted scanning system to check on incoming intruders. As any hungry fox would agree, nothing can creep up on a woodcock undetected. It is amongst the most successful ground-nesting birds and has the ultimate insurance policy. If by chance it *is* detected, it can take to the wing carrying its small brood with it.

NIGHT EYES

The visual world is more simple for the 250 species or 3 per cent of the world's birds that are nocturnal. Of these, even fewer are truly night active. Most, in fact, are active at dawn or dusk and rely not only on sound (see pages 169–71) or smell, as does the kiwi, but also sight. The kiwi is a true night forager, scrabbling about for worms and insects. Without fear of being out-competed for food or eaten itself, it did not need to invest in sophisticated optics. In fact an efficient worm-sniffing nose is much more useful and it has been developed by the kiwi at the expense of its sight; its eyes are probably the smallest of any bird's. As with the eyes of hedgehogs, moles and shrews, whose niche the kiwi occupies, it is a case of 'use it or lose it'.

Living alongside the kiwi is the nocturnal and monumentally awkward kakapo, the world's largest flightless parrot (see page 160). It has a peculiar hunched walk and uses its feet to crawl slowly and clumsily over the forest-floor debris. It has relatively tiny eyes and poor vision and so it too relies on a keen sense of smell, feeding on the commonplace plants and fruits it stumbles upon. Both sexes have dull olive green plumage which blends well into the foliage. Unfortunately, however, these myopic gentle giants evolved without the need for defence. When rats, cats and other alien predators were released into the forests the kakapos were ill-equipped to survive the onslaught. In the 1970s only twelve birds, nearly all males, were known. Due to the sterling work of the New Zealand Wildlife Service, more birds were eventually located, raising the number to forty-three. Now with commendable dedication a combination of pest eradication, translocation and reserve creation seems to have brought the remarkable, but poor-sighted, kakapo back from the brink of extinction.

Oilbirds and cave swiftlets rely on sound (see pages 163–5) to find their way in the dark, but some night hunters must depend solely on night-adapted eyes. Some have good night vision. The giant frogmouth is an Australian relative of the nightjar. Masters of camouflage, these mottled grey birds sit upright, fully exposed on a tree limb by day, looking for all the world like the stump of a branch. By night they open their huge owl-like eyes and hunt geckoes, mice and even small venomous snakes.

Others see less well in the dark. The American cousin to the frogmouth is the whip-poor-whill of the southern woodlands. It has good but imperfect night vision. It hunts its insect prey most actively when there is a bright moon, as in total darkness it is effectively blind. The raising of a hungry brood of youngsters therefore presents special problems for these still-evolving insectivores. Breeding is timed so that the eggs hatch about ten days before the full moon. Then the available light is sufficient to help the parents catch enough food for the tiny chicks. The moonlight increases nightly as the chicks grow. After ten to twelve days, when the moon is less bright or obscured altogether, the chicks are over the danger period and are large enough to survive with an unpredictable food supply.

The nightjar and owl families are the only two groups of birds which have sufficiently mastered nocturnal vision to fly in darkness through 'cluttered' habitats such as woodlands. The European tawny owl is probably the most familiar and best studied nocturnal bird. Recent studies have demonstrated that it has two and half times the nocturnal sensitivity shown by humans. This makes its eye about as sensitive as an eye could become, given the constraints of the laws of physics. If owl eyes were any more sensitive, they would not be able to see what they are looking for. The photons of light scattered from leaves would make their prey indistinguishable from the background 'noise'. Given the limits of night vision, owls must use every trick in the book if they are to become successful hunters.

Memory is extremely important to them. The birds learn exactly where every tree, branch and clearing is. This takes time, so the birds are territorial, defending their memorized hunting ground from intruders. The endearing facial disc of an owl does two jobs. It funnels extra photons of light into the eyes and also acts as a parabolic reflector, funnelling sound into the ears. An owl's ears are as important as its eyes (see pages 169–71). Typically the rodent prey is first heard, the owl swoops down towards it, and then the eyes take over to guide the talons for the last few metres to the kill. Owls usually restrict their hunts to a few favoured spots within their territory. These are usually dead trees with relatively open ground below. The birds alternate between sites through the night. They do not actively fly around searching for prey. Their 'sit and wait' strategy is far more economical and effective.

Only about fifty out of 135 species of owls are truly nocturnal, most are crepuscular, appearing in twilight. This is especially important for the three African and four Asian species of fishing owls. Hunting fish from the air at night cannot be easy. Like tawny owls, these little-known birds seem to use preferred branches overhanging rivers as look-out posts. They need exclusive rights to these if they are to secure such difficult prey and they are fiercely territorial. In Africa the 'hooooom-hut' call of Pel's fishing owl is usually all that is ever recorded of it. This territorial declaration periodically rises to a screech and a terrifying wail to warn off interlopers. (Fishing owls are amongst the noisiest of all owls.) This activity is interspersed with periods of intense concentration. The birds must strain to see the ripples from a fish's snout as it breaks the surface or listen for the tiny splash as it turns. Some of the Asian species hunt in ice-cold mountain brooks. How the birds can see or hear anything below the moving, gurgling water is a mystery. Their remarkable fishing techniques and specialized senses have yet to be studied. Somehow the birds are able to hunt successfully even on cloudy, moonless nights.

Other species like the long-eared and burrowing owls are crepuscular and find hunting reasonably easy in their relatively open habitats. Here prey is much more easily located. These birds are more easy-going and only become territorial in the breeding season. Long-eared and snowy owls may even come together in loose flocks of several hundred birds at favoured winter feeding grounds.

Many seabirds are largely nocturnal. This is because sea fish generally swim closer to the surface at night. Another reason is that adaptations for swimming such as rear-mounted legs tend to make specialists vulnerable to attack by day. Birds such as the Manx shearwater, rhino auklet and many petrels are typical nocturnal fishermen. They only come ashore to breed in hidden burrows where they rest by day. Each night they fly out to fish, often covering hundreds of miles on journeys which may take them from south-west England as far as the coast of Spain. Parents may be away for several days at a stretch and will not even risk returning to their burrow on dangerously moonlit nights. It has always been assumed that these specialists have powerful nocturnal vision but research has shown this not to be the case. The shearwater's eyes are in fact more similar to those of diurnal birds than to those of owls. Their night vision is therefore rather poor. Instead, to find their way back to their burrows they use a combination of an improved sense of smell and pungently poor nest hygiene! The mate left guarding the single chick probably also helps by producing beacon calls as an *aide-mémoire* for its partner (see pages 166–7).

Seabirds do, however, have various optical and mental modifications to help them navigate the enormous distances. The birds fly at a height of just a few centimetres above the waves far out to sea where there are no landmarks to aid orientation. The shearwater's fovea is horizontally elongated. The birds use it to align with the horizon (the line of brightness where the sea meets the sky), which enables them to keep their heads dead level when flying. This feature is combined with a good mental map built up through experience and their keen sense of smell to allow them to navigate featureless oceans. Using the starry line of the horizon can cause problems for the birds near developed areas. The birds run into trouble when towns are sighted as the lights dazzle them. The fledglings in particular are innately pulled towards lights and may crash exhausted in seaside towns. In Hawaii, islanders help rescue the dazzled birds as they fall out of the sky. They are allowed to recuperate and take their bearings before being released to fly out to sea.

Most nocturnal birds, like the oilbirds or Manx shearwaters, are drab grey or black to help them blend with the night sky. There is no point in nocturnal birds developing bright colours as they could never be seen. Many diurnal birds, however, are just the opposite: they are very colourful – either with gaudy colours to attract attention or with more subtle hues with which to blend it to the background.

BIRD COLOUR: ILLUSION OR REALITY?

As a group, birds are the most vividly coloured vertebrates. Diurnal birds are often very brightly coloured and use their colours and markings to save energy, solicit a mate and capture food as well as to help avoid being eaten themselves. There are two ways in which a bird can produce colours. Structural colours are produced by tiny barbules on the feathers which cause interference or the scattering of light of particular wavelengths. This works in the same way as a glass prism. The system is also used by butterflies. If the wing of a butterfly or hummingbird is boiled, no colours can be leached out. Their apparent colours are an optical illusion. These birds often have very bright iridescent colours which seem to change as the bird moves. This is because the angle and wavelength of light reflected from the bird to our eye changes, and with it the colour we perceive. It is exactly like rotating a prism or diamond and watching the colours change. Because this method does not involve producing coloured chemicals it is energetically inexpensive. In effect, the bird obtains this structural colour for free.

Iridescence is usually found only on the feathers of the head, neck and body, and not on the wings. Most flight feathers have hooks on their barbules which strengthen the feather. Hooks would block the passage of light hitting the barbules and prevent the colouring effect. Because birds using structural colours cannot have these hooks, the feathers are weaker. On the large, flight feathers strength is essential and so they are equipped with hooks but exhibit no iridescent coloration.

The alternative is to synthesize coloured chemical compounds to produce more costly pigmentary colours. The cost of manufacturing them is offset by the fact that they can be used on every feather without the loss of feather strength. It is very much a case of getting what you pay for. The commonest pigment is melanin, the dark pigment used to colour our own skin. In birds melanin can be black, brown, ochre or yellow. It is responsible for the black in blackbirds and crows as well as the yellow in chickens and is synthesized by the birds themselves.

The other main group of colour compounds are the carotenoids. These are named after the orange colour compound found in carrots and are absorbed continuously from the bird's diet. This is true of several colour compounds. If yellow canaries are fed seed laced with paprika powder they soon turn red! Gentoo penguins manage to remain uncoloured despite a diet of pink prawns, but their egg yolks are bright red. Conversely, if a bird is denied foods rich in essential colour compounds its colours soon fade. This has long been a problem with captive flamingos fed on a crustacean-free diet. Unless the extraordinarily expensive pigment is added to their daily feed, the birds soon fade to white. Haemoglobin, the iron-rich compound in human red blood cells, is used to produce the blood-red wattle of turkeys and the gaudy red heads of some vultures. The range of colour compounds used by birds is so diverse that even humble budgerigars possess red or yellow pigments which are chemically unknown.

Not all bird colours come from within. Great Indian hornbills, for example, produce an oily yellow secretion from their preening glands. This is used to stain some of their white feathers a more attractive yellow. Other birds make the most of naturally occurring dyes and practise body painting. Bearded vultures have white underparts in captivity, whereas in the wild they are a rusty brown. This is because of the birds' habit of annointing themselves with iron oxide (rust) deposits exposed on the cliffs where they nest. It is carefully spread into the plumage by preening. The iron deposit acts as a finger-nail repairer or hair-conditioning lotion. It seems to help strengthen feathers and is mostly taken up by worn or damaged feathers, so reducing further wear. Preening with the compound also acts as a flea spray, helping the bird to shed some of its parasite burden.

Darkening the plumage of nesting birds also makes them and their nest less visible to predators. Unfortunately this multi-purpose paint is not waterproof and the birds look decidedly pale after a tropical downpour. It takes them about six days of busy preening to fully restore their deep brown colour. The birds apply the stain very carefully. Whilst it does make the feathers stronger it also reduces their windproofing ability. To compromise, only the outer feathers are stained, leaving the underlying layers white and windproof.

COURTSHIP COLOURS

Whereas mammals, reptiles and even amphibians primarily use scent to identify the sex of strangers, most birds have a poor sense of smell and rely on colour. Many birds have differently coloured males and females. This saves time and energy both wooing mates and repelling intruders. With their sophisticated colour vision it is natural that birds use their great range and detail of colour to communicate. But, in the same way that birdsong exposes an individual to danger, birds face a fundamental conflict between being brightly coloured to attract a mate and being cryptically coloured to avoid being eaten. Where the risk of predation is minimized, and especially amongst polygamous species, males often become vibrantly coloured. This trait is most common where the males have little or no role in raising the chicks. There is rarely the problem of a gaudily coloured male leading nest predators to the brood. In fact, they scarcely even know where the nest is! Conversely, females have to bring up the brood alone and must do nothing to increase their risk of being eaten. Females of polygamous species are therefore usually cryptically coloured.

Some males which are less cryptically coloured than their mates do help raise the young. Some of them actually use their distinctive colouration to lure predators away from the nest. Ptarmigan males often keep some of their white winter plumage through summer. The hen is cryptically heather-coloured whilst she incubates the brood. If danger threatens, the more obvious male takes to the wing and acts as a decoy, drawing the hawk or fox away from the nest.

Preliminary research suggests that only the biggest, fittest males maintain their white feathers. Less able birds would not benefit by drawing attention to themselves as they are more likely to be eaten. The best males can confidently advertise themselves to both predators and their highly selective hens. Hens probably prefer to breed with these successful exhibitionists.

The most stunningly colourful birds in the world are almost certainly the birds of paradise from Australia and New Guinea. These starling- to crow-sized birds are probably most closely related to the corvids – the crows, jackdaws and rooks. They inhabit dense rainforest, particularly high mountain areas where there is plenty of cover. These forests provide an abundance of food throughout the year. The birds feed on fruits, which makes it easy for a solitary female to provide for her brood. As the males are surplus to requirements and therefore are not needed to help with parental chores they are released to court further females. This polygamous strategy has led to the most breathtaking plumage and courtship displays in the animal kingdom. Because females always select the most beautiful male, intense competition results. As all the females for miles around may mate with just one or two outstanding males, their genes for 'extra beauty' soon spread amongst the population. The next generation are therefore all 'extra beautiful' birds. Evolution progresses rapidly in polygamous systems and leads to the rapid development of new 'fad' or 'in vogue' plumages and even new species.

As well as vivid colours, males also use ritualized movements and mesmeric songs to attract and then hold a female's attention. To compound the attraction of their dance-like displays, males of some species come together in competitive displays called 'leks'. A lek is a congregation of soliciting males held in an arena which itself has no value, that is, it is not a feeding ground or breeding territory. Leks are nature's singles bars where males demonstrate their reproductive prowess. Visiting females have the opportunity to select from many performing males. The chosen mate, like the ultimate human male chauvinist, will contribute nothing but his genes to the hen's reproductive effort. One such lekking species is the archetypal Count Raggi's bird of paradise.

Count Raggi's is a large bird with a short yellow-plumed crown, metallic green throat and, most memorably of all, translucent orange plumes which extend backwards over the tail. From three to six males occupy a traditional display tree at which they display intermittently for most of the day. As food is quickly found they have the bulk of their time free to pursue their sex life. The season continues for most of the year, only pausing for the brief annual moult. From each moult the birds develop longer and more seductive feathers. This makes mature males more successful than their inexperienced juniors.

Each morning a raucous caw announces the first male's arrival at the display ground. His cries summon not only the occasional female but also his competitors. The males are in a 'Catch-22' situation. On their own, they have no competition. However, a solitary bird has almost no chance of initially attracting a mate so it must join the parade and perform, alongside several other great pretenders, at the lek. By about 10 a.m. the whole group is assembled and in fine form. At about that time the first of the dowdy hens arrives to sample the wares.

Then pandemonium breaks out. The rivals call excitedly, bending towards the only available hen and casting their plumes towards her. The cries change to a deafening high-pitched electronic buzzing which becomes faster and louder as the sexual tension rises. The initially coy hen coquettishly enters the area to hop between now frantically displaying males, but she is never touched by them. The cumulative effect of a dozen clapping wings, iridescent green and gauzy orange plumes and hypnotic noise is enough to quicken the pulse of any impressionable maiden, but the Count Raggi's hens are a little harder to satisfy.

When the hen has decided on her partner she sidles up to him and rests on his branch. This brings out an immediate change in the proceedings. At once his behaviour changes from frantic agitation to balletic ritual. His calling is quieted and he hangs almost upside down to perform a stationary nuptial dance. He throws his amazing pectoral plumes over his head so that his richest silken gold feathers and rhythmic swaying dazzle the hen into submission. If sufficiently aroused she will be drawn nearer and will even nibble his neck. Ultimately she will mount him. The mesmeric display of swaying colour is so essential that even then the dance continues. This courtship almost overwhelms the hen into a trance-like state. If the male bird's attentions are successful he can now right himself and gently pummel her with one of his wings. Whilst doing this he draws his beak back and forth across hers. With the hen quite entranced the male can consummate the courtship. Without further ado the hen then departs as suddenly as she came, to rear her chicks alone.

In contrast the blue bird of paradise prefers to woo his mates alone. The males are evenly spaced throughout the jungle and are rarely less than 300 metres apart. Each male is an extremely elegant bird whose black-marked body is contrasted with startling azure wings, two long trailing plumes, an ivory beak and bold eye rings. He spends almost every day of the year near his personal display perch. There he calls repeatedly hundreds of times a day to tempt itinerant females to watch the display. If a female is attracted to his arena he proceeds to change his song and hangs upside down from his perch. He then forms an azure umbrella around himself by encircling his wings and tucking his head in. To increase the power of the display he bobs rapidly up and down. It is impossible for the dancer to see what effect his performance is having on the visitor. So less fortunate birds may continue giving their all for some time after an unimpressed hen has moved on. Successful males are approached by the hen, which signals her willingness to mate.

Both species use colour to attract a mate but pursue different mating strategies. Communal displayers like Count Raggi's spend little effort in attracting a hen to the display site. The more males there are calling, the less effort each of them must make. Also the birds use traditional, even ancient, display grounds which are known to local females who need a mate. At these sexual super-markets females have the benefit of selecting the best of many performers. This enables the best males to mate virtually all the hens whilst inexperienced or inferior birds may fail entirely. Ironically the successful males profit from the fruitless attempts of unsuccessful birds. The energy used is shared between successful and unsuccessful alike.

Solitary birds of paradise perform alone, and must invest enormous amounts of energy. They must call incessantly to entice females to visit. But they gain in other ways. As it costs the female more in terms of time and flight to sample the many males spread out across the forest, she is more inclined to stay and watch a solitary male display. As each female visits fewer males, each has a more even chance of breeding.

Not all members of the birds-of-paradise family are polygamous. There are several monogamous species, including the black-coloured Macgregor's bird of paradise, whose males are similar in appearance to their equally drab hens. These birds form pair bonds which can last for several years. As the males need not devote themselves to the job of continuously impressing consecutive females, courtship is short and simple. A few wing flaps and tail flicks and a flight chase round the forest and it's all over. The male settles contentedly down to help his mate raise their offspring.

On the other side of the world lives a bird unrelated to the birds of paradise but which leads the same lifestyle – another example of 'convergent evolution'. Given the same set of environmental circumstances, animals which fill a similar ecological niche in different parts of the world will often evolve to resemble each other. Evolution will use the same design many times over in unrelated groups and come up with similar results. In this way ostriches evolved in Africa, rheas in South America and emus and cassawaries in Australasia.

The equally gaudy South American equivalents of the birds of paradise are the cocks-of-the-rocks. These too are jungle-dwelling fruit-eaters with spectacular orange males and drab females. In the tropical rainforests of Suriname noisy groups of about ten males assemble at lekking grounds each morning. The females are brown and bear sole responsibility for building the nest and raising the brood. Within the lekking area some sites are better than others. Birds left out on peripheries are less likely to be noticed than the central performers. Males continually jostle for ownership of the best sites. In order to reduce the chance of injury from such encounters, the males posture and threaten before resorting to combat. As the success of their lovelife depends largely on the quality of their appearance, they will always do their best to safeguard their gorgeous plumage.

When a female is persuaded to visit the lek, each male jumps into his own individual display court. He rapidly beats his wings to gain the hen's attention and to sweep the floor clear of obstructing leaves. If a male can catch a female's eye he will take up a rigid display posture. He keeps his back to the female and spreads his bright orange feathers like a fan to dazzle her. The Mohican-style crest on the male's head is at all times angled side-on to the spectator to show it to its best advantage. As the whole effect depends on the brightness of a male's plumage, the stage lighting is extremely important to his success. Males always strive to acquire the sunniest spot from which to display, as the brighter the light the more vivid their colours appear. Males may fight with locked beaks and talons for up to three hours to gain prime sites. If ownership cannot be established even then, the birds rest a while and then return to combat. The costs of site territoriality are doubled by the birds' requirement for both aerial perch and floor arena. With dozens of males displaying simultaneously, it is not surprising that hens take their time in selecting a mate. Only the fittest males can stand the test. The displays are exhausting, the selection ritual being a cross between a boxing match, a beauty contest and a marathon.

In being so particular about her consort, whether using visual or auditory cues to help her selection, the female is probably picking the most vigorous healthy male as well as the prettiest or noisiest. These outstanding qualities will then be transferred to her offspring. This will make her sons stronger and more handsome and hence more successful in seducing mates. If her own line is to continue to succeed she must carefully choose male qualities which subsequent generations will find irresistible. Even if a hen did have a quirky preference for bald males, she would still have to mate conventional males to continue her lineage with grandchildren. Conformity pays. Such important tasks cannot be decided in a few minutes. The female will visit the lek daily for four to six days. With each visit her shortlist of movers and shakers is narrowed down until the lucky and probably exhausted mate is selected. Once the hen has chosen her mate she will sometimes save time by using him in subsequent seasons.

Overall, the odds are firmly stacked against most males. Whilst all the females mate, less than half the males at a lek will succeed in doing so. Of the ones which do make the grade, the most popular male will often sire 30 per cent of all the chicks produced. Females need not compete as all of them breed. The situation amongst males is closer to all or nothing. Hence the fierce competition for positioning within the lek and the ever-intensifying development of feather colour and dance routines.

COLOURFUL DANCERS

South America is also home to the fifty species of manikins which form leks in dense tropical undergrowth. The birds are very brightly coloured but small and difficult to observe. Each species has a different range of colours and a unique arrangement of specialized feathers. Some of these feathers have recently been found to be used to physically stimulate females once they have been enticed with their colours. The males are mostly boldly coloured, with fine elongated tail plumes which contrast with their dumpy bodies. They fit the pattern of polygamous fruit-eaters whose drab cryptic hens are chained to a solitary life at the nest.

The manikins have evolved a peculiar dynamic three-dimensional display. The males bounce rapidly between the ground and bare horizontal twigs above. They call to attract females, changing to a repertoire of strange courtship sounds when they arrive at the lek. As they hop frantically from twig to twig their bright wing and body colours are exaggerated by rapid wing fluttering. The black-and-white male white-bearded manikin of Trinidad spends up to 90 per cent of its time throughout the year dancing to woo a mate. The males methodically clear small areas on the forest floor and use thin vertical saplings as display posts. They bounce and bound frantically between posts, stopping to slide slowly down them and let the females take stock. The dancers produce an inimitable range of incessant cackling, whirring and wheeing sounds to stupify the onlookers. After an hour of passionate displaying, the selected male will unite with his spouse for only a few seconds before she flies safely back into the undergrowth.

In Venezuela, the wire-tailed manikin has developed a further trick to overwhelm a mate. The males have a bright, bi-coloured head and neck and lustrous black wings and tail. The courtship feathers in the tail are very long and are reduced to single filaments. They have, in effect, a fine, delicate brush instead of a tail. Loud calls and bright plumage are used to usher in local hens. After a fairly typical display, the male will try to land on the same perch as the hen and then gradually sidle up to her. At first his landings seem almost accidental, like trying to 'casually' manoeuvre an arm around a first date at the cinema. At first, too, the hens often move to distance themselves. Gradually they become familiar enough to share their perch. Then the male can deploy his secret weapon. He backs up to the female and tickles her under the chin with his brush-like tail. The feathers are flicked from side to side in an arousing 'twist' assault on her senses. The stimulation is continued until the melting hen is sufficiently stupified to accept mounting. Interestingly, experienced hens will actually make the first move in soliciting the males' 'brushing'.

At dawn on the plains of North America colourful leks comprising anything from twenty to thirty males take place. These are spectacular aggregations of sage grouse and occasionally several hundred birds may take part. An early start is essential and the prime sites in the centre of the open lek are quickly taken by dominant cocks. The males have a spiny fan-type tail which is held erect as dark backdrop to a surprising display. To grab the hens' attention the males rapidly inflate two bright red air sacs of naked breast skin, which periodically erupt from a thick ruff of pure white feathers. A constant gurgling is produced by the males as their visual display is brought to life with a waggling, foot-stomping display. The performance is quite startling and has a drawing power of hundreds of metres across the open land. The display is so outstanding that it inspired many of the dances performed by indigenous Amerindians. As with most leks, the exceptional prowess of one or two performers leads them to mating virtually all the females. Clusters of fifty to seventy hens have been witnessed queuing up in tight clusters around master dancers.

Every bit as strange as the sage grouse is the unique lekking behaviour of the European ruff. Ruffs are fairly small birds of open marshes and bogs. They take their name from the enormous collar of feathers around their necks which gives them the appearance of flamboyant Elizabethan artistocrats. Their flight is not fast and they are exactly the kind of prey preferred by falcons and harriers. The males have reduced the duration and complexity of their calls to a short two-note whistle. Instead, they rely on the hens' familiarity with the generations-old lekking ground to guarantee an audience. The males come in two models. Large dark-ruffed birds are terri- torially dominant within the lek and are attended by smaller white- ruffed males. The two groups also show differences in behaviour.

The birds arrive at the lek as early as visibility permits. Dark- ruffed males form individual territories which they fight to maintain. White-ruffed birds do not even try to compete with the physically superior dark males. The white plumage seems to act as a flag of neutrality signalling non-combative status to the belligerent terri- tory holders. The dark birds do not attack white birds, which become 'satellites' moving around the edge of the display and even walking between the territories. The two groups seem to have reached an evolutionary compromise in their courtship strategies. The dark birds are large and fight to show their dominant status to visiting hens. The white males do not enter this particular compe- tition but do add to the impact of the dark birds' display by conferring greater numbers and brighter plumage to the lek, which is then more obvious at a distance. The white males benefit by allowing stronger and more vociferous birds to pull in the females. In the satellite systems of antelopes or amphibians, non-competitive satellite status is less successful than active territory-holding, but this seems not to be the case with ruffs. Female ruffs are just as likely to mate with a white satellite male as they are with a territory holder. Friction is reduced between males as both groups depend on the other for their success. The females perpetuate this evolutionarily stable strategy as a result of finding both systems equally attractive.

EVOLUTIONARY EXTRAVAGANCE

One way of reducing the energy expended in daily displays is to initially invest more heavily in a colourful advertisment which says it all for you. This is exactly what birds such as peacocks and widow birds have done. Peacocks are a communally lekking species from India. Their displays rely on holding their enormous tail feathers aloft and shimmering their iridescent markings to best effect. This represents substantial energy saving compared to more frenetic species, and this saving means that the time saved foraging for fuel can be spent in displaying. Experimental studies have shown that peahens are more likely to mate with males showing the greatest number of eye-spots on their tails. Males with fewest eye-spots are often young birds and may not mate at all. Female selection of males with the most elaborate and beautiful tails accounts for how the outrageous plumage has evolved. Males rarely fight. They have no need to as no amount of combat can increase a bird's tail feather display. Conversely, fighting would only lead to the damaging of their all-important sexual signal and no male is prepared to risk that. The large tail tells the female a lot about the male's age and status and his ability to survive a multitude of predators and parasites. The tails become larger with each year's moult so the largest tails belong to those individuals best able to survive.

East African widow birds or whydahs are members of the weaver family. Unlike weavers, they are solitary in the breeding season and males fight to maintain the best possible territories. Territory quality has two components. Ideal territories are both large and well stocked with suitable nesting bushes, with ample food and water provision. Only the strongest and most experienced males can hold on to such utopian pastures. The males are polygamous, which makes territory quality all the more important. As we have seen, the top one or two cocks are liable to acquire a disproportionate share of the hens. The territories are scattered over miles of flat bush and females cannot afford to waste time visiting the whole area to see who is the dominant male. To accommodate them the males all sport tail feathers which tell the hens at a glance who is the top cock and who holds the best breeding ground.

The males of each species are jet black, with or without a line of contrasting yellow or red on the wings. The broad tail feathers can be several times the bird's body length and are visible at great distances. The hens fly over the bush at the start of the breeding season to size up the local talent. On sighting a passing hen the male's interest switches immediately from territorial concerns to affairs of the heart. The male jumps excitedly up to about a metre in the air from specially cleared floor arenas. The fluttering wings and leaping black tail feathers soon draw the hen's attention.

In lekking species, the hen takes some time to discriminate between the local males assembled for her pleasure. Hen widow birds still need to assess the many hopefuls but distance dictates a swift appraisal. As males age so their tail plumes lengthen. If they are top-class survivors, their plumage will also be free of tears and parasite damage. The hen can see in an instant whether a male is an inexperienced dandy or a more mature safe bet.

This can be easily tested experimentally in the field. Three groups of male widow birds were netted and their tail length altered. The first group were the controls. The last third of their tail was cut off and then stuck back together before the bird was released. These birds 'scored' the same number of females as they did before the procedure. The second group had the last third of their tail removed and then they were released. The breeding success of these birds plummeted. Whilst they were still just as strong and fit, the hens lost all interest in them. The more fortunate third group had the missing third of the second group's tails glued to their own. These birds, therefore, had spectacularly long tails the likes of which had never been seen in the African bush. It did not matter whether the males had been top dogs or losers before the operation. After it they could do no wrong. The numbers of females mating with them and nesting on their land rose to new all-time records. Quite simply because, in nature at least, tail-length accurately reflects the quality of the males, the hens had abandoned all other criteria. This is a simple matter for polygamous birds whose males contribute nothing but a great floor show and their genes to the offspring.

There is another theory apart from female choice which attempts to explain why some birds have such conspicuous plumage. It is called the 'unprofitable prey' theory. It suggests that in some cases female preference does not explain bright advertisement plumage. Instead, the colours are a signal to potential predators and actually advertise the birds' presence to them, not to the hens. It is a bit like pronking behaviour in Thompson's gazelle. When chased by a predator the fittest gazelles leap or 'pronk' high into the air when we would be running away at full tilt. This is a signal which carnivores have learnt to understand. It says 'if I can spare the time to jump about I am obviously so fit that I will outpace you.' These signals are apparently very honest in that only uncatchable individuals pronk. The bright plumage of birds and long display feathers in particular may work in the same kind of way.

If a predator chases but fails to catch a distinctively marked bird, it may remember not to waste energy in trying to catch the same sort next time. Long tail feathers may still signal fitness, but to predators rather than or as well as hens. The long tail feathers of a peacock or widow bird are an obvious burden in flight. The bird may be advertising the fact that it is so fit that it can even survive attempts to eat it when so obviously handicapped. It is generally true that more mobile birds do tend to be more brightly coloured. Slower ones, and females of species which sit tight on a nest, tend to be cryptic in colour.

There is a time when all females are extremely vulnerable to predation and even rape. This is for the day or two immediately before they lay an egg. Eggs often add an additional 10–25 per cent to a female's body weight which drastically reduces their flight performance (see page 293). Males and possibly some predators such as raptors can spot this change. There is no point in females going to the expense of developing bright 'you can catch me' colours if for two weeks of the year they are not only eminently catchable, but advertised their disability as well. The theory is perfectly plausible and does not actually exclude the role of female choice in the uniquely colourful evolution of birds.

STAGEMAKERS AND ARCHITECTS

Some male birds initially attract a female's attention, not by extravagant plumage or raucous dances, but by building a structure, like an advertising hoarding, that does the job for them. One of the simpler creations is offered by the male tooth-billed catbird.

September in the dark, damp mountain rainforests of north-east

Queensland is the start of the curious courtship performance from this drab little bird. He is a little larger than a thrush, and he makes up for his rather dowdy plumage with an unusual display.

First the tooth-billed catbird male creates an irregular, roundish arena, about one to two metres square, in amongst the trees. He spends a considerable amount of time meticulously removing dead leaves and twigs until the area is swept clear. Having made his stage, which earned him the local name of 'stagemaker', he flies to a nearby tree. Here he uses his serrated-edged bill to saw off large, fresh leaves. Each leaf stalk may take about a quarter of an hour to saw through. Once completed, the leaf is carried to the stage floor and deposited not in a haphazard fashion but with the light under-side facing uppermost so that it shines in the gloom of the forest.

Most birds gather about twenty large leaves, although some enthusiastic catbirds have been known to collect as many as 200 small ones for a single display arena. Some birds prefer to obtain their leaves from one species of tree while others collect them at random. One population of birds has taken to using the 46-centimetre-long leaves of the wild ginger plant. As the leaves wither and dry, they are moved to the edge of the arena and new ones are cut to take their place. Late in the breeding season the stage begins to take on the appearance of a circus ring.

The stage is set below a song perch from which the male bird sings its extraordinarily loud and complicated song, which can be heard for hundreds of metres through the forest. Birds have been known to sing solidly for over two hours.

In East Africa, another strategy is employed by the rare Jackson's whydah. It lives in the highlands of Kenya and Tanzania, where the male birds gather in leks in open grassy areas. Like other widow birds they leap into the air displaying their long tails, but this particular species of widow bird has another trick up its sleeve. Each bird confines his performance to a 0.8–1.2-metres circular arena. In its centre is a tuft of grass with two cup-like depressions moulded into each side. Females enticed within the circle show considerable interest in the nest-like tuft and copulation takes place while the female is inspecting it. She then leaves to build her simple egg-laying nest elsewhere, independent of the male with whom she has mated. The male's nest look-alike is an example of avian subterfuge and the courtship routine demonstrates a shift in focus from the functional to the symbolic nest. This switch is seen most obviously amongst the bowerbirds of Australia and New Guinea.

Male bowerbirds build and attend complicated open nest-like structures, called 'bowers', but these are not nests at all. Eggs are not laid in them. The bowers are supranormal nests, built in clearings, and designed to attract and stimulate a willing female to ovulate and mate. In the bowerbird world females are turned on by architectural achievement and the focus of attention has been drawn away from a male's body and more towards his bower. Of the eighteen known species of bowerbirds, fourteen construct bowers, which are often decorated with objects such as feathers and leaves or are painted with natural dyes from fruit pulp or charcoal. One species even uses a 'paint brush', consisting of a tuft of fibrous bark. Some bowers are titivated with fresh flowers or fruits and freshened regularly. The bowers themselves range from a simple platform of twigs to great avenues, towers or thatched huts. The drabber the male, the more ostentatious is his bower.

The males do nothing to help raise the brood, for the females build their own nests and bring up their offspring unaided. All of the males' considerable reproductive effort goes into building his bower and defending it from other males. As a result there is intense competition amongst males to build the most beautiful bower. They have two approaches to ensuring success. Firstly they are dexterous builders, they work diligently and they search for the rare decorative materials that are sure to impress a female. Secondly, they are notorious sneak-thieves and saboteurs. They not only plunder other birds' construction materials but also actively damage their rivals' bowers.

One of the simpler bowers is made by Archibald's bowerbird. The male clears a small area of forest floor and simply lays a mat of mosses and dry ferns. Here he performs his display. The aptly named male flame bowerbird goes one better and builds a simple avenue of twigs through which it struts to show off its flame-like plumage. Unlike the builders of more elaborate bowers, the flame bowerbird relies on his attractive uniform as well as his building skills. The colourful yellow-and-black regent bowerbird of Australia also constructs an avenue but complements his handsome appearance by painting the walls of his avenue with yellow leaf juices. Similarly the spotted bowerbird has a painted avenue, but adds to his overall display by presenting his back to the female and showing off a bright pink patch of feathers on the back of his neck.

The golden bowerbird also has attractive plumage but breaks all the bowerbird rules by building an enormously elaborate bower. It is the smallest bowerbird, yet it constructs one of the largest bowers. Two 3-metre-high towers of sticks are woven around the trunks of two small trees about a metre apart. A branch at the top or a buttress root at the bottom, spanning the gap between the towers, is similarly embellished with twigs and from this bridge platform the male sings and displays.

The golden bowerbird at its twin-towered bower.

Macgregor's gardener bowerbird follows the rules. It is a little 'light-brown job' about the size of a thrush, but it makes up for its dull colour with a giant bower, shaped like a maypole, and consisting of a column of twigs attached to a sapling. Around the base, twigs are broken off so that they have a uniform length and mosses and lichens are anchored to them in such a way that a circular moat is formed. The entire edifice is embellished with pieces of leaves, the iridescent wing covers of insects, fungi, lichens, leaves of the *Pandanus* tree, charcoal and anything else that takes the bird's fancy, particularly objects coloured black, orange-brown or bright yellow. The most obvious decorations are strands of insect frass produced by wood-boring moth larvae. Frass consists of silk mixed with sawdust, and it is hung from the twigs on the maypole where it dangles in the breeze. In the bushes around the bower, bunches of fresh fruits are placed. A single bower might have as many as 500 decorative objects.

Macgregor's gardener bowerbird at its 'maypole' bower.

Another very ornate and elaborate bower is constructed by an equally inconspicuous New Guinea bird that lives in the mountain forests, the Vogelkop gardener bowerbird. Birds from different mountain ranges, however, build different shaped bowers. In one area, males go for large, towering 'maypole' bowers, each about 2–3 metres high. They weave thin twigs around upright saplings and glue the sticks together with a white substance, thought to be saliva mixed with plant juices. Like Macgregor's gardener bowerbird, they also place a circular mat of black, dead moss around the base of the bower. The wing cases of beetles, leaves, acorns, snail shells and stones adorn the nest, but curiously they are covered with a shiny black layer of oily secretion produced in the bird's excrement.

In another area, the same species builds a completely different shaped bower, probably the most expansive of all. The superstructure consists of one or two 60-centimetre saplings, around which towers of twigs are weaved. Unlike its Kumana relatives, it does not use glue. The towers are roofed over with a wooden stick canopy to produce a thatched hut that can stand up to 2.2 metres tall, nine times the bird's own height. The entire structure has a large and cavernous front entrance that faces downhill, and in front is a lawn of green moss. The 'garden' is lavishly 'planted' with parts of beetles, bracket fungi, bark, flowers and fruits.

The Vogelkop gardener bowerbird at its remarkable tent-like bower.

The only decoration common to birds from the two areas is beetle-wing cases, although some individuals keep the heads and make separate piles in front of the bower. There are also individual differences amongst birds of the same population. Some birds collect mixed piles of brown and grey snail shells, whilst other birds keep the colours separate. There are also speciality collections – a pile of yellow flowers here, a display of butterfly wings there. Curiously, one population ignores acorns, even though they are locally abundant.

The decorations sought by bowerbirds, however, can be quite extraordinary, including spent shotgun cartridges, clothes pegs, bottle-tops, silver paper, metal buttons, hair curlers, nails and polythene bags. There is one story told by the German wildlife film-maker Heinz Sielmann of a male great bowerbird in Australia reaching the climax of his display to an interested female, at which point he produced his number one prize possession – a tin mug. There is also the tale of a farmer who visited all the bowers in his area and recovered several lost silver spoons and a set of car keys.

It is thought that male bowerbirds achieve their architectural and decoration skills mainly by learning from other birds and by trial and error. Different shaped bowers in isolated populations of the same species and individual differences within a population indicate a pupil-tutor relationship, although it is the females who ultimately influence the construction by preferring males who build the best bowers. Common to all bowerbirds is the propensity to wreck and steal, and this clandestine behaviour has been best studied in the satin bowerbird of Australia.

Male satin bowerbirds must roam far from their avenue-shaped bowers in search of decorations. This means that they must be away from their territory for long periods of time, and while the bird's away the neighbours start to play. They watch with interest the comings and goings of other bower builders. Given the briefest opportunity they will sneak into an unguarded bower and make off with the most valuable ornament, most usually the blue feathers of the rosella parrot. Indeed, satin bowerbirds have been known to kill small blue birds in order to obtain their feathers. Not surprisingly there is a high degree of reciprocal stealing between neighbours. Thefts occur once every ten days on average, and blue feathers will pass from bower to bower. Stronger, more alert birds are able to acquire more of the highly prized items. Females assess a male's fitness by investigating his stock of treasures. The male with the greatest hoard wins.

It is, perhaps, significant that although female bowerbirds mature at the age of one or two, males are not ready to mate until about seven. Probably it takes this long to learn how to build a better bower. This means that a small number of eligible males are present in a population and they get to mate with many females. Master builders, assiduous collectors and artistic decorators are three times more successful than barely competent novices.

The bowers of great bowerbirds often contain the bones of kangaroos and snail shells. Heinz Sielmann counted 500 bleached bones and 300 pale yellow snail shells in front of one bower alone. For archaeologists this passion for collecting can be a nightmare. The great bowerbird, like people, tends to stay close to water, and so the collection assembled by a bowerbird will closely resemble an archaeological site, maybe an ancient encampment. It is unlikely that an archaeologist would be fooled by the collection, but the bird could confuse the composition of an open assemblage by removing some of its contents, not for food but just for the 'aesthetic' quality of the object.

Bowerbirds, though, are not the only collectors. Their successful European relatives, the magpies, have long been known as sneak thieves. But a curious collection of items gathered by the European wryneck has long puzzled ornithologists. Adult birds bring ants back to feed their youngsters in the nest, but that's not all. In a Finnish study, it was found that wrynecks also gather up an enormous collection of inedible objects, such as stones, broken glass, air-gun pellets, porcelain, eggshells, pieces of cement and bones, that they store on the floor of the nest. There are, on average, about forty items per nest, with the top collectors accumulating up to 200 objects. Why they do it is a complete mystery.

DANCING ON WATER

All of the above examples show the lengths to which male birds will go to attract a mate. In monogamous birds, pairings which stand the test of time are the most successful in reproduction terms. The secret of these matches relies not so much on the initial wooing, but on the regular demonstration of their affections, a behaviour known as pair bonding. The colour and plumage of these birds is built to last. The beauty, for example, of the great crested grebe's plumage is such that it has long been coveted by man. Another victim of 'we always kill the thing we love,' grebe populations were decimated for fashion conscious Victorians. The demand for 'grebe fur' in ladies' muffs and stoles brought western European populations to the brink of extinction. Both sexes were equally pursued, as the courtship plumage of males and females is very similar.

The birds have a spectacular courtship dance requiring large areas of open water. The birds snake-dance together, swimming towards each other at speed with their crests erect and their heads shaking vigorously. They stop advancing when each can touch the face of the other with its stiletto-sharp bill. The bills are simultaneously drawn rapidly across the partner's face just lifting its facial feathers. As well as this colourful display of controlled power the birds perform a symbolic plant-presenting ceremony. Both sexes dive to pull up an aquatic stem and then run along the water side by side whilst standing upright. At the end of the run the birds slowly sink into the water in synchrony and start to bill and headshake.

The western grebe of North America has an even more extravagant display. The pair dash across the water at an incredible pace with their necks stiffly arched and wings folded back. Even at high speed the birds' sense of timing is such that the one bird resembles the mirror image of its mate. At the end of the run the birds simultaneously deep dive.

The grebes are the bird world's ultimate precision dancers. The ritualized movements enhanced by the colour are essential to the bird's breeding success. Not only do they serve to bring the birds together and then keep them together, but they frequently underlie the whole biological basis of reproduction. Initial dances stimulate the male to produce hormones which increase the sexuality of his performance. This then stimulates the female to produce breeding hormones. There may be several hormonal 'rebounds' or reciprocal stimulations between partners, leading to mating and egg production.

Colours not only serve to trigger reproduction, they also serve to make sure that birds only mate with the correct partners. Deficient individuals or suitors of other species would not have the right colours, signals and displays to trigger the reproductive cycle in their would-be mate. Hence the genetic isolation between species is ensured.

ECLIPSED BUT NOT FORGOTTEN

Relatively few birds are able to breed throughout the year. Where bright colours are used solely for courtship, there is no benefit from birds advertising their whereabouts out of season. It could be dangerous. Also, at the end of each arduous breeding season a bird's plumage becomes worn and in need of replacement. Once the chicks have finally fledged, the parents have the chance to moult and grow a new set of healthy feathers. This will ready them for the coming winter, dry season or migration. This post-nuptial moult gives the birds an opportunity to develop a less conspicuous coloration, known as the eclipse plumage. In some species, notably the ducks, the normally conspicuous drakes become quite drab until they grow a new outfit of breeding colours which they wear throughout the year. Other birds grow non-breeding or winter plumage that is designed to help them blend in with, rather than stand out of, the background. In the tropics it is usually light brown or straw yellow. In temperate areas birds such as ptarmigan and willow grouse develop snow white camouflage to see them through the winter. It is often extremely difficult to identify male birds in eclipse or non-breeding plumage and nearly impossible to differentiate between similarly drab females of many species. When the breeding season comes round the winter plumage is by then in poor condition and can again be replaced by bright breeding dress.

CAMOUFLAGE

Bold colours and flamboyant displays are only of any use when a bird has the vision and speed necessary to flee from predators. Many birds simply cannot do this and use a different approach in order to disguise themselves. They opt for camouflage, with feather patterns and colours cryptic or hidden. Cryptic coloration is shown by the nightjars, which are virtually invisible against their background. Whilst not very useful for attracting a mate, cryptic colours are an inexpensive way of surviving. The bird just has to keep quite still. This is especially suitable for nocturnal birds, which cannot use colour for courtship (even cats and owls can only see in black and white at night) and remain quietly hidden by day. However, there is another selection pressure which tends to push birds towards camouflaged plumage. If a bird is a hunter itself it stands a better chance of a successful kill if its prey can't see it. Ambush and the element of surprise are maximized. Cryptic colours can be equally effective for predators and prey.

There are, however, several different ways to achieve anonymity. Birds such as the red grouse and ptarmigan have cryptic summer plumage which matches the moorland plants on which they feed and amongst which they nest. Other birds, seabirds especially, employ countershading. Here the back is significantly darker than the belly. When viewed from the side this cancels out the natural shading of light, which tends to make the upper sunlit parts of the body lighter than the shaded belly. The strategy is particularly effective when the bird is resting flattened against a branch or on the ground. In addition, shoals of fish beneath the surface are less able to pick out the white bellies of seabirds against the bright sky. Similarly, skuas or other predators flying above find it difficult to spot dark-backed birds moving above the waves. The success of countershading is demonstrated by the fact that most seabirds the world over have the same colours and pattern.

Some seabirds do go against the norm and sport white upper parts. Recent research has shown that seabirds, including black-headed gulls, benefit from hunting in large flocks. It is believed that white backs may act like the striped tails of ring-tailed lemurs in attracting other birds to the flock so that everyone can benefit from better fishing.

Another example of colour used to help fishing is the hunting stripes of Humboldt's penguins. Most penguins are simply coloured – black above and white below – in accordance with the usual fishing seabird pattern. Humboldt's penguins are white below, but have a white streak running within the black area down both sides. This is their hunting stripe. Experiments have shown that the stripe of white confuses fish shoals into breaking up. The penguin can then select the easiest target from the scattered fish. The lines seem to confuse the fish, which know how to evade other predators but are surprised by this unfamiliar object. As the bird's image has its outline disrupted by the irregular markings its body may be perceived as several distinct hunters or one unrecognizable one. Whatever the explanation, the strategy works. The penguins have hit upon a successful means of confusing and exploiting their prey. (It seems likely that the same pattern effects underlie the disruptive coloration of several races of striped dolphins.)

On the defence side of coloration, birds frequently develop concealing behaviours to increase the effectiveness of their cryptic patterns. A tern chick will flatten itself to prevent casting a tell-tale shadow on the speckled beach. Long-eared owls and bitterns are reed-patterned birds which improve on the effect by elongating their bodies to better blend with willows and reeds. A number of owls, like Scops, and other groups, such as potoos and frogmouths, spend their days sleeping, exposed in trees. With their hind quarters nestled into the bark they are almost undetectable.

Disruptive coloration is best seen in chicks and juvenile birds. The young of many birds are stripey, spotted or blotched. At close quarters these babies are quite distinctive, but as soon as they are seen from a distance of a few paces against their natural background they merge into it and seem to disappear altogether.

The habitats in which chicks with disruptive patterns are found are all quite similar. They tend to be open featureless places such as beaches, scrub, moors or arid plains. Because the land is seen as homogeneous, it is essential that the chicks themselves do not provide any distinct outline to attract a predator's attention. The chicks are patterned so that they are not only the same colour as the background but also visually disrupt their own silhouettes. Their markings run at all angles over their bodies. It is difficult for a predator's eye to follow a line when trying to trace a bird-shaped outline from its background. The chicks, therefore, merge into the 'noise' of the background.

A chick on its own can quite easily blend into the background and freeze, but the movement of one chick in a crowded nest might give the game away. So they must cooperate to create the illusion. The nestlings of the bar-tailed flycatcher-shrike do just that. They sit in their lichen-covered nest with their beaks facing one another and pointing skywards. To a casual observer the effect is that of a snapped-off branch requiring no further investigation.

Camouflage works because most predators rely on detecting an object which matches their mental 'search image' of what their prey's outline should look like. This is especially true of raptors which are the principal enemies of most small birds. Predators have a mental picture in the form of an outline or silhouette of their quarry locked in their brain. If their eyes find an outline which matches their mental template, alarm bells are sounded in the brain attracting the hunter's attention to the possible prey. Camouflage, therefore, evolves to make birds appear as un-bird-shaped as possible.

Birds, as we have seen, depend more on their eyes than on any other senses. Their different lifestyles have posed different problems which their eyes have evolved to overcome in many unique ways. Birds not only have brighter colours than any other group of animals but they also have much better sight. They can see things which we find hard to imagine. To a white stork, with its vision extending into the ultra-violet, another stork appears exactly like a zebra! Other birds have 'two eyes in one' systems, or developments unique to themselves, like single colour discrimination accurate enough to assess toxicity. With such eyes and such a sophisticated visual sense, how different and bright must a bird's own plumage seem? The lekking spectacle as seen through the eyes of a female bird of paradise must be overwhelming! We are now only just beginning to understand how birds view the world. Already it seems like a strangely unfamiliar and magical place.

7

BRINGING UP BABY

EVERY DAY JUST BEFORE DAWN, ABOUT 200 SOMBRE, BROWN, CHICKEN sized birds emerge from the tropical forests of Savo in the Solomon Islands and gather in a sandy clearing. They are scrub hens and they are looking for somewhere to deposit their eggs. For most of the year they forage on the forest floor, scratching around in search of a mixed diet of lizards, grubs and fruits, but when it is time to lay they head for the 'geu' or 'megapode field'. There has been no prolonged courtship and no pair formation. Scrub fowl, or 'bigfoots' (megapodes) as they are known, are intolerant of other scrub fowl. Somehow males and females overcome their mutual dislike and mate for just a few seconds, before going their own way once more. The cock birds play no further role, it is only the hens which arrive at the geu.

The geu is a special place. Deep under the ground, volcanic activity warms the sand from below and it is this geothermal energy that attracts the birds to this, the only geu on the island. Each bird scratches around, looking for sand that is easy to excavate and begins to dig. About 60 centimetres down the sand temperature is 33°C, just right to incubate her eggs, and a temperature more suited to the incubation of a reptile's eggs than to those of most birds. She checks that she has reached the right place by inserting her beak into the warm sand. Temperature receptors on her tongue tell her whether it is time to lay. She deposits her eggs, covers them up, and is away back into the forest before the sun is up. She never sets eyes on her eggs or her offspring again.

The unattended eggs are three and a half times larger than those deposited by similar-sized birds. They have a high yolk content, thin shells – half the thickness of other eggs – and take about 60 per cent longer to hatch. The hatchlings are well developed; they have to be. For the first 15 hours of their life they must struggle to the surface. They are fully feathered and are able to regulate their body temperature immediately. Within an hour of reaching the surface they can run and within two hours can flutter into the forest. By their first nightfall they can fly strongly enough to evade snakes, cats and the occasional passing Savo islander. (The geu is divided by the islanders into rented units from which they can take bigfoot eggs.) From the onset, the scrub fowl chicks are entirely independent, finding their own food and shelter and relying on their wits to avoid being eaten themselves.

Other megapodes have other heating systems. One species on Celebes relies on the warmth from hot springs, while another uses the heat from the sun on the sand, birds prefering black sand to white. In the Soloman Islands the eggs are laid in rotting tree trunks, while compost heaps (see pages 287–9) are built in New Guinea and Australia.

Whatever the method of incubation, the 'bigfoots' of Savo, and other brush turkeys and scrub fowl of Australia, New Guinea and the islands of the western Pacific, are unusual amongst birds. Most birds invest enormous amounts of energy in pairing, deliberately choosing a nest site and then building a nest. This care is generally extended to warming, protecting and feeding the brood and may well continue until well after the young have left the nest. With about 9,000 different species of birds, it is not surprising that a whole range of bizarre sexual strategies have evolved to ensure successful breeding, and that birds have explored a whole range of possibilities for nest-site selection, nest building and ways of obtaining food for the chicks. But once a female is ready to breed she must first decide precisely where is the best place to do so.

NEST SITES

A bird's choice of nest site is affected by the duration of the breeding season, the availability of materials, the possibility of predation, the proximity of food supplies and the species rarity. In most species both sexes contribute equally to the selection of nest site and to nest construction. In cold northern latitudes, the breeding season is too short to allow birds to be too fastidious, and many, having found a site, return to it year after year. In warmer latitudes, birds may spend several weeks rather than a few days in choosing the right spot. Others are not so finicky and simply squat in someone else's nest. In the tropics, nest predation is common.

Most birds have access to a wide range of serviceable nest materials, but some specialist builders are confined to within close flying time of particular building materials or scarce nest sites. Indonesian palm cockatoos and African blue-bellied rollers only nest on tall palm trunks from which the crown has been lost. With such penthouse accommodation at a premium, competition for sites can be fierce, and successful tenants can spend as much time protecting their nest from would-be usurpers as they do from predators intent on snatching their chicks.

European house martins glue cup-shaped mud and saliva nests under the eaves of houses. Though small, these nests may require a thousand beakfuls of suitable mud to construct, so high-quality mud, dry eaves and feeding sites catering for the martin's mainly midge diet must be sought. Scarcity of such places means that these birds often have to pack into the sites and nest gregariously.

The white-collared swift, one of the larger swift species, builds its shallow-cupped nest of moss and lichens in fissures and grottoes behind waterfalls. It does not actually fly through the falling water but hovers outside until a gap appears through which it can quickly dart. Thousands of birds might hide behind one large waterfall.

Limited nest-site availability not surprisingly gives rise to fierce competition. Failure to find and retain a site will mean a failure to breed, and specialized nesters such as swifts, whilst nesting in loose colonies, battle for hours for suitable sites.

Amongst the most remarkable colonial nesters are the weaver

birds of Africa and India. The birds live in noisy colonies often visible to predators at great distances. To thwart boomslangs, genets and other wily predators, colonies are often founded in trees or palms standing in water. The weavers sometimes seek the protection of others, siting their nests close to wasps' nests or the nests of other birds more capable of defending the site. Pendulous nests dangle from a grassy thread on the ends of the finest twigs in order to limit the size of uninvited guests. Really bold weavers have been known to hang their nests from the twigs beneath an eagle's eyrie.

In South American forests, the hoatzin builds its untidy nest in mangroves or trees over water. In this way it too reduces the risks from predation. Birds of prey and some seabirds take inaccessibility to the extreme. They nest on tiny crags high on mountains or on sheer 300-metre-high cliffs overlooking the sea. Andean condors, for instance, find sites high up in the great Andes mountain chain. A pair will seek out convex cliff faces, some as high as 900 metres, and make their bare scrape of a nest in shallow cave-like hollows on the least accessible part of the face.

Safe from all but avian predators and with abundant fish stocks in the sea below, seabird breeding colonies may be summer home to millions of birds (see pages 60–3). One of the factors restricting colony size is the limited number of suitable rocky ledges. Experience and physical prowess ensure a choice site for some, but for those at the bottom of the pecking order there is the prospect of being restricted to using ledges narrower than their own breast width. Bickering and theft of nest materials are commonplace, so a good knowledge of available sites is valuable at the beginning of the season. The fulmar, which takes several years to mature, starts its prospecting two to three years before it is actually ready to breed.

Hole nesters, such as titmice, select sites at a height in the forest canopy where their preferred caterpillar diet is found. Holes must be of sufficient size to enable ease of access but small enough to exclude predators. Males of migratory species like pied flycatchers arrive at breeding sites before the females. They defend a territory containing several nest holes, and when the prospective mates arrive they are taken on a guided tour of the accommodation on offer. The final choice is made by both sexes. For whitethroats and garden warblers, it is the female's choice. She is taken on an inspection tour of several rough nests built at potential sites and she chooses one site. Hornbills share the responsibility. Every dead and suitably holed tree in a pair's territory is visited many times before the final decision is made and the hole-of-their-choice is occupied.

Cryptic shorebirds, utilizing a simple scrape in the sand or shingle, are spoilt for choice. But miles of featureless beach may make returning to the nest difficult, so some birds find suitable landmarks. Greenshanks often nest close to a large stone or a piece of driftwood. Pairs of red-necked phalaropes in northern Europe tend to use the entire beach. In this way they ensure they are not caught short as the time for egg-laying approaches. They dig many scrapes along the beach, apparently at random, and about an hour before laying the female frantically visits as many as she can find. Her four eggs are deposited in whichever scrape is nearest at the time. She then abandons them, leaving the male to incubate the eggs and raise the brood.

Other birds are more discerning. Early birds not only catch the proverbial worm but also have first refusal on the best available nest sites. At breeding time, males of migratory species arrive as early as they can at breeding territories. The first redwing arrivals – a migratory species of European thrush that nests in trees – select nest sites in the uppermost branches where they will suffer less from predation. Latecomers must do with the lower branches where they are more likely to be plundered.

Another anti-predation strategy is to site a nest close to where larger, more aggressive birds confer a degree of protection. In this way, mixed colonies containing different species of birds are formed. Bramblings – a small European finch – often take residence amongst colonies of the larger fieldfares, a species noted for its successful mobbing of predators. Similarly, tufted ducks nest, where possible, amongst mixed colonies of gulls and terns (see page 61). They benefit from the seabirds' constant aerial surveillance and very effective mass mobbing of unwelcome visitors.

In areas where climate can be unpredictable, potential nesters must keep one eye on the weather. White-crowned sparrows in the southern states of the USA begin to nest even before the winter snows melt. They prefer to nest on the ground, but if they sense that the snow will lie well into spring they build nests in bushes and low trees.

Weather forecasting has been developed to an amazing degree by the emperor penguin. These Antarctic giants produce a single enormous, slow-growing, fluffy chick which must be ready to learn to swim and hunt for itself during the brief summer thaw. With a sixty-four day incubation period and several months more before the chicks actually start to swim, the parents must back-time egg-laying to the middle of the long, dark winter when the sea is still frozen. Their choice of breeding site is also critical, and is usually far inland on the Antarctic continent itself. If they nested at the water's edge, close to where they could feed with ease, the ice sheet beneath them would melt before the chick had even hatched. The adults, therefore, must select sites at the point to which the ice will have retreated by the time the chicks are ready to swim.

One of the most reliable ways of choosing a good site is to use the one that has proved itself successful in previous years. Many eagles use the same nest year after year, even generation after generation, and the nests can be enormous. The nest of a pair of bald eagles and their successors in Vermilion, Ohio, was reported in Gerald Wood's *Guinness Book of Animal Facts and Feats* and Brian Martin's *World Birds* to have been occupied annually for thirty-five years. It measured 2.59 metres across and was 3.66 metres deep and weighed about 1,814 kilograms. Another pair in Florida built a nest 2.90 metres across and 6.10 metres deep which weighed more than 3,000 kilograms. A golden eagle's nest in Scotland, which was used for forty-five years, was reliably measured as being 4.6 metres deep. Guillemots and other seabirds return to the same nest site each year and make do, not with a vast nest, but with a section of narrow ledge on the side of a sheer cliff face.

But, whether returning to a gigantic bowl or a convenient scrape, by using the same nest site birds save time and energy in searching and a pair are assured of proven food supplies within easy reach of the nest. For the big-nest birds, it also saves on time used to build the structure and, given the enormous size of bald-eagle nests, guarantees the strength of the supporting branches. When nests can be several metres deep and weigh tonnes, it is a valuable indicator of nest safety to find that the old nest has withstood the ravages of winter storms. However, this is not always watertight – the Vermilion nest grew so big that during a storm it crashed to the ground, killing the eaglets of that year.

BROOD PARASITES

Given the enormous energy spent in building and defending a nest, it is, perhaps, not surprising to learn that birds of one species will cheat the system and place their eggs in the nest of another pair.

This is known as brood parasitism and it has evolved independently in at least seven families or subfamilies of birds. In fact, the trait is surprisingly common. About 1 per cent of all bird species are brood parasites. Even birds which normally raise their own young have been tempted by the easy way out and have laid their eggs in the nests of other birds.

Cliff-dwelling swallows dupe their neighbours. A bird might carry one of its own eggs, visit the nest of a neighbour, and leave without the egg. Other birds, like starlings and ducks, *lay* their eggs in the nest of a bird of the same species, but these swallows carry an already-laid egg. Scientists monitoring a population in Nebraska found that 6 per cent of nests contain transferred eggs, and they believe that the figure is an underestimate. They even watched one cheeky individual slip an egg into a nest right under the beak of the sitting bird. There was a fight and the intruder was quickly evicted. But in those ten seconds the bird had successfully deposited its egg. The resident, ruffled but unabashed, continued to sit on the nest, blissfully unaware that it had gained an extra egg.

Why these birds should behave in this way is uncertain. Survival in the colony generally is not assured. About a quarter of all eggs fail to hatch. But only 10 per cent of transferred eggs are unsuccessful. Maybe, thought the researchers, the nest parasites focus their attention on birds which are better incubators. The nests of these birds are also in canyons and cliffs prone to rockfalls, so by spreading the brood around the survival of at least some is assured. On the other hand, the parasites may simply be getting a free ride – they increase their reproductive success by reducing the costs of parental care. Ostriches also spread risks by laying in the nests of several hosts, but most other nest parasites avoid the nests of their own species and leave their eggs in foreign nests.

Lapwings are reported to have deposited eggs in the nests of ruffs, and bearded tits occasionally take advantage of Savi's warblers. Some parasitic chicks are totally independent as soon as they leave the nest and have little impact on the breeding success of the host birds. South American black-headed ducks, for example, add one or two of their eggs to the nests of herons, ibises, rails and other ducks and even to the nest of the vicious, predatory caracara. The foster parents simply incubate and protect the black-headed duck eggs along with their own. On hatching, the precocious ducklings immediately leave the nest and fend for themselves.

Such casual arrangements are thought to have developed quite recently. Birds only evolve the ability to spot alien eggs after many generations of exposure to brood parasites. In Europe, ruddy ducks lay in cinnamon teal nests and shelducks parasitize red-breasted merganser nests. In these cases, the parasites lay more of their eggs in the nests already containing host eggs. As the hosts only continue to lay their own eggs until their normal clutch size is attained, the parasitic birds directly reduce the number of offspring their hosts can produce.

These 'trial and error' attempts at brood parasitism are not always successful. Merganser parents tend to lead their mixed brood to deep water to feed. Young shelducks, however, are at a distinct disadvantage. They are unable to dive as deep as the merganser chicks and cannot reach the bottom where they would normally feed. Frequently they simply starve to death.

Other parasites are more closely adapted to their hosts and have become dependent on them for their own success. There are fourteen species of African whydahs and indigo birds and each parasitizes a particular species of finch. The parasitic chicks carefully mimic the colour and begging calls of the host chicks and the parasitic adults might even mimic the host birds' songs. The parasites and host chicks are raised successfully in the same nest, and while the finch parents raise no fewer of their own chicks the extra work required to raise such a large family may reduce reproductive success the following year. The birds are simply exhausted.

In the New World, the cowbirds are the most important brood parasites and they offer a glimpse of the origin of this kind of behaviour in birds. The bay-winged cowbird lives in South America and is quite capable of building its own nest, but if the opportunity arises it will occupy abandoned nests or forcibly evict residents from their nests and take over. It is not a far cry from eviction to parasitism, and its more widely distributed relative, the common cowbird, is known to parasitize the nests of over 100 species of finches, the hosts raising parasites and host chicks together.

Most host parents are seemingly unaware of the intrusion and are unable to detect aliens in the nest; but not so the hosts of the Mexican giant cowbird. These hosts are able to recognize the eggs of the giant cowbird, but even so they do not always eject them from the nest. The chicks of the host finches are plagued with botflies. The parasitic flies deposit their eggs on the chicks, and the maggots, which grow up inside the chicks, usually kill their hosts. So, where possible, finches build their nests close to wasp or bee colonies and are afforded some degree of protection. These protected finches do not tolerate cowbird eggs; they throw them out. But finches without such protection ignore the foreign eggs, for the cowbird chicks have a useful function: they eat the botfly larvae before they have a chance to burrow into the finch chick's body.

A more sinister relationship has developed between the African cuckoo finch or buffalo weaver and its warbler hosts. The nest parasite deposits two of its eggs among the eggs of its host. At fledging, however, only the two buffalo weaver chicks remain, the warbler chicks having disappeared under suspicious circumstances.

Old World cuckoos have developed brood parasitism to its self-serving extreme. Common cuckoo parents do not form lasting relationships. After mating the female identifies several suitable host nests within her territory. Some time in the afternoon – the timing is crucial – the male creates a diversionary rumpus which is sure to bring an outraged resident away from one of the targeted nests. The female cuckoo meanwhile waits quietly hidden nearby until the unsuspecting foster parent has her attention turned elsewhere. When she sees the coast is clear, she visits the target nest. This behaviour is repeated at several nests. At each one she picks up a host's egg in her beak and deposits one of her own – it might fall from a height of 15 centimetres – and then she makes off. The whole performance takes just 10–15 seconds and culminates in the hen cuckoo eating the stolen egg. The timing is critical because eggs deposited in the morning tend to be recognized and ejected.

This diversionary role of the male is important too for several species of African and Indian brood parasites. Male parasitic honeyguides have been known to battle for several days with nesting rollers, attempting to divert their attention away from the nest in order that the female honeyguide can discreetly enter the hosts' nest hole and deposit her own eggs.

If the nests of host birds are too well advanced to receive the parasitic eggs, female cuckoos will remove eggs or chicks, and maybe even destroy the nest. Thus, the host is forced to build a new nest or start a new brood, giving the cuckoo an opportunity to breed. This kind of sophisticated behaviour has made the cryptic cuckoo a very successful bird, and the key to this success lies in the choice of host.

In Britain, cuckoos target the nests of four main species, the choice depending on local conditions: on moorland, the nests of the meadow pipit are parasitized; in marshland the reed warbler is selected; around farms and in woodland the hedge sparrow or dunnock; and in open habitats the pied wagtail. Recent observations have revealed that cuckoos and their offspring specialize in one particular host species, and scientists refer to pipit-cuckoos, pied wagtail-cuckoos and other cuckoo races as genetically distinct groups or 'gentes'.

Female cuckoos of each gens deposit eggs which mimic the colour of those of their hosts, so cuckoo eggs can be brown, green or grey-white depending on which species is parasitized. The exception is the dunnock-cuckoo. The female dunnock lays blue eggs, yet the dunnock-cuckoo deposits pale spotted eggs in her nest. Dunnock-cuckoos, it seems, do not need to mimic the colour of their host's eggs. Unlike other hosts, they should be able to recognize the cuckoo's eggs, which are a different size and a different colour from their own. It is thought that this anomaly might be due to the fact that cuckoos have only turned to the dunnock recently and the dunnock has not yet caught up in the evolutionary race. On the other hand, dunnocks may just be amazingly stupid birds.

Records of cuckoo activity in Britain have been kept for over fifty years, and they show that on average only 0.4–5.5 per cent of host species nests are actually parasitized, although in some localities this figure might rise to 16 per cent. Cuckoos seem to strike the right balance between acceptance and rejection by removing only one egg. If more eggs are removed, the parents may desert the nest. Also, a single parasitic chick will be raised by its hosts, but a single egg will not be incubated.

Unlike some other brood parasites, such as whydah and indigo bird chicks, which mimic the begging calls, mouth colour and markings of their host's chicks, a cuckoo chick does not copy or resemble the chicks of its host. When it hatches, the cuckoo chick automatically backs up against any host chicks, raises them up onto its shoulders and pushes them over the side of the nest. Unhatched eggs are dealt with in the same way. The foster parents are left with a rather large and unusual chick, but they seem unable to recognize it as alien. In experiments, warblers have shown that they cannot distinguish between the chicks of a whole range of species. So, with foster parents that are not able to tell what they have in the nest, a cuckoo chick need not disguise itself.

And the remarkable story doesn't end there. The warbler-cuckoo requires the daily food intake that would normally be offered to three or four warbler chicks; the number, in fact, which it has replaced. Cuckoo growth, it seems, is tailored to the demand that its foster parents can manage to meet.

Evolution, though, favours the ability of host birds to detect the presence of cuckoo eggs. Similarly, the ability of the cuckoo to dupe its host gives it an advantage. So this has led to a kind of evolutionary 'arms race' in which host and parasite try to outdo each other. On the one hand, bird species with limited or no incidence of cuckoo parasitism may have evolved better powers of recognition and can spot a take-over. Some may just have eggs with patterns that cannot yet be matched. On the other hand, the unfortunate dunnock may represent a recent switch to a species which is unfamiliar with the villainy of the cuckoo and which, at present, is ill-prepared to deal with it.

AVIAN ARCHITECTS

Birds generally are model parents, and having selected a suitable nest site they set about constructing the nest itself. Nests come in all shapes and sizes, from 10-centimetre scrapes in the sand to decades-old structures of mud and sticks more like a tree-top beaver lodge than a bird's nest. Traditionally, a bird is depicted 'living' in a nest of twigs that rests in the fork of a tree. Indeed, some birds do have just such a nest but they do not live in it the whole year round. The nest, be it simple or elaborate, is the place where the eggs are laid, the chicks fed, and the youngsters fledged. When the new brood has left, the nest is usually abandoned.

The simplest nest is probably that of the emperor penguin. It uses no materials at all. It incubates its single egg for over two months, balancing it on its webbed feet and therefore clear of the chilling ice and snow. Holding it close to its belly brood patch, the emperor incubates its egg at 37°C, up to 80°C warmer than the temperature of the antarctic air outside.

Some birds have very simple nests. Many ground-nesting birds place their eggs in a scrape in the ground, sandgrouse have been known to deposit their eggs in large hoofprints, and the water dikkop lays them on hippopotamus droppings.

Seabirds, nesting on cliff ledges, typically have untidy nests using a few dozen strands of dry seaweed, feathers and droppings. Within large colonies, like those of gannets and penguins, materials are scarce and theft is rife. Less powerful birds, like puffins, manage to avoid the ledge squabbles by digging themselves nesting burrows on the cliff top. Some birds, like the Manx shearwaters of Skomer off the west Wales coast, don't even bother to dig, they simply take over old rabbit burrows.

The giant albatrosses of the Southern Ocean build large, crude nests of grass and moss, nestled amongst clumps of tussock grass. They nest in loose colonies, set back from the sea cliffs, protected from the buffeting of southern gales. The adults commute daily along well-worn tracks to take-off points at the cliff edge. While most seabirds nest on the shore or cliffs, some species exploit other sites inland. One drawback with nests is that they smell and can therefore be detected easily by predators. The diminutive fairy tern from the tropical Pacific overcomes this by precariously depositing its single egg on a bare branch. The branch selected is usually a little wider than the egg but it is remarkable that it does not fall off. In fact, young, relatively inexperienced birds do have problems. A trail of broken eggs below impossibly steep or narrow branches are witness to early learning accidents.

The tiny marbled murrelet forsakes the nest-side squabbles and material shortages by building a moss-lined, cup-shaped nest mainly of guano at the very tops of conifer trees. Indeed, its nest is the highest so far recorded and nobody had ever seen one until 7 August 1974 when the first marbled murrelet nest was discovered 45 metres up a Douglas fir in Big Basin State Park, Santa Cruz County, California. Another auklet, Kittlitz's murrelet, flies even further from the ocean to nest. It heads for the mountain tops above the tree-line, where it builds a simple moss-and-down nest on the ground. At these high altitudes, it avoids the attentions of most predators.

One of the most extreme anti-predator strategies must be that adopted by the grey gull or 'garuma' of Chile. Whilst feeding, courtship, and mating take place on the coast, gull parents fly fifty miles or so inland to nest; but their nest site is not on the top of a tree, a cliff or a mountain – they nest in the middle of the Atacama desert where the daytime temperature can reach 50°C. The nest is just a scrape in the sand, and one parent always remains on the nest to shade the eggs and chicks from the sun. No other creature, save the odd snake or scorpion, would venture into such an inhospitable place so the nesting birds are safe here.

Flamingos often inhabit brackish, inland lagoons where the

salinity makes plant growth difficult, if not impossible. Nesting is safest in groups, and to further reduce predation flamingos nest in colonies far out in the lagoon. Denied easy access to other building materials, the birds use what they find at their feet – mud. Using their peculiar-shaped beaks and their webbed feet, they back-pile soft mud, often mixed with excrement to bind it together, into small mounds. Once a mound begins to form it is left to dry in the sun before more layers are added. Eventually, the nest-makers sculpt a foul-smelling, rimmed bowl about 30–50 centimetres across. With successive years of renovations the mound can reach a height of 45 centimetres. It is effectively unlined, although a few feathers are stuck to it accidentally. The stench is a ready beacon for predators, so chick survival depends on how far from the shoreline the birds decide to breed. Those nesting in the middle of caustic soda lakes in East Africa are effectively isolated from most predators, although on one lake fish eagles have taken to hijacking flamingos. Faced with a shortage of fish, the fish eagles changed diet and the flamingos are fair game for a bird the size of an eagle.

Mud features in the nests of birds in the New World too. South American savannahs are often punctuated by the famous mud nests of the ovenbird. In the eyes of man the ovenbird makes amends for being possibly the drabbest bird on the continent by living in close association with human settlements. On the seemingly endless pampas of Argentina, fence posts, stakes and broken farm machinery can be seen decorated with football-sized mud nests. They are found about a metre above the ground, shaped like giant eggs, pointed-side up. They have thick mud walls and a narrow entrance leading to an 18–25-centimetre-diameter chamber lined with fine grass in which are deposited three to five eggs. Some species of ovenbird produce deluxe versions, mixing a cement of fine sand and fresh cow dung. Architecturally elegant, the design has a major design flaw, making spring cleaning difficult. The thick walls successfully insulate against the hot sun by day and keep the nestlings warm at night. But these conditions are also ideal for the hordes of bed-bug-related parasites which feed on the blood of ovenbird chicks. They become so numerous that they reach plague proportions and much of a chick's energy is used up in scratching and shaking.

Ovenbirds and their relatives have a strong architectural flair. The tiny wrenlike rushbird weaves its grass nest around strands of reeds. When the grass skeleton is complete the sphere is neatly plastered with clay. A small porch keeps the rain off the entrance and the opening is even fitted with a grass-hinged trap-door. Outside the entrance the bird has a clay patio on which it sings.

Other species forego architectural niceties for thorny defences. The rufous-breasted spinetail builds an oblong nest 80 centimetres long and 50 centimetres tall. It too has a singing platform at the entrance, which leads through a thorn-fringed tunnel to a central nest chamber neatly thatched with sticks and straw and lined with special velvety leaves.

The cordilleran castinero builds huge columns of thorny twigs which will withstand the weight of a man. The nest is generally invisible, hidden somewhere in the middle of a thorn pile. This is an idea that has been developed by the rufous-throated thornbird, which constructs large thorn mounds to protect its double-chambered nest. Each season new chambers are added and these may be occupied by immature helpers from the previous season's brood. Even other species of ovenbirds have been known to move into the loose colony.

The largest internally chambered nests are those made by the African hammerkop or hammerheaded stork. This 60 centimetres long brown bird has a head shaped like a clawed hammer and is something of a scientific enigma. It has been variously classified as a stork, a heron and a 'not sure'. Its nest is enormous. It is constructed from inside out, starting with the nesting chamber. This consists of a damp bowl of reeds, twigs and grass cemented by mud. Three of its sides are extended upwards and roofed over with remarkably sturdy sticks and small branches 60–80 centimetres long and 2–4 centimetres thick. Roofing starts by placing sticks diagonally across the corners and then working inwards until the whole chamber is capped. More and more sticks are piled on and the birds begin to decorate the dome with a thatch made from all manner of unexpected objects – plant debris, snake skins, feathers, refuse, aluminium cans and bits of dead animals. The lower parts are plastered with mud to insulate, waterproof and keep the nest chamber rat- and snake-proof. The single entrance is largely invisible, the birds entering or leaving through a hole beneath the dome.

New nests are over 1 metre wide and 1.5 metres tall and are built 12–15 metres up in a tree. They take about six weeks to two months to complete and may contain over 10,000 sticks. Those used in successive years have materials added each season and can grow to truly gigantic proportions, up to 2-metres wide and deep. The entire edifice will withstand the weight of a man and, perched in tree forks over water, is often visible from great distances. The nests are so solid and dependable that many other species of birds may decide to cohabit. Pel's fishing owls and milky eagle owls sometimes invade the dome. Several species of bulbuls and wattle-eyes nest amongst the mass of side sticks. Weavers and penduline tits may hang their own covered nests from protruding sticks. Unfortunately for the industrious hammerkops, other birds covet the nesting chamber itself. Barn owls, Dickenson's kestrels, and Verreaux's eagles may oust the residents after years, or even generations of careful ownership. Egyptian and African pygmy geese may take over a vacated nest. But all these interlopers may be in turn supplanted by colonies of the legendary African honey bee.

The other prime contenders for the title of 'holder of the world's most impressive nest' are the large eagles. Bald eagles pair for life and usually return to the same nest year after year. Nests are built high in trees or rocky promontories and constructed of sticks with a softer pine needle lining. After thirty or forty years, the nest can be huge (see page 269). New nesting material is added daily throughout the breeding season and the nests grow appreciably from season to season. Instead of merely restoring the previous year's nest as other birds do, bald eagles effectively construct an entirely new nest on top of the old one. The nest building procedure itself appears to be an important part of the eagles' courtship behaviour and of the pair-bonding process.

The weight of the structure, particularly after rain, can bring down the entire supporting tree, a factor that bald eagles in the Aleutian Islands do not need to worry about. Nest materials here are hard to find and the eagles simply nest on the shoreline in a pile of seaweed.

Weeds, particularly freshwater weeds in lakes, can be loosely woven to form floating mats. Several species of grebes use mats to provide safe nest platforms away from the lakeside. They are anchored to water lilies or rushes and require the daily addition of fresh waterweed to prevent them from sinking.

Even nests surrounded by water, however, are susceptible to predators that can swim and, more importantly, predators attacking from the air. In fact, being in the open is not the ideal strategy for survival; it is much better for a bird to hide its nest, in a hole, for example. Hole nesting is a simple and widely used nesting tactic which improves brood safety. A survey of fledgling success in birds generally revealed that about half of 22,000 eggs laid in open nests fledged young. Birds using closed or cavity nests did better. Of 94,000 eggs laid in enclosed nests, about 70 per cent were reared successfully. And there are other benefits too, for the more secure a nest is, the longer the parents can safely spend away from it gathering food.

Birds do not necessarily dig their own holes, but take over vacancies. The cinclodes, a dipper-like relative of the ovenbird, searches out bank-side rodent tunnels. The nest chamber is usually some 1.2 metres into the bank and is lined with feathers and dried moss. The brood is protected from large predators and extremes of temperature. But not all ovenbirds are so particular about their nesting habits. The sharp-tailed streamcreeper also nests in tunnels in stream banks, but in the less salubrious parts of town. This inconspicuous bird has benefited from the insect-rich open sewers of Brazilian shanty towns. Little else thrives here and the stream-creeper is known locally as 'The President of Filth'.

Some birds take advantage of the protection afforded by the nest structures of other creatures. The violaceous trogon of Central and South America, for instance, must use one of the most extraordinary enclosures. It invades wasps' nests, eats the wasps and excavates the comb for its nest cavity. But probably the most highly evolved hole nesters are those that excavate nest chambers inside the nests of termites, some becoming wholly reliant on the protection afforded by their hosts.

The brightly coloured orange-fronted parakeet of central Mexico and Central America nests solely in the termite mounds of the *Nasutilermes* colonial termite. The distribution of these birds is closely tied to that of the insects, and has been recorded from only a few places where the termites do not occur. The parakeets benefit from the enhanced protection of the concrete-hard termitarium walls and from the resistance put up against predators by the soldier termites during an attack. The 'house proud' termites also keep the parakeets' nest meticulously clean, removing bird-nest lice and their larvae, as well as the chicks' faeces. What the termites get in return is not clear. It could be that the squatters provide valuable salts and other compounds in their faeces, or the termites steal nutritious nest materials from the birds. It seems certain that the soldier termites would soon evict the birds if they provided nothing in return for their safe haven.

Other birds nest in termite mounds if the opportunity arises. Cotingas, puff birds, parrots, trogons and kingfishers are all known to take advantage of termites, but the relationship is less highly developed. The termites simply seal up the sides of the excavations made by the birds, and often the birds take over the tunnels made by other animals like rodents. The mound can get mighty crowded. Birds, mongooses, cobras, monitor lizards and scorpions have all been reported as sharing the same termite mound.

Many hole-nesters dig their own holes. The kingfisher benefits from the secrecy of its solitary nest hole, but others, like the carmine bee-eater of Africa, get together in huge colonies. They are busy, colourful and noisy places, but the high profile they offer to predators is compensated for by the ability of the birds to work together and to mob predators and defend their chicks. Though not large or powerful birds, bee-eaters possess sharp bills which are especially effective when a skyful of irate neighbours is on the warpath.

Large territorial birds cannot rely on the neighbours for protection. The bird next door is probably a rival and not to be trusted. Therefore they must adopt another tactic. Woodpeckers excavate their own nests in trees with the smallest practical entrance and the widest possible outlook. The nest as such is no more than a typically unlined, hollowed trunk.

Excavating holes in trees is a nesting strategy best developed by the African and Asian hornbills. Hornbills pair for life and the pair bond is particularly strong; it has to be, for the nesting procedure requires the birds to have absolute trust in their mate. With the exception of the two species of African ground hornbill, hornbills nest in excavated tree holes, and they seal the female and the young inside.

The great Indian hornbills of the rainforests of south-east Asia are nearly a metre in length, the size of a turkey, and enormous birds need enormous holes. The massive bill is a specialized feeding and digging implement and can account for 10 per cent of the bird's overall weight. Males are more active at finding holes and they tempt the females to adopt them with offerings of food. Both birds then share the task of laboriously chiselling out their new home. These large birds are restricted in what trees they can use. The trunk must have a minimum diameter of 1–1.2 metres at the nest height of 20–45 metres, and those kinds of trees are fast disappearing. They occur only in remnant stands of unlogged forest and that is becoming desperately rare.

Once the nest hole has been made sufficiently large, the female lines the floor with a mixture of guano, wood shavings and food scraps. The entrance is then gradually walled up. The female provides excrement mixed with wood chips on the inside and the male provides beakfuls of mud on the outside. A week later only a slit the width of a beak is left open. The female inside continues to excavate into the roof of the nest, throwing the wood chips out through the slit. In the top of the chamber she digs out a 'funk-hole' or retreat. All the while the male brings gifts of calcium-rich snails, lizards and fledglings as the female prepares to lay. Egg laying is delayed after fertilization to enable entombment and internal home improvements to be completed. Great Indian hornbills deposit only one or two eggs, whereas smaller species may lay four to seven.

The incarcerated female is now totally dependent on her mate. Ventilation in the hole is maintained by convection, and rising tree sap helps to keep the nest cool. One problem, though, is the nest parasites, and it could be that the huge build-up of these irritating interlopers is responsible for the fact that a pair of hornbills never use the same nest hole twice, despite the effort that went into its construction.

The tiny elf owl of North American deserts is a hole-nester and it has found a solution for nest parasites. It nests in the giant saguaro cactus, in holes made by the gila woodpecker. Aerial, sap-cooled homes are few and far between in the desert and are almost always occupied; so birds have to double up and gila woodpeckers find themselves cohabiting with elf owls. At dusk the peace of the desert is disturbed as woodpeckers are trying to get ready to roost and the owls are just waking up. But the woodpecker tolerates the owl, for it has solved the problem that because precious nest-holes are used time and time again there is a build-up of parasites. To combat this, the elf owl has learned to catch western blind snakes and, instead of eating them, takes them back to the nest. The snakes are about 10–20 centimetres long and thread-like. They usually burrow for ants and insect larvae, but in the nest they make short work of lice and other parasitic insect larvae. New nests do not need pest-control snakes, but an old nest may have as many as half a dozen slithering about. When the owl chicks fledge and the snakes' ready food supply is gone, they wriggle out of the cactus and back down to the ground.

Prions are hole-nesters. They dig their own burrows, but on Poor Knights Island off the New Zealand coast they share the hole with a strange choice of nest-mate. On returning from the sea, the birds plunge through the forest canopy and scramble down their burrows only to be confronted by a tuatara – an ancient lizard-like creature and a left-over from the days of the dinosaurs. Why the prions should tolerate the tuatara is not clear, for the lizard preys upon any prion chicks left by the adults.

Holes or mud do not suit every bird's lifestyle and a surprising number use another, more unlikely material from which to construct their nests; their own saliva. By using saliva, one group of birds unwittingly supplies the main raw ingredient for a multi-million dollar soup industry. Bird's nest soup is made from the cup-shaped nests of the cave swiftlets of south-east Asia (see also page 165).

The nest collectors arrive at the caves in January, when the first nests are built. To reach the nest sites in the roof of the cathedral-like galleries, which can be 50 metres high, the collectors construct a flimsy scaffolding from bamboo and vines, which is wedged into cracks in the fluted cave walls. The harvest is controlled. Only the first nests are allowed to be taken. Even so, many eggs and nestlings are tipped out. The parent birds, though, simply rebuild and attempt to raise another brood.

The nest, which is built precariously on cave walls that overhang slightly, is started with a U-shaped strip of rubbery saliva, the 'hinge'. Clinging somehow to the rock face, the birds add thinner layers until the cup-shaped shelf is finished. It is just large enough for the female to sit tight to the rock face and incubate her eggs. Some nests consist of alternate layers of saliva and feathers, and appear striped. Red nests are coloured by iron leached from the damp cave walls. But oriental gourmets are interested in the nests made only from saliva, the so called 'white gold'.

Such are the supposed aphrodisiac and curative properties attributed to the nests that, to the alarm of conservationists monitoring the birds' decline, Hong Kong alone imports 18.7 million nests a year. Entire villages have made their livelihood from nest collecting for centuries but it is very dangerous work. In the first week of the collecting season in 1991, at least eight collectors fell to their death.

Cave swiftlets build their saliva nests in the dark in caves, white-rumped swiftlets build on cliffs, but the palm swift of East and Central Africa builds a new nest each season on the undersides of palm fronds. The nests of all these birds are difficult for predators to reach and they are well protected from inclement weather. They also do not accummulate heavy parasite burdens as do the nests of some of their 'lousy' relatives.

Another relative, the cayenne or lesser swallow-tailed swift from South America has learned to make its valuable saliva go further by mixing in feathers and plant material. With this mixture the swift constructs an inclined, open-ended tube up to 70 centimetres long. The outside of the tube is made from rough plant material which disguises the nest, while the inside is painstakingly plastered with saliva and down. About halfway along the cylinder is a tiny shelf where the eggs and chicks are incubated.

This 'plastering' technique is also utilized by the scrub birds of Australia. Saliva is used to moisten chewed fragments of plants until they are wet and pliable. The papier-mâché-like building material is then moulded into a nest shape and dries to produce something resembling cardboard.

Other small birds construct elaborate enclosures. The aptly named Argentinian firewood gatherer collects large sticks, seemingly out of all proportion to its size. It stacks them to form a drum-shaped structure 70 centimetres deep and 30 centimetres in diameter. A single entrance is left in the top, and to prevent rain from entering the nest a crooked passage leads down to the small off-centre chamber.

Most birds, however, produce simple open nests of dried plant material, such as twigs and leaves, lined with feathers. They are supported by branches or held in the forks of trees. In the tropics, South American antbirds, vireos, African orioles, crombecs and Australian honeyeaters construct cup-shaped nests that are slung precariously by their rims under terminal twigs or at the tips of thin branches. Australian riflebirds make crude, bulky nests from any available plant material, but they finish them off by draping sloughed-off snake skins around the outside; why they do so is a mystery.

Crows and rooks build their nests in what seem to be the most inappropriate places. Their heavy untidy nests are placed on the tops of old trees. Here they sway in the wind, suffer storm damage, and offer no protection from freezing winds, rain, direct heating from the sun, or aerial predators, yet the corvids do well and some species have expanded their range in recent times, despite the efforts of gamekeepers and farmers to control them.

In contrast, African sunbirds and their New World relatives, the hummingbirds, produce jewels of nests. They use tiny fragments of plants and down, carefully bound together with spider or caterpillar silk. The smallest is that crafted by the female bee hummingbird, the world's tiniest bird and an inhabitant of Cuba and the Isle of Pines. The female bird, with no help from the male, builds a silken sphere only the size of a thimble. Its relative, the vervain hummingbird from Jamaica and Hispaniola, builds a similarly tiny cup-shaped nest of lichens, silk and cotton, the size of half a walnut shell.

Other hummingbirds, like the hermit hummingbird, construct hanging nests which are strung below large leaves, while lancebills, metaltails and hillstars hang their nests by spider silk from the roofs of caves.

But the masters of nest construction must be the weaver birds. There are fifty African and twelve Indian species, and most build intricately woven, covered nests. As colonial nesters, individuals of many species benefit from communal food location and nest defence, and the activity and excitability within the colony stimulates reproduction. Nest designs vary from species to species and closely related species can go about nest building in quite different ways.

Male village weavers from Africa gather at the nesting sites in advance of the females and start to construct their nests in the trees. They carefully select pliable lengths of green palm frond fibres or grass and begin by weaving a ring under the tip of a fine branch. Further strands are woven around the ring and on one side the top is extended. Using hundreds of 30–60-centimetre-long strands, the weaver constructs the dome, the floor and back of the nest, producing a structure resembling a cup hanging on its side. Construction continues, to form a porch. A circular opening, pointing downwards, is left level with the floor.

The weaver's nest-making ability seems to be inherited. Young males, reared in isolation, can build quite serviceable nests but their skills improve with practice. Females are quite fussy, so young males must spend the first two years before reaching maturity simply practising nest building. The females prefer strong, tightly woven nests, able to withstand the battering of tropical storms and downpours. The nest must also be fresh. Females only go for green nests. They probably surmise that a green nest has been constructed rapidly by a successful, practised male. The yellowing, dried-out nest of a young bachelor is ignored. Unsuccessful candidates, despite ten to eleven days' work must cut loose their first attempts and start the construction all over again.

A male advertises his efforts by hanging upside down from the entrance of his nest, whistling and flapping his wings in a display which is an echo of the begging behaviour of chicks. If a female is enticed in, she will line the nest with soft grass. Females reach maturity after one year so, coupled with the high rejection rate of young males' nests, there is an imbalance of the sexes. Males constructing the most desirable residences therefore build additional nests in efforts to attract more females. When a female is in the nest, the male's construction work continues. The entrance hole is extended as a 10–15-centimetre-long tube to protect the hen sitting inside the nest from the unwelcome attentions of goshawks and snakes. If a snake should poke its head into a nest, the rest of the colony attacks the now vulnerable tailend and the snake usually withdraws.

Being relatively drab birds – with black heads and yellowish bodies – male village weavers rely on their elaborate nests to attract the females. A more 'showy' weaver, the vivid red-and-black-coloured red bishop, produces a simpler nest and attracts a mate with its song and distinctive bobbing advertisement flight.

The male Cassin's weaver is relatively drab and as a consequence produces one of the most spectacular weaver nests, a grass nest with an entrance tunnel over a metre long. It is a monogamous forest dweller, and the older, more experienced males do not construct their nests alone but get a little help from younger males. Whether the helpers are related to the nest-builder is not known, but they receive little thanks for their efforts. When the nest is complete the younger birds are simply chased away. This apparently selfless act on the part of the immature birds is hard to explain. The youngsters, in effect, are helping a rival get the girls. On the one hand, if they are related – say, sons of the father – then they do have some genetic interest. After all, some of their genes are shared; by helping father they are helping their own genetic line. On the other hand, if they are not related, then the youngsters are learning the skills and gaining the experience to go into business themselves one day. By copying a successful builder they enhance their chance of constructing the best nests and gaining access to the pick of the females.

Buffalo weavers in East Africa have a similar 'helper' system. Adults and immature males work together to construct distinctive communal nests using thorny acacia twigs. The helpers do not breed and the dominant male usually has two or more mates. The nest is divided into compartments, providing each female with her own, individual brood chamber.

In Kenya, the white-browed sparrow weaver also builds a communal nest to house five or six adults. The nests cleverly have two openings, which allows birds to escape from an incoming predator. Whilst all the inhabitants maintain the structure of the nest, individuals have their own nest chambers. However, only one pair per colony breeds. The others collect food and help rear and protect the offspring. The relationship between the birds in each communal nest has yet to be established, but it is thought that they might be related.

Sociable weavers from southern Africa build huge communal nests up to 8 metres in width and looking to all intents and purposes like a haystack in a tree. The nest encompasses up to sixty chambers, each with a single entrance hole extending upwards and protected by a communal, umbrella-shaped roof. While all the birds help construct the roof, only the males maintain it. The females look after the roosting and breeding chambers below. Outside the breeding season, three or four males huddle in a single chamber to conserve warmth. During the season, a pair of sociable weavers will exclude all visitors from their chamber and the male adds a threshold ridge at the front of the chamber to keep the eggs from falling out.

One major benefit from such a communal dwelling is temperature regulation. The thick walls ensure that the chambers are insulated from the extreme temperature fluctuations outside. The nests stay cool in summer and warm in winter. In fact, the air temperature outside can vary between 16 and 34°C, but within the nest the fluctuation is reduced by half.

Sociable weavers' nests have been found with over 300 chambers, making them the builders of the world's largest bird communes. Their nests can dominate a tree, with several communes on one large tree. As with all large nests, the weavers' have uninvited guests including the small, 19-centimetres-long pygmy falcon, which is sometimes seen perching on the topmost twig of a nest tree. Curiously, although the falcon is a net consumer of small birds, it ignores its weaver hosts. Below, rosy-faced lovebirds, with their distinctive green plumage and pink faces, take over vacant nest-holes.

The builders of the world's largest nests must be the megapodes – the scrub fowls, brush turkeys and mallee fowl. Unlike the 'bigfoots' of Savo, some species build enormous nests in the ground. Instead of volcanic heat, they rely on heat from fermentation or directly from the sun to incubate their eggs.

The common scrub fowl builds the biggest nests, some measured at 11 metres across and 5 metres high. In the nineteenth century, a member of the crew of HMS *Rattlesnake* discovered a mound with a circumference of 45 metres. Although the mounds were recognized since 1521, when one was reported in the Philippines, it was not until much later that science came to terms with what or who had constructed them. When the European explorers began to explore Australia, they discovered these curious mounds of earth in the arid Eucalyptus scrublands. At first they considered them to be aboriginal burial mounds, but the locals denied any involvement and insisted they were made by birds. Nobody believed them at first, and it was not until 1840 that naturalist John Gilbert opened a mound and discovered a clutch of eggs. They were the eggs of what is now called the mallee fowl or lowan.

During the winter, before the rains come and the breeding season gets underway, a pair of birds will dig a large pit, about a metre deep and up to 5 metres in diameter, and then scrape and carry every piece of dead vegetation within a radius of 50 metres to fill it up. With the arrival of the rains, the rotting process is accelerated and the temperature within the pit can rise to 60°C. The birds cover in most of the pit with a layer of sand about 50 centimetres thick, leaving a small section where they mix sand and leaves to form a chamber in which the female will lay her eggs.

The remarkable part of the whole story is the role played by the male. He must maintain the mound at a constant 34°C throughout the period of incubation, and that can go on for many months, for the female lays her eggs, up to thirty-five in a season, in small batches over a long period of time. The male's is by no means a simple task, for, during the summer, the air temperature can fluctuate by over 16°C during the day and night, and it varies considerably through the seasons.

The bird's beak and tongue are inserted into the mound to keep a close check on temperature changes. In some related species in the mountains of New Guinea, the bare skin on the head is thought to be used to monitor temperature. Temperature testing is important at the moment the female lays her eggs. The surface temperature of a mound might be, say 15–19°C, while that deep inside might be 40–60°C. The female checks the temperature of a nest-hole before laying, and only deposits her egg at a depth where the temperature is 33–34°C.

In the spring the male opens the mound in the early morning in order to let heat escape; in the summer, when soil temperature can reach 60°C, he scrapes on sand to protect the eggs from the vicious heat of the midday sun; and in autumn, when the sun's rays are weakening and the rotting process is declining, he will spread out sand to warm it up before scraping it back onto the heap. All the work is done with his big feet and the mallee fowl male is a tough bird. Two naturalists studying mound building once saw a 1-kilogram male shifting a 7-kilogram boulder. Another scientist found that it took him half an hour with a large shovel to dig a hole that the mallee dug with his feet in just an hour and a half.

Like the 'big-foots' of Savo, the mallee fowl's young scratch themselves free of the nest mound and are self-sufficient from the word go. Each egg takes forty to ninety-six days to hatch and, as eggs are laid a week or so apart, the chicks emerge as if from an assembly line. Each must dig itself free, struggling through 60 centimetres of mound before emerging. There is no further parental care. Indeed, on one occasion, a male mallee fowl was seen digging a nest hole in which his partner was to deposit an egg, when he uncovered one of his emerging young. The chick was kicked out of the way like a stone. It survived, however, and, in a rather dazed state, crawled past its mother, which ignored it, and then crept away to start its life in the scrub.

Why mallee fowls and their relatives should embark on such a complicated breeding cycle is a mystery. Chick survival is not enhanced particularly. They do no worse or no better than birds from conventional nests. Many eggs fail to hatch because they are at the wrong temperature, some chicks succumb while trying to dig out, particularly in the hot summer, and there are many nest predators, ranging from foxes to large monitor lizards. This has led to some bizarre sights. One researcher on the Indonesian island of Komodo witnessed a Komodo dragon digging into a mound in search of eggs while the male megapode was feverishly scraping up sand to fill in the hole. As fast as the lizard dug the hole, the bird filled it in.

Although the mallee fowl's method of nest building and incubation appears advanced and sophisticated, it is, in reality, based on a more primitive reptilian system. Many reptiles have underground nests, lengthy incubation periods and precocious young that receive little or no parental care after hatching. So have megapodes developed mound building as a secondary nesting strategy from normal nesting birds or are they, perhaps, a throwback to that ancient dinosaurian past?

THE EGG

Once a mate has been found and a nest constructed or dug, a bird can prepare for egg-laying. The female may store sperm after mating for several hours or sometimes several days. The egg is basically a fertilized ovum surrounded by a protective coat. All the materials necessary for the developing embryo must be placed inside before the egg is complete.

The yolk is laid down in concentric layers. The quantity varies from species to species – 50 per cent in ducks and as little as 15 per cent in cormorants. The white-shelled kiwi egg contains 61 per cent yolk. The cells that will form the embryo sit on top of the yolk. The albumen surrounds the yolk and is also in four concentric layers, the inner layer of which forms the chalaza, a system of supporting structures that stabilize the position of the yolk and developing embryo.

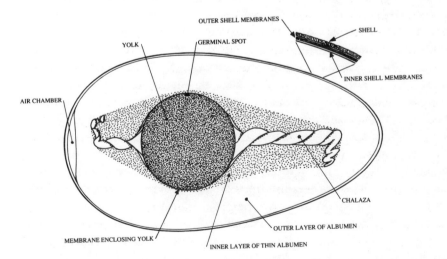

Cross-section of a bird's egg.

Birds deposit hard-shelled, calcified eggs with a surface pitted with microscopic pores to allow for the respiratory exchange of oxygen, carbon dioxide and water. Shell thickness varies. Fast-hatching eggs, like those of the pigeon, are generally thin-shelled. Birds like francolins have thick-shelled eggs. Up to 30 per cent of the egg's weight is in the shell. The megapodes have surprisingly thin-shelled eggs. If they were thicker the chick would be unable to escape. Indeed, if birds in general produced eggs with shells that were too thick then the chick inside would be unable to break free. Hence, some eggs are thick at one end and thin at the other. A guillemot egg, for instance, has a thick pointed end which lies in contact with the rocky nesting ledge and a thin rounded end that allows the chick to emerge.

Tragically, birds with thicker-shelled eggs are particularly vulnerable to the insidious effects of agricultural chemicals. Many persistent pesticides – such as DDT – reduce a bird's ability to metabolize the calcium essential for egg shells. At the top of the food chain, where it can accumulate vast quantities of pesticides which have built up in the body fats of animals in the chain, the peregrine falcon may eat dangerously high levels of poisons. The result is egg shell thinning; the eggs crack open part way through incubation and the embryos die. It was a crash in peregrine populations in Europe and then in North America that first alerted the world to the dangers of pesticides, and that story continues.

Although peregrines inland have benefited from a ban on many persistent pesticides and their populations are recovering, those living by the sea are only just beginning to suffer. Chemicals like DDT, for instance, were banned many years ago. But those washed all that time ago via streams and rivers into the sea are only now working their way up through the marine food chain. Today's coastal peregrines are in danger from chemicals that were thought not to be around anymore.

A similar and even more insidious problem is now coming to light in the forests of northern Europe where the soils are poor in nutrients. Acid rain is reducing the ability of trees to take up calcium. Caterpillars feeding on their leaves have reduced calcium levels and, in turn, so too have the great tits and other insectivorous creatures feeding on them. The outcome is that these birds are laying calcium-deficient, thin-shelled eggs, and, as with DDT, they are prone to rupture prematurely.

It seems odd that after so many years of industrialization and pollution this problem should suddenly emerge, but it may have taken this long for the calcium levels in the poorest soils to become exhausted. The dipper, a bird which walks underwater on stream beds to hunt invertebrates, shows a similar problem. On the nutrient-poor Welsh soils, acidification is affecting dipper egg shells via their leaf-eating, aquatic prey.

For those birds unaffected as yet by pollution, embryo development can continue unabated. Inside the egg, this is facilitated by an air chamber which acts as a lung. The embryo can draw oxygen from this air space and pass carbon dioxide back into it. These are then exchanged with the air outside through the pores in the shell. Food is obtained from the nutrient-rich yolk.

Egg shapes vary according to a bird's lifestyle. Owls and kingfishers lay the most rounded eggs, while hummingbirds, swifts and swallows lay long, elliptical eggs. Pear-shaped eggs are normally deposited in clutches of four. The eggs being arranged so that the points face inwards, they can be densely packed in the nest to reduce heat loss, and this also reduces the external diameter of the clutch to be incubated. Seabirds nesting on ledges also tend to have eggs pointed at one end. If bumped accidentally, they roll in a circle, which may help save them from falling over the cliff.

Birds' eggs, unlike the white eggs of reptiles, can be almost any colour and pattern. Some are plain, like those of ducks, while others are blotched, and there are two levels of colour. Colours deep in the shell are laid down at an early stage during the shell's production when it is high in the female's oviduct. Surface colours and patterns are deposited at the cloacal end of the reproductive tract. The colours are produced from blood pigments and bile. Iron-based compounds, such as those in haemoglobin, the oxygen-carrying compound in the blood, produce red-brown colours. Copper-based compounds from the bile result in blues and greens. On the iron-rich red laterite soils of southern India and Australia, local birds frequently lay red eggs. Herring gulls are particularly susceptible to these variations derived from the ground on which the birds live.

Spotting, blotching and speckling are dependent partly upon the pressure applied to an egg as it passes down the oviduct. Spotted patterns are produced when the egg is held still. If pigments are added while it is on the move, streaked patterns are formed. Ground-nesting birds have particular patterns that match the ground on which they are deposited. On the burned ash soils of

Senegal, for example, the plover-like Temminck's courser produces almost black, perfectly camouflaged eggs. On other soils the birds lay sandy fawn-coloured eggs. Within a given family, birds' eggs often show this adaptive coloration which relates to the conditions at the nest site. The eggs of tree nesters have large blotches to mimic leaf shadows. Crevice nesters have plain blue or speckled eggs. Some eggs laid in scrapes on the ground, like those of some plovers, are so well camouflaged that they are virtually invisible.

Guillemots probably have the most variability in egg colour and pattern. Each bird lays its pear-shaped egg with a distinctive pattern that it can easily recognize when returning to the nesting ledge. Other colonial nesters, such as grackles and weaver birds, have a similar adaptation. The great-tailed grackle, living in the crowded coconut palm colonies of Central America, is thought to recognize its own eggs by the distinctive individual pattern on its egg shells.

White eggs tend to be produced by the more primitive species of birds – cormorants, pelicans and albatrosses. And hole-nesters, in danger of trampling unseen objects, usually lay conspicuous white eggs. White eggs laid in open nests by owls and grebes are usually covered up with nest-lining material when the parents leave the nest.

Just as body size varies from species to species, so does egg size. The minute bee hummingbird has a 0.3-gram egg, while the ostrich has eggs weighing 1.6 kilograms each. Interestingly, this represents an investment of 25 per cent of the hummingbird's weight but only 1 per cent of that of the ostrich. The largest egg relative to body size is that of the New Zealand kiwi. The single gigantic egg is a third the weight of the female carrying it.

Egg size in birds of a similar size, however, can be variable. Doves, some cuckoos, falcons and shearwaters weigh roughly the same – about 100 grams, yet their eggs are widely different. The cuckoo lays 4.5-gram eggs, the dove 6-gram, the falcon 15-gram and the shearwater 21-gram. Egg size relates to the habits of the chicks. Precocial chicks must be sufficiently well developed on hatching to fend for themselves. Such species tend to produce larger eggs with a larger volume of yolk, about 35 per cent of total egg volume. Atricial species tend to produce smaller eggs containing only 20 per cent of yolk.

Cuckoos produce very small eggs relative to their body size because the eggs must be accepted into the nests of very much smaller birds. The host birds would reject inappropriately large eggs, so evolution favours the cuckoo producing eggs the same size as the host's.

A female producing smaller eggs reduces the amount of energy she uses and reduces the risk of predation when she is heavy with eggs. A hen bird with unlaid eggs carries roughly 10 per cent more body weight. This reduces her speed and manoeuvrability in flight. To reduce the threat of predation, therefore, it is important for her to lay as soon as possible after fertilization.

When a female does came to lay, the eggs of one female may be a different size from those of another, even though the two birds are of the same species. Experienced females produce larger eggs than first-time breeders, but very old hens revert to laying smaller eggs. Egg size is related partly to female size, so fit, healthy females produce large, healthy eggs. This ability to produce top-rate eggs is passed on genetically to the offspring. But if food supplies are low at the critical egg formation period, smaller eggs would result. Smaller eggs are less successful at producing viable fledglings, so in order to avoid this scenario most birds are able to vary their clutch size. When times are hard, fewer eggs are laid. Some birds, though, do not have this luxury – the Manx shearwater, for example, has only one egg each season. Instead, if food supplies are down, the bird takes longer to produce its single egg. European swifts do both. They depend on good conditions to catch sufficient flying insects, and during a bout of sunny weather will normally lay three eggs at two-day intervals. In bad weather they produce only two eggs, three to four days apart.

Female birds have a limited amount of energy to invest in producing eggs and they may adopt a variety of ways in which to vary the number and weight of the eggs laid. In spring, house martins, like swifts, depend on good weather. Foul weather might make it impossible for a female to find sufficient flying insect food and she will lay small eggs. In 'boom' years her large eggs give the chicks a good start in life and most survive to fledge. In 'bust' years, the smaller eggs may result in her losing the entire brood. Some bird species avoid this by hedging their bets. Most of their eggs are of normal or near-normal size, but the last one laid is smaller.

Herons and gulls, with unpredictable food supplies, adopt the small-last-egg strategy. Herring gulls on the Isle of May, off Scotland's west coast, have been found habitually to lay two large eggs and one small one. Two advantages have been proposed. Firstly, the two large eggs assure that the chicks have a good start at hatching. The two chicks from these eggs should fledge successfully. If the resources are spread evenly between three eggs, there might be insufficient to give the chicks a good start and the entire brood would later perish. The small egg is a kind of insurance policy. Its sacrifice enables its siblings to gain sufficient resources to fledge successfully during a bad season. Only under extraordinarily good conditions will the runt survive, providing the parents with a bonus.

Secondly, the small egg is used as a diversionary tactic. It is less well camouflaged with speckles and is therefore more obvious to predators. Herring gulls are powerful birds and it would benefit a nest thief to make off with the smallest, most obvious egg rather than risk an attack trying to make away with the larger eggs. Interestingly, if the first egg is experimentally removed immediately after laying, the gull will produce two more large eggs and a small fourth egg. The experiment shows that the bird is actually quite capable of producing three large eggs, but 'chooses' to lay its third egg as a small one to reduce the effects of predation on the rest of the brood.

Coots use a different strategy to achieve the same goal. Females lay a graded series of progressively smaller eggs. The size of the chicks and their ability to compete and survive are therefore also graded. So, if food is particularly scarce, the first chick alone will secure enough to live. With increasing abundance the second, third and sometimes some of the smaller chicks get a look in and make it to adulthood. The parent bird's strategy guarantees the survival of the greatest number of her offspring that the unpredictable season can support.

Some birds take the sacrificial route to extremes. Snares Island crested penguins and macaroni penguins lay a first egg that is not incubated. It is 42 per cent smaller than their second egg. If the second egg hatches, the first egg is ignored. If, however, the second egg fails to hatch or is attacked and broken open by predators, the penguin returns to the first egg and incubates that. Bird eggs are viable for many days before the onset of incubation, so despite being ignored at first, the first egg – predators and frosts aside – can still develop normally.

Optimal clutch size for a species has evolved to yield the greatest number of surviving young during the course of the parent's lifetime. Small birds are short-lived and produce a relatively high clutch weight. Some finches have clutch weights equalling or even exceeding the female's body weight. Egg production can be quite exhausting. Parents of these large broods need to work incessantly to provide sufficient food at the nest. They die from exhaustion, increased predation and because they are less able to lay down fat reserves for the moult and for winter survival. Long-lived raptors and ostriches, on the other hand, will survive to breed for decades. In order to be in good condition for the next breeding season, it is important that these females do not use up too much energy in producing any one clutch.

If a brood is too large, particularly those with altricial chicks needing much care and attention, it would be difficult for parents to keep them well fed. The number of chicks fledging and the weight of those fledglings would be reduced, and low-weight fledglings have a reduced chance of survival – they are less able to evade predators and obtain their own food, and have no body reserves to tide them through lean periods. So birds with small clutches ensure their chicks' survival by feeding them up, and small clutches tend then to contain heavier offspring than large clutches.

Large clutches are also more obvious. This is important for precocial birds, like ducks, geese and curlews. In effect, the parents of these birds do not have to find food for their relatively independent offspring and, in theory, could therefore lay very large clutches. They don't. Smaller clutches suffer reduced predation and so are more successful.

Clutch size is also related not unexpectedly to the condition of the female. This is influenced not only by events on the actual breeding grounds but also by conditions months previously. This is especially so in large geese which take a long time to gain or lose weight. Summer breeding ability is determined, to some extent, by winter feeding success or failure. Lesser snow geese, for example, must fly from their winter feeding grounds in the southern parts of North America to the high Arctic to breed. The summer thaw is so brief that the birds must arrive at the nest sites, nest and start incubation before the winter's snow has even melted. Feeding is impossible, so birds must rely totally on the fat deposits built up over the winter months whilst they court, build, mate and breed.

Experiments have been carried out involving the supplementary feeding of these geese at the start of the breeding season. Birds receiving the additional food did not lay any more eggs but did start to lay earlier. This seemed to show that the parent birds are more interested in the number of chicks that they can care for than in the number of eggs they are capable of producing.

Birds, apart from those consistently laying a single egg, rarely lay a fixed number. They usually have a range for the species. The quality of the parents' territory and their ability to acquire food determines where an individual will fall within that range. Female great tits which are better at finding food not surprisingly lay more eggs and produce more fledglings than do less able birds. In experiments, if able and less able birds are given large broods, the able females raise more chicks than less able ones. It follows then that hen birds laying large clutches are those birds most able to raise young.

Territory quality can be measured by the number of successfully fledged young it produces each season. Birds fight to hold territories, but will sometimes continue to fight to obtain better ones. Magpies produce larger clutches in high quality territories, where previous pairs raised more young, than they do in territories with historically poor performances. A comparison of territorial breeding records shows that large clutches in good territories produce more surviving offspring than do smaller clutches.

With so many factors influencing egg laying, clutch sizes can vary enormously from group to group. Petrels, shearwaters and albatrosses have a single egg. At the other end of the scale, the European grey partridges of Ostrobothnia in Finland regularly have a record-breaking clutch of nineteen eggs. One hen bird in Sussex in 1974 had twenty-five eggs of which twenty-four hatched and all chicks were alive at six weeks old. The bobwhite quail has been reported to have up to twenty-eight eggs at a time, but this is unusual, the average is more usually eight to fifteen.

Hole-nesters produce more eggs than their more vulnerable open-nest relatives. Blue tits that have taken to nest-boxes in Europe produce an average of eleven or twelve eggs per season with nineteen in exceptional years. Those laid early in the season tend to be larger than those deposited later. The birds take advantage of an abundance of food earlier in the year.

Some large clutches are due not to the activities of the parent birds but to the sneaky behaviour of the neighbours who go 'dump-nesting'. Several females, deprived of suitable nest sites, might lay in the same nest. This sometimes happens with ducks and gamebirds, and the resident birds will sometimes attempt to incubate their enlarged egg collection. Some redheads from North America practise nest parasitism while others don't. Some lay some eggs in another's nest and then go on to rear some more in a normal way. One North American redhead was visited by so many of her neighbours that she eventually had a nest filled with eighty-seven eggs.

The ostriches of Tsavo in Kenya dump eggs in each others' nests. A breeding pair might incubate the eggs of several females, the male bird taking the night shift and the female sitting by day. During the day, the male is able to mate with several solitary females, but for their genes to have any chance of immortality they must be deposited in the nest of the main breeding pair. The breeding pair, however, also put some of their eggs in the nests of other pairs, and the tactic pays off. By laying in the nest of another, at least some offspring are assured survival, especially if the mother's own nest is raided. But she can comfortably sit on twenty or so eggs and only lay about eleven in her own nest. By taking in the eggs of others she dilutes the chances of her eggs being attacked. The insurance policy is important, as seven out of eight nests are destroyed each year.

Also, the ostrich produces an egg every two days. A normal clutch of twenty would take thirty-nine days to complete and the first to be laid would be cooking in the sun. By laying in other nests and accepting the eggs of others into her nest she ensures that the clutches are built up more quickly.

The pair, however, don't just accept the regulation twenty; the two breeding birds might gather thirty or more. Twenty of them are selected, including the main female's own eggs – no mean task as they are seemingly identical – and they are placed centrally to gain maximum benefit from incubation. The rest are placed in a ring around the edge of the nest, an insurance against sneaky nest predators.

Clutch size is also dependent upon the part of the world in which a bird builds its nest and the type of terrain. Island birds typically lay fewer eggs than mainland birds. Islands tend to have more birds packed into a smaller area than on the mainland. Even large islands the size of Great Britain appear to influence clutch size. Little owls were introduced from Continental Europe in 1840 and initially their clutch size was maintained as before. But now, 150 years later, British owls produce significantly smaller clutches.

Nests in the tropics contain fewer eggs than those nearer the poles. The tropics are regarded as more stable environments, with predictably low rates of mortality. Every available ecological niche tends to be permanently occupied and so populations of animals are said to be 'saturated', that is, they are very close to the limit of available food. Parents, then, need to produce fewer young. If they produced more they would outgrow the niche and probably die out. In the Arctic, say, where relatively few birds arrive to breed each spring, there is abundant food. Arctic breeders therefore produce large broods.

On the tropical savannah, however, conditions are not unlike the tundra. Few birds can be supported in the dry season, but come the rains there is a sudden superabundance of food. Savannah birds, then, living in low densities, also produce large clutches. If the population density increases food supplies and available territories shrink, so birds there produce smaller broods or even fail to breed at all. In these situations birds which might otherwise have bred may opt out and help their parents nest instead.

If prey is scarce, entire populations of raptors may fail to nest. Flamingos too may not breed for two or three consecutive seasons. The reason for this abstention is unclear. On high-altitude saline lakes in South America, lesser flamingos sometimes forego breeding, even when the food supply is adequate. But this luxury is largely confined to large, long-lived birds like flamingos and raptors which can afford to maintain their body weight for future breeding attempts.

To beat the fact that clutches have an optimum size beyond which success actually decreases, some birds have adopted yet another strategy. Reproductive rates *can* be increased by having more than one clutch per season. Most species of birds attempt just one brood a year, but certain short-lived species will have a go at more. Zebra finches in Australia can continue to produce further broods as long as there is an adequate food supply to support them. In captivity some have been known to raise twenty-one consecutive broods. In the wild, old and experienced blackbirds do well, often raising seventeen youngsters from four broods each containing four to five eggs. The moorhen is another prolific breeder with two to three broods each with five to eleven young in a good year. Red-legged partridges succeed by the male and female raising broods at the same time.

The time spent actually laying the egg or eggs can be different depending on the circumstances. Cuckoos, which have to be in and out of a host's nest as quickly as possible, lay their egg within seconds. Most birds take just a few minutes. Turkeys and geese take up to two hours. Songbirds lay at dawn, while doves lay in the early afternoon. The interval between first and second eggs can be anything from a day, which is most common, to three days amongst raptors. The masked booby has a seven-day interval between laying its two eggs, and the kiwi may take up to thirty-three days between eggs.

There is some evidence that the sex of the offspring can be chosen by the mother. In lesser snow geese, goslings hatched from the first two eggs are inevitably male. The larger male goslings are more costly in food terms and therefore are given a head start. In ring-billed gulls, the ratio is similar as long as food is plentiful. The first egg is male, the second female and the runt egg can be either. But if food is scarce the reverse happens and females are preferred.

Having created such a miraculous thing as an egg, a parent bird must then look after it. Eggs must be kept warm and safe from nest predators. To do this birds have developed different incubating methods.

The majority of birds do not start incubating until the last egg has been laid. This ensures that the brood hatches at the same time, and that no chick exploits an advantage over its siblings. If the food supply is good, then the whole brood will be raised successfully. If the food dries up, however, then with each chick being fed at the same rate, the entire batch could perish. Some birds avoid this predicament by incubating eggs as they are laid. The first out of the egg is fed well and becomes stronger than its later hatching siblings. The second in line is second in the pecking order and so on, until a point is reached where there might be insufficient food for late-hatched chicks and they starve.

This 'Cain and Abel' approach is exemplified by large raptors. The first to hatch is invariably the only one to fledge. It not only consumes most of the food brought by the parents, allowing its less able brother or sister only scraps and leftovers, but also it frequently prevents the sibling from feeding altogether. This may even result in murder in the nest. Egret chicks stab their younger brothers and sisters to death, baby eagles sit on and suffocate their weaker siblings, hawks and owls tear at each other with their bills and cliff-nesting birds push their close relatives over the edge. Sibling rivalry can be pretty extreme, and the parents just stand by and do nothing as this fratricide or 'cainism' carries on right beneath their beaks. The reason is that when times are hard a parent would rather one bird survived to perpetuate its genes and so they leave the birds to reduce the brood size themselves. The strongest wins and lives. This is facilitated by the mother laying the eggs asynchronously so that one chick is inevitably ahead of the others. In many raptor nests, the eventual death of the second chick is almost a foregone conclusion. Why then produce it?

Again, this is a form of insurance. The first egg might fail, be eaten by predators, trampled by clumsy parents or yield a sickly chick. In these circumstances the second chick is standing by to assume the dominant position in the nest. Bee-eaters tend to have a reserve chick stuffed away in their breeding burrow. If an eagle or snake invades the tunnel it will probably take the fat dominant chick. If this happens the runt of the nest takes over. It is fed well and grows normally, seemingly unaffected by the trauma it went through during its early chickhood.

Birds like great tits rely on a combination of tactics to ensure success. The first clutch, early in the season, is hatched synchronously. This is the time of peak caterpillar abundance and the entire brood feeds well. Hatching of eggs in later clutches is staggered. Late in the season, food resources are less predictable, so the parents play safe with asynchronous hatching.

Brooding birds, both male and female, develop a featherless 'brood patch' to warm incubating eggs. Feathers are lost from under the belly, the skin thickens and extra blood vessels keep the exposed skin very warm. Some birds have a single large patch, while others develop several small patches, one for each egg.

The sitting time varies from less than an hour at a stretch in many passerines to the uninterrupted sixty-four-day stint of the emperor penguin. And the total incubation period can be as little as eleven days in some small finches, up to a maximum of eighty days in the wandering albatross. On average a doubling of egg weight lengthens the incubation period by 16 per cent.

As incubation progresses, the embryo develops the ability to produce significant amounts of its own heat and can be safely left for longer periods; that is, if it is not an emperor penguin egg in the middle of the Antarctic winter! Incubation temperatures vary at 34–39°C, although about 75 per cent of bird species aim to have a constant temperature of 35°C.

Temperature control is difficult to maintain in a hot desert, but the Egyptian plover has developed a novel approach. The clutch of two to three eggs is covered by sand. During the night when the temperature drops somewhat, the eggs are partially uncovered and one of the parents sits on the eggs incubating them with the heat of its body. At dawn they are reburied and left. About three hours after sunrise the temperature rises dramatically and the parents return to the nest. Taking turns, they sit on the eggs, but every now and again the bird on duty jumps up, kicks sand over the eggs and heads for the river. There it wets its belly feathers and returns to the nest. The bird settles and soaks the sand with the water. The water cools the eggs.

During incubation eggs lose about 15 per cent of their weight through water loss. Parent birds move and roll eggs to prevent the embryo inside sticking and to counteract any temperature fluctuations within the nest. After turning, the embryo normally resettles itself across the width of the egg. When it is ready to hatch it presents itself longways.

THE CHICK

The embryo moves inside the egg. It turns longways so that it can pierce the airspace with its bill. It switches from obtaining oxygen from the amniotic fluid to breathing air. Like reptiles, most bird embryos use an egg tooth, a thorn-like projection on the upper bill which is used to pierce the egg shell. But there are a variety of ways in which the chicks of different species arrange themselves in order to push themselves out.

The most common is known as 'symmetrical' hatching and it is done in three phases. Firstly, the chick chips a circular cap. Secondly, it moves its shoulders and chest to push against the cap, and finally, it twists its body leftwards in the shell and uses its legs and wings to push through the hole. Chickens, blackbirds, geese, ducks and several species of owls use this way. Ostriches also rotate in the shell but not as much as the others, usually less than 90 degrees.

Then there are the 'asymmetrical' hatchers, the ones, like oyster-catchers, avocets and lapwings, which have long beaks. They rotate very little in the egg; instead they push hard against the chipped hole, enlarging it to an irregular shape.

A third style of hatching is reserved for the megapodes. The chicks do not chip away at the inside of the egg at all. They stretch and tear at the shell with their claws, whilst rotating at the same time. In this way they clear enough space above the egg to be able to raise their heads and begin to escape from the mound.

While most chicks hatch unaided, eastern bluebird chicks and those of a few other species receive some assistance from the parents. Barn owl parents also help their chicks escape the egg.

On hatching, the wet ball of skin and soggy down soon dries. Extreme precocial birds are immediately independent. Scrub fowl chicks, having endured several hours of battling with ants on their way out of the mound, get their own back as they start to probe for insects in the dense undergrowth in which they hide. They are unguarded by either parent, and left to fend totally for themselves.

Having invested so much energy and time in their offspring, however, most birds do not leave things to chance and continue to care for their young.

Right from the moment they hatch, baby birds draw attention to themselves. They leave evidence, which if left for long will surely place the hatchlings in danger. The white, reflective inside surface of an egg shell is a beacon for nest predators. Studies of barbary doves have also shown that unremoved shells might cover unhatched eggs and prevent chicks from emerging. So parent birds are fastidious in removing broken pieces of shell.

Faeces are also regularly removed. Good nest hygiene reduces attention from predators. Passerine chicks produce faeces contained in a mucilage envelope for easy disposal or even to be eaten by the parents. Chicks produce faeces soon after they are fed, so parents often wait at the nest for them to lift their tails in order that the little package may be collected and removed. Some parents seem so obsessed with their offspring's bodily functions that they peck at a chick's vent to stimulate egestion. Faeces, by its very colour, can be spotted by predators, so some birds go to great lengths to ensure it is far from the nest. Swallows and martins often fly several hundred metres to drop the faeces over water. The female lyrebird from Australia either digs a hole and buries it or submerges the droppings under a stream bed.

As they get older, chicks become better toilet trained. Faecal sacs may be deposited on the side of the nest for collection or voided directly over the side. Baby kingfishers develop the remarkable ability to shoot liquid faeces at high speed and with some accuracy through the narrow tunnel entrance. Nightjar and Montagu's harrier chicks move out of the nest and along a branch to relieve themselves, but many species of heron chicks simply defecate into the bottom of the nest, where the liquid goo drips through the collection of rough sticks. Some scientists believe this might have some cooling effect in the nest, but it might simply be that herons –

as we shall see – are not that fussy about their daily bowel habits.

Spilled food can also be a bit of a problem for scraps can give rise to bacteria and disease. But the gannets of New Zealand's Poor Knights Island have little helpers. Tiny lizards, clambering around the nest site, pick up the debris spilled from the beaks of young gannets as they are fed.

Nest hygiene is important, particularly among animals nesting gregariously. It is easy in a colony for blood parasites to be taken from one nest to the next and, once in place, they can remain active for a long time. Bugs like the bloodsucking *Oeciacus vicarius* can survive in an unused nest for three years or more. They account for almost all the deaths of nestlings of some species of birds, such as cliff swallows in North America.

The nests of swallows, martins and swifts are notorious amongst bird nests for their high ectoparasite populations. Two entire families of specialist lice-like flies feed on the birds' blood, whilst their maggots feed on skin fragments and chicks' blood. The adult flies deposit light-sensitive, explosively capped eggs on the rim of the nest. When an egg is momentarily shaded, it explodes its larva in the direction of the arriving bird. In this way the parasites are able to disperse their larvae quickly to any birds visiting the nest. In badly infected nests, a dozen or more parasites can be released each time a bird lands.

Cliff swallows nest in colonies and they have a big bug problem. And the bigger the colony the bigger the bug population in each nest. Unfortunately the more bugs in a nest the more weight a nestling loses each night when the bugs bite. A ten-day-old nestling, from a nest in a large colony, loses about a sixth of its body weight to blood-suckers, and only half the normal number of youngsters survive at all.

The cliff swallow's answer to this is to be careful in selecting a nest at the beginning of the season. Heavily infested nests are avoided, and if all the nests in a colony are bad, the colony moves elsewhere. Swallows will tend to build new nests rather than move into an infested one, and this gives the parents a head start of one or two weeks on the parasites.

Starlings have another solution: every day or so they continue to provision their nests with fresh plant material. The plants have no structural or insulatory value but only a few species are chosen. Investigations have revealed that all the plants incorporated into nests have similar properties. Starlings, for example, pick madder, chrysanthemum, asters and other plants which produce volatile compounds that kill or deter insects. The birds have a specially developed sense of smell which enables them to identify plants with insecticidal properties.

Cold is another killer. Both altricial and precocial birds need to be kept warm for several days after hatching. Parental brooding is important for, as yet, they are unable to maintain body temperature adequately. Large broods require less brooding as the many bodies conserve heat more efficiently. Hole-nesters or those species in covered nests are similarly at an advantage. Parent birds, though, do not know instinctively when to brood, and nestlings must trigger their parents to get brooding.

Rain can bring a fatal chill to very young birds, so the parents of even precocial chicks use their bodies and outstretched wings to shelter their offspring during a shower. Birds like swifts and swallows, though, must leave their chicks alone in the nest in order to maximize their food-collecting abilities. Their chicks, sheltered from the rain in a semi-enclosed nest, are none the less prone to chilling. Swift chicks, therefore, conserve fat reserves by remaining torpid until their parents return. Whereas most chicks would die without daily feeding, swifts can survive for a week or longer.

Overheating can be as serious as chilling. Out in the open, raptors shade exposed nestlings with their wings. Some tropical terns dip their breast feathers into the sea in order to give their chicks a cool sponge on their return. True to form, herons have their own cooling solution. They defecate over their overheated offspring and cool them by evaporation.

For chicks brought up in the safety of hot deserts, not only is heat a problem but also the lack of water nearby. The male sandgrouse overcomes this problem by flying to a waterhole, immersing its belly feathers in the water, and then carrying it like a wet sponge back to the young in the nest. The returning bird stands near the nest site where the female shelters her little ones from the sun, and the chicks run out to drink from the wet feathers. The feathers themselves are specialized to carry water with the minimum of evaporation, and the bird can fly over 18 miles without any significant loss of the water it is transporting.

One of the more obvious reasons for chicks not growing up, though, is predation. Skuas, gulls and caracaras patrol the seabird colonies of sub-Antarctic islands waiting for an opportunity to strike. A careless parent will soon lose its offspring. On the tropical island of Fiji, ground-nesting brown boobies must contend with the local land-living hermit crabs. Worldwide, chicks are helpless and vulnerable and parents must play a major role in protecting them. The first line of defence is the alarm call (see pages 153–7). On hearing this, chicks freeze, making them less obvious to predators. Egyptian plover parents help disguise their chicks by throwing sand over them.

Some waterfowl can carry their young to safety. Grebe chicks can ride on their mother's back. The male lilytrotter gathers his brood up under his wings, the only sign that they are hiding there being their spindly feet sticking out from underneath. The woodcock improves on this and can hold its chick securely between the legs and body, even while flying. The American finfoot has specially hollowed pockets of skin under each wing. The chicks dash to the pockets when danger threatens and they can be swum or flown to safety. Less sophisticated carriers like some hawks and moorhens carry their chicks in their feet. Some African rails simply carry their chicks in their beaks and walk sedately away.

Most birds cannot transport their brood and must rely on other ways to stay clear of trouble. Subterfuge is popular. Hole-nesters rely on concealment and may resort to some clever vocal tricks. A predator outside a nest-hole is unable to see what is inside, so if the chick can hiss the predator might leave its examination of the 'snake' until later.

The long-legged, 23-centimetres-tall, American burrowing owl nests in burrows abandoned by rodents and can hiss like a rattlesnake. To test its effectiveness researchers took one group of ground squirrels from areas frequented by rattlesnakes and another group which rarely encountered them. In the laboratory, the squirrels were presented with an artificial burrow in which was placed a loudspeaker. The playback included real rattlesnake rattles, the mimicry hiss of the owl and some control sounds. The squirrels unaccustomed to rattlers were cautious about all sounds. Those familiar with the snakes responded more strongly to both the rattle and the hiss. And if the ground squirrels were alarmed at the way the owls could mimic an agitated rattlesnake, then it was reckoned that the owl's predators would be equally effectively deceived. It was thought that weasels and coyotes, both of which put owl chicks on the menu, would be reluctant to tangle with a rattler and avoid burrows in which they thought the snake might be.

This behaviour gave rise to an owl myth. Pioneers, opening up the west of North America, were convinced that the owls shared their burrows with rattlesnakes, for each time an inquisitive human bent down to inspect a burrow the owl gave its lifelike imitation and the startled person withdrew immediately.

Distraction displays also work. The parent bird is usually alone and a ground-nester. The eggs and youngsters tend to be well camouflaged, with speckled egg-shell colour or plumage blending in with background rocks and vegetation. The display works if the parent bird makes itself very conspicuous by calling and flashing white patches of feathers and is able to lure the predator away. Some birds, such as the African courser and the ringed plover, feign injuries, flapping about on the ground as if crippled and unable to fly. But each time the predator gets close, the bird is just out of reach. A broken wing trailing on the ground is an effective way in which to entice a hungry fox, and birds have been known to lead predators to over a mile from the nest site. When the bird considers its offspring safe, it miraculously recovers and flies away, leaving an exhausted and confused predator behind.

The display itself is thought to be an evolutionary compromise between a bird's wanting to flee a predator and at the same time wanting to defend its nest, and it has been honed into an effective display by natural selection. Other distraction displays include the 'rodent run' in which some waders imitate the hurried movements of small rodents and attract both aerial and ground predators away from the nest.

Gregarious birds are more up-front. They rely on group attacks and mobbing, and a flock of gulls, terns or skuas can be quite determined, using their sharp bills to draw blood from the exposed head of a human interloper. Some solitary pairs can be just as determined – hen harrier parents will harass any animal or person approaching a nest, diving fast and close at eye-level whilst calling with a harsh 'yikkering' call.

During dive attacks birds can also bring in their main weapon – defecation. European fieldfares are masters of the faecal blitzkreig, and some attacks have been so overwhelming that the intruder has suffocated and died under a blanket of guano. Roosting herons can be relied upon to do what seems to come naturally to herons. Scientists studying crocodiles at night report 'faecal rain', from the disturbed heronries overhead, as an occupational hazard!

Some chicks have their own effective methods of defence. Fulmar chicks can squirt a disgusting, foul-smelling regurgitated fishy oil into the face of an unwelcome visitor, whilst young hoopoes anoint guests with a secretion from special garlic-scented odour glands.

In South America, seriemas normally run about in scrubland but they have nests about 3 metres off the ground. The chicks, covered in brown down, happily remain in their open tree nest until it is time to fledge; that is, if they are not disturbed. If danger threatens, then as one they jump out of the nest and dash into the tall grass to hide. They start their ground-dwelling life prematurely, but the parents, unperturbed by the change of plans, herd the brood together and continue to feed and protect them albeit at ground level.

Precocial chicks, whilst able to feed themselves, are still dependent on their parents for defence. Indeed, the survival of Canada goose goslings has been demonstrated to be directly related to the size of the gander protecting them. And although parents of precocial chicks might not provide food directly, in many species they do guide their brood to where the pickings are rich or dredge up deep-water foods from the bottom of the lake.

Another form of defence is to gather young birds together in a crèche. Eider and shelduck chicks are vulnerable to skua and large-gull predation and so parents improve their guarding capability, yet reduce the parental investment in protecting their offspring, by gathering their broods together. Parents may gather together several broods to form crèches totalling dozens of ducklings. The edges of this floating mat of youngsters are patrolled by several of the parents, aided by successful aunts and sisters. Old, experienced but non-breeding hens as well as immature birds might also help. The parents can then spend more time away from the kids and replace spent fat stores. Without these crèche facilities, the parent would not be able to gain weight quickly and would be forced to breed late in the following season. Pelicans, flamingos, penguins and some terns rely on crèches in order that parents can recharge their batteries.

By contrast, female willow grouse are quite capable of raising their precocial brood unaided. Yet the male grouse hangs around, attending to the daily chores and trying to be useful. If he finds another mate, his original hen couldn't be bothered; she just gets on with life and the chicks do just as well. If, then, the cock's contribution is superfluous, why does he do it? Males experimentally left to look after the family are a disaster, so why do they expend all this energy helping the hen? The answer is as yet a mystery.

FAMILY HELPERS

Breeding goes well if food is plentiful, the weather is kind, and the pair of dedicated parents work hard to feed and protect their youngsters. But what happens if things start to go wrong and, say, one parent dies?

When one of a pair of monogamous birds is widowed, a replacement mate is often recruited to help raise the brood. This is true of altricial birds. The new mate, though, is not related to the offspring and, by the simple laws of nature, should not waste its energy on them. Yet he does. If the bird is territorial, it might be that territories are hard to come by. Adoption by a widowed bird virtually guarantees the new mate co-ownership of the territory and with it the ability to breed in the future.

Very young tits are likely to die if one of the parents is lost. After six to eight days chicks can be successfully raised by one parent until they grow to half their maximum bodyweight, but beyond this point, demand outstrips the food the single parent is able to supply and the chicks decline. So, a replacement spouse is recruited from the non-breeding birds waiting on the peripheries of the territory. Permanently widowed birds are likely to lose weight and so may not survive the winter to breed again, so there is a pressure on finding a new mate.

Work with dark-eyed juncos in Indiana, USA, has shown that in order to raise the brood unaided, widows, not unexpectedly, must spend twice as long looking for food. This leaves the nest unattended and exposes the brood to a higher risk of predation. This extreme case suggests to the scientists that the need to provide food competes, even under normal conditions, with the urge to protect the brood. These duties might be segregated between the sexes. Both guillemot parents spend equal time incubating their single egg, but when it hatches it is the more aggressive male which performs the bulk of the nest-guarding duties. The female concentrates on finding food, both for her offspring and her mate. Later it is the male who takes the chick to sea and teaches it to fish. This devotion to his offspring is unusual amongst male birds as a 'father' cannot be entirely certain of the chick's paternity. Rape is not unknown amongst guillemots. The male must be sufficiently assured of his mate-guarding success to believe that the chick is his.

Parental care systems can be very complicated in the avian world, at times reading like a steamy paperback novel or television soap.

White-winged choughs in Australia stoop to kidnapping to secure a childminder. Baby choughs receive a specialist diet of insects that are so scarce that four adults are needed to supply it. The birds live for about ten years and the flock grows slowly. Every fledgling is vital, not only to survive the parents and continue their genes, but also to help with the raising of successive broods. There are never, it seems, enough helpers to go round. In order to overcome this labour shortage, larger families begin to harass smaller ones. At first they destroy their eggs and nests, but at the end of the breeding season things come to a head. The aggression takes the form of exciting display battles, and during the confusion fledglings from the smaller group are coerced into joining the larger group. Alternatively, they are seduced. Adults from the large group will display and preen at young birds from the smaller group and the fledglings are left in no doubts about what very personal favours they might enjoy. The wide-eyed youngsters often succumb and are lured into an exchange of allegiance. As it happens, both parties stand to gain, for although a lost chick is a serious blow to the future reproductive capability of the raided group, the kidnap does benefit both the 'victim' and the recipient flock. The recruit brings new blood into the group in which it will eventually breed. It also provides badly needed assistance, by helping to raise the fastidious chicks. In doing so, however, it is gaining skills it will find essential when it comes to raising its own brood.

The use of helpers by birds that spend their lives together is more widespread than was once thought. The first species to provide ornithologists with new insights into this behaviour was the Florida scrub jay. Jays were observed at the nest where a dominant pair bred but several birds were seen to raise each brood. The scientists thought it odd that the helpers were not raising their own offspring, and the mystery remained for several years until the true picture was finally unravelled.

Scrub jays are territorial birds living in patchy, open scrub. Some territories are more successful than others and birds compete for the better patches. Both parents feed their brood, but they are assisted by several immature birds and young adults. With the support of the helpers, the parents are able to feed and protect their young successfully. Their help also prevents the parents losing bodyweight, so they breed more frequently and can better defend their territory. The territory holders do well from the arrangement, but what of the helpers?

Gradually over the years, as the parentage of the birds was established, it became clear that the helpers are the parent birds' offspring from previous broods. The picture now began to make sense. Brothers and sisters are as related to each other as they are to their own offspring with 50 per cent shared genes and so there is some genetic benefit in helping your own family rather than someone else's. Young, inexperienced birds in the scrub jays' circumstances are unable to maintain viable breeding territories and have poor reproductive success. Therefore they don't try. Instead, they achieve greater overall reproductive success by staying to help raise further broods of siblings. There are other benefits too. The helpers receive 'on-the-job' training, the exercise improving their knowledge and experience for when it is their turn to breed. They also gain detailed knowledge of the lie of the land and where the best territories are to be found. From the relatively safe position of helper, they are better able to capitalize on any territories that become available. And, as the parents age and decline, one of the helpers might attain the dominant position of breeding bird and take over the family territory. Sometimes, they might even succeed in splitting off a section of the ageing parents' territory. It pays, then, to be a helper.

Galapagos hawks have helpers. Pairs of Galapagos hawks produce large stick nests about 1.2 metres in diameter and lay one or occasionally two eggs. But life is hard on the arid islands and food is scarce. Birds are often reduced to scratching about in the dirt for centipedes or locusts. And, for some reason, female mortality is higher than that of males so there is a surplus of adult males. Spare males – either the previous season's immature birds or even apparently unrelated adults – attend the nest. With food hard to find, helpers are useful and a nesting pair may be assisted by one to three adult male helpers in chick feeding and guard duties. Again, the female has a reduced workload and she can better regain her stamina and shape to breed again successfully the following year. Helper males gain from the experience and, like the helper scrub jays, can check out available territories and be ready to take over when the ageing breeding male has had his day. The hawk's behaviour has evolved in response to a harsh environment where it is difficult to provision chicks and in which females are scarce.

Harris hawks, living in a similarly harsh environment in North America, rely on helpers to feed their chicks, and have developed a unique cooperative hunting arrangement by which they can enhance their otherwise unpredictable and relatively poor food supply.

That food and its availability are an important influence on whether a pair of birds tolerate or even seek out the assistance of helper birds has been shown by pied kingfishers in Kenya. Two colonies have been studied: one on the shores of Lake Naivasha and the other at Lake Victoria. Like their European relative, pied kingfishers feed almost exclusively on fish and they feed in the same way. On spotting a fish, they hover and then plunge. But the fish available to the two East African groups differ considerably.

At Lake Naivasha, the fish are numerous and have a high nutritive and energy value, whereas the prey at Lake Victoria is sparse, of poor quality and of low energetic value. The Naivasha birds do well, the Victoria birds less so. Naivasha kingfishers take no more than 5.9 minutes to catch a meal. The Victoria birds must labour for 13 minutes or more. Solitary pairs there successfully rear half as many chicks as at Naivasha.

But not all pairs go it alone, and both colonies of kingfishers employ helpers. They are of two types – primary helpers, which are the yearling sons of at least one of the breeding birds, and secondary helpers, the unrelated surplus males which have failed to breed that year. The difference in fishing success is reflected in helper policy. At Naivasha, only primary helpers are tolerated. Prospective secondary helpers are seen off. But at Lake Victoria, both primary and secondary helpers are used. The birds there need every beak they can muster.

The secondary helpers lend a beak because they stand a chance next season of landing the top job. They have their eyes very much on the future. Thus they are a threat to the male of the pair. He must weight up the balance between losing his mate next year against losing his brood this year.

Not far away at Lake Nakuru another cooperative breeder has been studied extensively. This is the white-fronted bee-eater which nests in burrows in the eroded river banks. These birds live in 'clans', each clan composed of several generations of families and consisting of one to five mated pairs accompanied by a handful of non-breeding birds. About two thirds of the breeding pairs are partners for life, and during the breeding season each pair is helped by one or two helpers. The helpers are usually single birds or mated pairs that have postponed breeding for a year, and nearly 90 per cent of helpers are related to the pair they help. Nearly half are grown-up sons and daughters. They assist with the new nest, hunt for bees, butterflies and other insects, and help confront predators like spitting cobras. In the harsh and often dangerous conditions in which they live, there can be no doubt that these helpers sacrifice their own self-interest to help their relatives, and the closer they are related the more likely they are to help. Older birds will even 'birdsit' their grandchildren, thereby bringing help to their daughter.

In many cases, the helpers have a choice of families to help, but invariably they choose the most closely related. It seems that helpers receive the greatest genetic return by helping their closest kin. Inlaws, however, do not lift a feather. A female from another clan having teamed up with a clan male is accepted by her new family but she is unlikely to become a helper. Indeed, when times are hard, a female inlaw may very well desert her mate and return to her natal clan. There she will help her parents raise their family, returning to her mate after the breeding season. The help is important, for the researchers found that, in this savannah environment where food is unpredictable, a breeding pair assisted by helpers successfully raises twice as many chicks as a pair of birds without help.

POLYGAMY

Polygamous birds, that is, birds with many sexual partners, have different problems. Males might have several active nests within a territory and have no time to help their mates at all. Male widow birds from East Africa are highly territorial and take no part in nest building or chick raising. They attract females with their long conspicuous tails, and the longer the tail the more mates a cock can attract. Females are courted, mated and left to build the nest and raise the chicks alone. The male visits and mates his harem regularly but his sole job seems to be to flounce around attracting mates or chasing out intruding rivals.

Polygamy can be concurrent, as with widow birds, or sequential as in willow grouse. In the latter case, the male might actively assist in rearing the brood until such time as a new mate can be found. Even some, what were thought to be monogamous, passerines have recently been found to desert their first mate and brood once they are largely reared, in order to start an early second brood with a new mate.

But polygyny – in which a male mates with many females – usually only evolves if each female can raise her brood successfully unaided or with the minimum assistance. North American blackbirds and orioles turn to polygyny when an abundance of food permits the female to raise her brood alone. At such times, males become increasingly territorial and exclude rivals from approaching prospective mates. The Old World's woodcock similarly switches from monogamy to polygamy when conditions are good. And wrens, warblers and some penduline tits switch from monogamy to polygamy when the weather is good and many insects are on the wing. Birds of paradise and bowerbirds have access to abundant fruits in their forest home, so males, with little demand on time for looking after the offspring, are able to concentrate on mate acquisition. Birds in well-hidden nests, such as dome nests or holes, also have reduced brood demands and they are frequently associated with polygynous behaviour.

Sometimes the male does have some influence on the care of the brood, albeit remote. Several female hummingbirds nest successfully within the territory of a successful male. He defends the patch against all-comers, protecting the females' essential food supplies and nesting requirements. Hermit hummingbird males defend riverside territories in which two or three females nest, such waterfront locations, with direct access to fish, being vital for successful breeding. Females mate with territory holders whose help is needed to keep out potential nest thieves.

The common pheasant cock improves the reproductive success of his mates by feeding them prior to egg laying. He also defends them from other males and from predators entering his territory. Orange-rumped honeyguides, living in the cool Himalayan foothills, take this one step further and guarantee their own breeding success by ensuring that of their mates. Fledgling honeyguides need beeswax if they are to survive but the giant combs of the Himalayan bee are rare. Male birds fight vigorously to defend the exclusive right to feed on the wax. So several females nest in the territory of a hive-owning male and, in return for mating, a female's youngsters are allowed access to his comb.

Turkey cocks – male chauvinists amongst birds – do not assist in any way. They maintain polygynous harems but their only contribution to reproductive success is their sperm. But there are some females of the species which score a win for female avian emancipation. On the plains of Argentina male greater rheas are fiercely territorial and they collect together harems of up to fifteen females. Each male builds a single, enormous nest into which all his females lay. He then incubates and raises the dozen or so precocious chicks alone. Meanwhile the female rheas, having done with their first mate, move into adjoining territories in search of a second. Here they lay again for the resident and then move on once more, leaving the male, quite literally, holding the babies. It is not known how many males the females will approach and there is no information about whether they discriminate one from another, but as only a few males can hold territories many will fail to breed entirely. South American tinamous do the same. Many female birds lay for a succession of different male territory holders who are left to raise the brood unaided.

In a few polygamous species it is the female which monopolizes more than her fair share of available males. The female produces a clutch for her mate who then raises it without further help. She, in the meantime, moves on, free to deposit other clutches in the nests of other males. These polyandrous systems are typified by a form of role reversal in which the females are larger and brighter than the males and hold territories containing several subordinate males. The best-known examples are the lilytrotters or jacanas.

The simplest breeding system is shown by the pheasant-tailed jacana from India. Females produce one nest after another to be cared for by different males. They are successively polyandrous. The most advanced is that of the female northern jacana of Costa Rica, the only known example of simultaneous polyandry. The female is 75 per cent bigger and far more colourful than the male, and they breed on floating nests in vegetation in slow streams and marshes. Where invertebrate food is abundant throughout the year, the birds breed continuously, and even in seasonal swamps birds still nest for half of the year. Outside the breeding season, where there is one, birds are gregarious and highly sociable. But, when breeding, the males defend a small territory around their nests. Up to four or five of these male territories are encompassed by that of a single female, and females exclude any other female from their patch. Each male then only mates with the female in whose territory he nests, while the female nests with all the males she controls, and all in less than an hour.

The males have no say in the selection of their mate, and larger females may swipe husbands from the neighbours. The more-aggressive females capture males from the less competent hens and the males are held virtually as sex slaves, forming submissive pair bonds with their dominant hen. Having laid in each male's nest, the females neither incubate nor brood the young. They do, however, routinely patrol the territory, visiting each nest on a tour of inspection. The nests are prone to predation by blue gallinules and the hens defend their patch against marauding birds.

If a male is threatened and his mate is elsewhere in the territory, he will call in alarm. His giant mate will come running and rally to his defence. The hen will also oblige a male feeding away from the nest by watching over his brood. So, overall, female northern jacanas play an important role in protecting their genetic investment.

The sex ratio is generally even, but the operational sex ratio of birds actually breeding is skewed towards males. Males rarely have to fight for territories and virtually all adult males are coveted by females and breed. Life at the top for the 20–25 per cent breeding females is tough. While they have more mates than their male partners, pressure from rivals is such that they cannot hold their territories for long. Fresh, more powerful hens soon replace exhausted former tenants and the resident males are presented with a new mistress. Female northern jacanas, then, are mated by lots of males simultaneously – simultaneous polyandry; whereas males are adopted by several successive partners over a period of time – successive polygyny.

Most other polyandrous species tend to be successively polyandrous. Female button quail, plains wanderers and painted snipes lay an initial brood with one male and then leave to seek out further mates. The origin of this behaviour may be illustrated by Temminck's stint. The female lays the first brood for her partner to raise, but she incubates the second brood herself. The female spotted sandpiper goes that little bit further. She lays up to four clutches, which she leaves with a succession of males whilst saving the last clutch for herself.

Australian honeyeaters have a very complicated sexual lifestyle. They breed communally, but as their story unfolds it more resembles affairs at 'South Fork' than a natural history treatise. A female mates with at least three or four males from her section of the colony, but the chicks are looked after by up to fourteen different males, though not all with the same enthusiasm. Whilst the details of this conjugal confusion have yet to be unravelled, events do seem to depend on the loose living of the hen. She is openly

315

promiscuous. Any of the males mating with her might sire a chick. These males form a heirarchy in which dominant males ensure that they mate the most frequently. As paternity relates to mating frequency, the most successful studs father more chicks and so work hardest to feed them. Lesser males may still have managed to fertilize at least one egg and therefore they also make a small contribution to bringing up the youngsters. After all, one of them might be their own. On the hen's part, she is relieved of a considerable part of her normal workload, enabling her to breed again sooner, which is all to the advantage of the waiting beaux. They, in their turn, advance their own opportunity to breed in the next round of frantic, promiscuous matings, by helping to feed the chicks.

DEPENDABLE PARENTS

Polygamous behaviour, whilst full of anthropomorphic parallels and intrigue, is very much the exception in the world of birds. Most parents would be unable to raise their brood successfully without the help of both birds. Hornbills are an obvious example. Almost as soon as the female has been walled in she moults and soon finds herself nearly bald, unable to fly and imprisoned in a dark hole 20 metres up a tree. It is not surprising that bonding in hornbills is strong enough to last a lifetime. The doting male feeds his trusting female throughout the twenty-five-to-forty-day incubation period. Indeed, during one season in East Africa, a male silvery-cheeked hornbill was seen to carry 24,000 fruits in 1,600 nest visits during the entire 120 days' breeding cycle.

When the hornbill chicks hatch, they are blind and naked. At first the top half of the beak is much shorter than the lower part. Initially the chicks are unable to reach the nest hole, so the male must pass small items of food to the female and she feeds the chicks below. As the chicks get older, their legs grow rapidly and they can soon reach the opening to take food directly from the male. The adults, while sometimes taking small animals, are largely fruit-eaters. But to speed the baby's growth, hornbills, like many birds, switch to feeding them a high-protein insect-and-mouse diet. The amount a male, hunting on his own, can catch limits the size of the brood. The rare brown hornbill of South East Asia overcomes this restraint by recruiting young sons to help feed his larger than average brood.

But no matter how diligent father hornbills tend to be, sometimes things go wrong. They miscalculate the size of the slit-sized nest opening and spend many wasted minutes trying to squeeze outsized chunks of kingfishers or other prey into the nest. Food is often dropped in bungled attempts to feed the family.

Nest sanitation is a bit of a hit-and-miss affair. Baby birds defecate onto wood chippings in the bottom of the nest. The female mixes the guano with sawdust and throws it out through the nest hole. As the babies grow and their legs get longer, they imitate the female and raise their tails towards the nest hole to squirt out their droppings. Beetle larvae also infest the nest, feeding on food scraps. But the most serious problem is from ants. Armies of ants may invade the nest and begin to feed on the incarcerated birds. A hen must break open the mud-walled entrance and escape the hole if she is to save herself, leaving her babies to the dreadful fate of being eaten alive. Suffering such a loss, the parents will not breed again that season.

Some female hornbills, such as the African crowned hornbill, break out of their nests before the chicks are fledged. The youngsters replaster the nest opening and both parents feed them until it is time for them to emerge about two weeks later. Female trumpeter hornbills stay in the nest for the full sixty days after their chicks have hatched, and other larger species may be entombed for up to eighty-four days. Nest-holes are scarce, and it is believed that the southern African trumpeter hornbill reseals its nest once the young have fledged and it remains in 'mothballs' until the following season.

Devotion is tested to its extreme each year in the Antarctic. Emperor penguin parents are certainly as devoted parents as the tropical and sub-tropical hornbills, but they must cope with an infinitely less hospitable environment. Emperors are probably the only birds never to set foot on land, for even mating and egg-laying take place on the sea-ice close to the antarctic continent. Unlike other penguins, they start their breeding in the autumn while the ice is forming. When the Adelie penguins, which frequent the same areas, move north and back to the sea, the emperors head south, towards the Pole. They may travel considerable distances. Emperors breeding in the Bay of Whales in the Ross Sea have been found with recognizable pebbles in the stomach that could only have come from sites over 340 miles away. And for some, reaching the ice edge is only the beginning of their journey, for rookeries can be as much as 100 miles from the sea. They can travel quite fast by lying on their bellies and tobogganing across the ice. During courtship, both sexes are far from open water and cannot feed.

At the rookery, courtship itself is a noisy affair; the trumpeting call (see page 148) can be heard over half a mile away. Birds pair up but do not have their own territory to defend, simply 'personal space'. The female lays a large white egg, 12.7 centimetres long, which is immediately scooped up on the feet of the male, who covers it with a special fold of skin at the base of his abdomen, for it is the male who incubates the egg. The female leaves her mate, and sets out on the long journey back to the sea in order to stock up on food, mainly squid and fish. The male must stay fasting for nine weeks or more until the egg hatches and the female returns.

By this time, the perpetually dark winter has set in, and icy winds and blizzards, sometimes blowing up to 124 mph, send the temperature down regularly to minus 50°C and even occasionally to minus 75°C. The males huddle together, each with its bill resting on the bird in front, in a great circular 'tortue' which slowly rotates as several thousand birds press to get closer to the centre. In the huddle the birds need less energy to keep warm – a bird in the centre only uses up 100 grams of stored fat each day whereas a bird in the open would use 200 grams. When the blizzard subsides, the huddle disperses and the males space themselves out once more. If a male drops his egg, other males without eggs will rush in and scoop it up and start to incubate it. Such is the urge to carry an egg that occasionally fights break out.

The male rides out the winter storms for two to three months and throughout the incubation he just shuffles around, cradling the egg on his feet inside the skin fold, and does not eat. Heat loss from the exposed part of his feet is kept to a minimum as the penguin has a clever heat exchange system in the legs that diverts heat away from the feet. Arteries and veins in the lower leg lie close together so that heat passes from the warm arterial blood heading for the extremities to the cold venus blood heading back to the heart. In this way very little body heat is carried to the exposed feet and lost to the outside.

Eventually the female returns, fat and brimming with food to present to their newly hatched chick. If it hatches before her arrival, sometimes up to ten days early, the male can summon up a milky secretion on which the 15-centimetre-tall chick can feed for its first few days. By now, after over 115 days without food, the male has lost nearly half of his body weight. The female than takes over the brooding, using the same method – the chick rests on her feet – and the male heads for the open sea. She looks after the chick for twenty-four to forty days, but he will return again and brood the chick for its final week. The chicks, by this time, are large enough to live in crèches on the ice. Hundreds of great, brown, fluffy chicks may huddle together in these crèches for warmth, and here they will stay for another 100 days or more, fed by both parents. On returning from the sea they recognize their chick as their own and feed no other. On fledging the 13.5-kilogram juveniles are but a shadow of their 30-kilogram, 1-metre-tall parents. By the time they are ready to leave for the sea, the sea-ice will have melted and they need not travel the extraordinary journey over the ice that their parents made the previous autumn – the sea has come to them.

The parents of the wandering alabatross chick are no less diligent. Breeding on sub-Antarctic islands in the Southern Ocean, they must go to sea periodically to find food – mainly squid – for the chick; and when they go, they fly tremendous distances across the sea. A bird fitted with a radiotelemetry device which could be tracked by a satellite in space showed scientists that on each single foraging trip an albatross might travel 2,237–9,320 miles. The bird, which was on an incubation shift, flew at speeds of 50 mph and covered 560 miles a day, flying day and night with few stops for two to three days. The mate waits on the nest for the wanderer to return.

In the South American rainforest, the hoatzin parent (see pages 339–41) is not confronted with climatic problems, but with food problems. Hoatzins and their chicks are surrounded by the leaves on which their species feeds, but baby hoatzins cannot digest leaves. This is a problem facing all herbivorous youngsters. The animals themselves cannot digest plant cellulose, the material in plant cell walls, and therefore release the nutrients inside. They rely on a range of microscopic life, including bacteria, that live in their stomach or small intestine to break down the cellulose and make the cells' contents available. At hatching, hoatzin chicks do not possess any of this 'mid-gut flora', so they must be innoculated. The parents introduce the culture as a meal of either faeces or regurgitate and, once started, the baby hoatzins can begin to digest their own food.

The microbes they obtain may detoxify poisonous plants that other animals avoid, giving the species a greater range of plant foods and little competition for them. The parent birds are careful to select only the most succulent, protein-rich shoots to feed their youngsters in order to give them a good start in life. But even in the rainforest the tiniest shoots are hard to find and so immature helpers are recruited to protect and provision the demanding chicks, making a breeding unit of up to seven birds. There is, therefore, a premium on territories containing the best food plants and there is considerable competition for the best sites. Each breeding group defends a strip of river bank territory, about 46 miles long, against the intrusion of other hoatzin groups who are trying to improve their lot. Island sites are particularly sought after because they are less accessible to predators. The parents are very active in defining and maintaining the family's territorial boundaries. Their method, however, is rather unusual.

Hoatzins do not scent-mark or defecate or engage in the flamboyant breast or wing-flapping displays seen in other birds. Instead, they copulate. Adult hoatzins signal territorial ownership by performing dozens of copulations daily on the edges of the territory. And these are no ordinary copulations. The birds are noisy, making loud croaking sounds, and very aggressive. The unusual nuptial display apparently deters the neighbours. And if a pair of resident couplers fails to impress, neighbouring clans may engage in all-out battles.

Once things quieten down and the territories are established, the birds nest and incubate their two or three eggs for about thirty-two days. The atricial young are born naked, and they grow very slowly on the low-protein diet. For the first three months the babies are given a monotonous feed of regurgitated, semi-digested sticky green slime. About this time they start to snip off shoots and are largely self-feeding by the time they can fly.

Whilst parents and helpers try to defend their chicks, some predators are rather large and persistent. In fact, predators account for over half the chicks in any one year, the black-capped capuchin being a frequent raider. It can locate the nest simply by the pungent smell, the result of the peculiar diet. But the chicks are not entirely helpless. When danger threatens they can crawl out and away from the nest on branches and twigs. Fledgling hoatzins have a claw on the leading edge of each wing, at the point of the thumb, and another at the end of each wingtip. Using these four claws, together with the beak, they can clamber about in the undergrowth, looking very much like primitive birds must have done. If the danger persists, the young hoatzins dive over the side and into the river below. They swim about under the water until it is safe to return and then, using their claws, haul themselves up through the branches and back into the nest. When they have learned to fly – at about ten weeks – they lose their claws and escape predators, not by swimming, but by flapping off, in a rather ungainly fashion, to a neighbouring tree.

Hammerkops also have a baby-feeding problem. Parents have taken to feeding their youngsters with Africa's most slippery food. In some parts of their range, hammerkops feed almost exclusively on clawed toads. These entirely aquatic amphibians have been likened to muscular bars of soap with claws on their hind feet, and they are notoriously difficult to hold. Hammerkops often neglect to stun their prey, and a bungled attempt to feed a chick might result in an excitable toad slipping from the parent's grasp and out through the entrance hole of the enormous nest.

Inside the nest, the eggs are laid at one- to five-day intervals so there can be a range of chicks sizes at any one time. They are naked and in their early days look far more peculiar than their parents for the extended feathers on the back of the head, which lend the bird its hammerhead appearance, are the first to develop. But growth can be curtailed. With such a specialized diet, if feeding sites dry out, smaller broods can perish. Generally it is thought that rearing broods in a protective nest is a successful breeding strategy, but the very nature of that nest has meant that little is known of the birds' first few weeks of life.

More is known about ostrich chicks. The breeding pair of a male and major hen, together with their extended family (see page 297), gather up their chicks and escort them away from the nest. The family then becomes even more extensive, for the parents tour the district gathering up other chicks to join their own. A crèche of thirty to a hundred chicks forms and it is guarded by two or three of the original parents. In a few months the youngsters are on their own, their numbers reduced considerably by the attacks of lions, jackals, hyenas, hunting dogs, cheetahs, leopards and other predators. The predators, though, don't have everything their own way. Ostriches with young can be very aggressive, and they are powerful birds. There is one report from a local Masai tribesman in Kenya which describes how a lioness and her cubs chanced upon an ostrich pair and their chicks. The cock bird led the chicks away while the hen challenged the lioness and her family. In the fight, one young lion had its back broken and another fell with a kick to the head, but the hen ostrich was caught and killed by the lioness.

CUCKOLDRY

Monogamous birds, like swallows and martins, live in gregarious colonies, yet function as pairs. Both parents incubate the eggs and feed the young, but normally male birds only work hard when they are sure of the paternity of the offspring in which they are investing so much energy. And it has been found recently in sand martins that paternity is less obvious than was at first assumed.

The problems start a day or so before laying, when the hen is heavy with the developing egg. Females are about 15 per cent over their normal flight weight and males can spot their slower, less manoevrable flight. Unfortunately for the pair, this also signals the female's fertility, and eager males are poor respectors of others' fidelity. As the female flies out of her tunnel nest, up to half a dozen males swoop down and chase her. The mate does not give up without a fight, and he follows her, flying almost close enough to touch his partner. This is vital if he is to thwart the attempts of aerial copulation by the following flock of frenzied males. Sometimes the male gang will succeed in separating the pair, and chaser males succeed in performing sneak copulations with the outmanoeuvred female. The exhausted hen is, quite literally, raped.

The males are so keen to mate with slow-flying females that they will attempt to copulate with almost anything that resembles them. In experiments, both stuffed birds on wires and male birds carrying lead weights were eagerly sexually assaulted. Surprisingly, the assaulting males are not birds which have failed to find a partner. They are the respectable neighbourhood males which have mates and families of their own. And older, more experienced males are more likely to chase females than the younger paired or unpaired males.

Male martins can afford to chase and mate with females which are not their partners because their investment is limited to one or two droplets of sperm. If an egg is fertilized, they gain an offspring for no real cost. They do not provide any assistance with their victim's nest building nor do they take any part in feeding the brood. If, however, they fail to sire, the loss of such a tiny investment is negligible. So, they might as well have a go. For the female, things are different. She does not solicit these male attentions, the males just force themselves upon her. Each fertilized egg she lays represents days of intensive feeding, and each chick's appetite requires the attentions of not one, but both parents. As a partner is essential, his paternity must be assured, and it is in the female's interest to avoid being caught.

Males of the closely related swallow can assess the likelihood of the brood being their own. They can see the degree of interest other males show in their mates. The more frequently they are chased, the less certain the males become, and when they know for certain they have been cuckolded they provide less food for the offspring. And the effort a male delivers, measured by the number of feeds he provides, is linked precisely with the number of copulations he performs.

Solitary swallow pairs have near absolute certainty of paternity and provision the brood to the best of their ability. Only those in colonies show males feeding chicks at reduced rates. There is also a correlation with the male's mate-guarding ability. The more a male believes his partner might have been mated promiscuously the less work he performs. At worst he can desert her. On the other hand, the very act of mate-guarding might provide the female with a means of assessing her mate's fitness.

At times, male barn swallows may badger established pairs almost continuously. They chase flying females and follow them home, all the time trying to sneak copulations. They may even resort to infanticide – the second leading cause of deaths of nestlings in swallow colonies. By killing the brood which was sired by her regular mate, they ensure that the hen will lay another clutch. It is possible that the sneaky male might succeed in siring some of this new brood. And by hanging about a nest these males also gain a competitive edge. They acquire information about their rivals' strength and about breeding sites, as well as gaining access to the females.

In the main, infanticide is practised by males, but for house sparrows the female might be involved too. Infanticide in this species is the major cause of chick deaths, but the murder is committed by the two sexes for different reasons. The males, as with other species, kill the female's offspring to make the female available for breeding once more. But male sparrows might have more than one partner, and the murderous females are the second wives of bigamous males. The mates only help the first partner to feed the chicks, ignoring the second mate's brood. The second mate kills the first mate's offspring in order to redirect the male's attention to her own brood.

Generally, breeding systems in which males sneak copulation or engage in infanticide are becoming increasingly widely reported. But, while this benefits successful sneaky males, it may reduce the female's reproductive success. So bi-parental care may have developed in typically monogamous birds for three main reasons: firstly, two parents may be necessary to rear the young, as with emperor penguins and hornbills; secondly, because pairs breed in residential territories, the male is at hand and, with nothing else to do, might help to raise the brood; and thirdly, bi-parental care offers a degree of certainty that the male partner sired the brood.

Nevertheless, sometimes females *are* raped forcibly, and at other times they may successfully refuse mating. But even females refusing some sneaky matings will accept others. If these 'extra-marital' couplings can prove so costly, why do it? Where females willingly accept copulation, there must be some benefit to offset the costs incurred.

Females might enhance their offsprings' fitness by mating with additional superior males. But then one wonders why they did not choose these super-studs in the first place. Also, in some species, as we have seen, females can acquire helpers to assist in feeding the young, and these males might have a paternal interest in one or more of the offspring. If this is the case, those males are less likely to indulge in infanticide for risk of killing their own offspring.

FIRST FLAPS TO FREEDOM

Leaving the nest is the most hazardous step for a baby bird, and for some this can be a rather premature but nevertheless essential event. Wood ducks nest in high tree-holes, but almost immediately after hatching the precocious chicks are forced to follow their mother anything between 5 and 20 metres down to the forest floor. Mother, supported by her well-feathered wings, descends easily, but the ducklings are not so well equipped. She leaps first and on reaching the ground makes a special 'exodus' call to summon the brood. One by one they leap from the tree nest, tiny downy flaps held out like miniature wings. They bounce on the leaf litter at the bottom and, although there are some casualties, most chicks make it and run away with mother.

Barnacle goose chicks have an even more horrendous first flight. In parts of Greenland and North America, barnacle goose pairs nest at the tops of towering, precipitous basalt cliffs. In order to feed, however, the tiny fluffy chicks must leap over the edge and free-fall 150 metres to the bottom where a further 300 metres of shattered rock scree drops to the valley floor. Protected by their thick, downy coats many chicks float down and bounce on the tufts of moss and lichens at the bottom. Some are caught in crevices and become food for the waiting arctic foxes and ravenous gulls.

From the high, limestone crags near Hermann, Missouri, Canada goose chicks make the same remarkable descent to the riverbank below. Just a day after hatching they throw their 85 gram bodies over the cliff and, literally, bounce on impact at the bottom. Some land harder than others and one little tyke was seen to land head-first. Stunned but not dead, the gosling got up and, rather unsteadily at first, ran to join its mom. But that's not the end of their incredible journey. Next they must cross the 18-centimetres-high railway tracks, jump into the swift flowing currents, swim the breadth of the 2 mile river and walk the 1–3 miles to the brooding grounds where they spend the rest of the spring and summer.

Cliff-nesting guillemots also need to get their chicks down from their ledges and safely out to sea as soon as possible after hatching. At about fourteen to twenty-one days, their secondary feathers are just large enough to provide their developing wings with enough lift. The parents then use a special 'water' call to persuade the chicks to flap-fall to the sea below. The wings, though, are not sufficiently well developed for proper flight and the chicks are vulnerable to attacks from gulls. The parents, therefore, call the chicks down at dusk. And, as one parent calls from the water, the other may fly down with the chick, shadowing it protectively with its body. The male then takes the chick out to sea, the two birds swimming through the night so that in the morning the chick is safely away from marauding gulls.

Most precocial birds feed themselves from the moment they hatch and, with that experience, the chicks are usually free of their parents as soon as they can fly. Altricial birds, on the other hand, having fledged without ever having found their own meals, must be taught how to find food. This is easy, say, for a gregarious seed-eating weaver bird. Seeds are relatively common everywhere about the nest site and there are plenty of adult birds around to watch and copy. Fledglings soon learn to fend for themselves, releasing their parents to start another brood. In species with rare or specialized diets, more effort must go into teaching the fledglings how to become independent and survive. Just getting the brood to leave the security of the nest can be difficult. Bluebirds do it by withholding food and resuming feeding only when the chicks have vacated the nest. Only then are they shown how to find their own. Some species, such as robins, divide the brood into two manageable groups. The cock birds take custody of the daughters and the hen looks after the sons.

For the parent birds separation time can be quite a wrench. They must strike a balance between safe-guarding the investment they have already made and leaving the fledglings in order to nest again. Conflicts can arise. Youngsters may demand more care than the parents ought to supply. Bewick's swan cygnets try to stay close to their parents when danger threatens. Over the first four weeks of their life this is encouraged, but after this the frequency of the parents' guarding response reduces from an initial 87 per cent to 52 per cent.

Terns need time to teach their fledglings their specialized fishing techniques, and parents of British-born young have been seen tending their fledglings months after their departure south on their African wintering grounds. Terns invest much time and energy in their offspring and it pays off. They cannot have a second brood anyway, for they are constrained by the short breeding season, and none of their offspring would survive without a prolonged opportunity to master their fishing techniques.

Eurasian sparrowhawks must acquire more straightforward hunting skills. The brood fledges at twenty-six to thirty days, but remains around the nest, watching and learning, for another four weeks. At first the parents feed the youngsters on demand, but as they learn to hunt and start to catch their own food supplementary feeding is reduced. After four weeks the parents stop altogether and the young can be heard calling to be fed. After a few days they get the message and the need to feed forces them to disperse and go hunting. If sparrowhawk fledglings are provisioned experimentally with food at the nest for a further three weeks, they will remain. Only when the artificially supplied food is withdrawn will the birds leave.

On dispersal, males travel only 6 miles from the nest on average. Females go 12 miles. The difference between the sexes is common amongst birds. Males are more likely to establish a territory close to the nest site with which they are familiar. Females are less territorial and travel greater distances. The dispersal pattern also helps to prevent inbreeding amongst siblings.

Manx shearwaters have an unusual way of persuading their chick to leave the nest burrow. They feed it for precisely sixty days and then abandon it about fourteen days before it is fully fledged. The chick must wait alone and unfed in its dark tunnel for a fortnight and must be very hungry when eventually it can fly out. Its ability to hunt for molluscs and small fish must be entirely innate as it receives no tuition from its parents.

Species that recruit helpers seem to have hit on the ideal solution to the investment-dispersal dilemma. The fledgling continues to be protected by its parents and it learns a range of skills from their example. At the same time, the parents can have another family and even benefit from the presence of their previous brood by getting them to help with the new clutch. Dwarf red-billed hornbills from savannah areas often recruit their offspring to help defend the family territory during the harsh, dry season. The youngsters benefit from learning about the different foods that become available during the ten months the group is together. In places like the savannah where food is scarce or unpredictable and therefore constantly changing, a longer learning period is to a bird's advantage. In rainforests, where there is always something to hand, such long apprenticeships are unnecessary.

Brood parasites, such as cuckoos, have their own peculiar learning problems to overcome. Many species have generalized diets and so learning to feed is easy. When cuckoos fledge all they have to do is learn where to find insects like those brought by their foster parents and then eat them. Breeding is, on the other hand, a bit of a problem. Cuckoos have to recognize other cuckoos in order to mate with another of the right species, and they must recognize the correct host to parasitize. Some must learn and be able to sing their host's song.

Emperor penguins have a slightly less complex departure. Gaining independence can be a rather accidental affair. At fledging, emperor chicks have enough fat deposits to allow them a couple of weeks' unsuccessful fishing and so they have time to perfect their techniques. Youngsters may leave the breeding colony at any time of day or night and from the start they are on their own. Learning to fish is a matter of personal trial and error. Some birds become independent not by design but by accident as the pack ice breaks up beneath them. In dangerous waters, with killer whales and leopard seals abroad, just over 80 per cent of fledglings die in their first year at sea. Successful survivors spend four to five years at sea before they return to breed at five years of age.

When wandering albatross chicks fledge, they are enormous: about 104–137 per cent of the adult weight. They are independent at fledging and have sufficient fat reserves to enable them to learn to fish. They will then spend from four to fourteen years circling the earth, an average of 7.8 years on the wing, before returning to their natal home to breed. Survival rates are good, with 71.5 per cent of fledglings alive after their first five years and 91.8 per cent of these survivors making it to eleven.

Most baby birds will die, however, before they reach maturity. If an animal population remains stable, two parent birds, no matter how many chicks they succeed in fledging, will leave an average of two surviving offspring. Birds producing, say, three broods of nine chicks for several years will produce no more surviving progeny than albatrosses or penguins that have a single chick every year or two years. The enormous range of breeding strategies developed by birds has evolved to ensure that their lineage has, at least, this success.

But the entire process, while ensuring the continuation of the parents' genes, is not that good for the parents themselves. This was confirmed by a study of collared flycatchers in Sweden. Early breeding female birds are aged by the experience to the extent that in subsequent years they produce smaller clutches than females starting late. Having children, it seems, is bad for your health.

8

HUNTERS, GATHERERS
AND PIRATES

THE FARALLON ISLANDS LIE DUE EAST OF SAN FRANCISCO OFF THE
coast of California. The setting is a placid, idyllic one, but its
serenity belies the fact that here nature can conjure, in an instant,
frenzied life-and-death struggles; they are short-lived, almost
bizarre interruptions lasting a matter of minutes before the
relentless action of waves and wind restores normality. But this
place is the setting for a macabre event, one which is witnessed both
by the local flock of western gulls and by the scientists studying them
at the isolated Point Rayes Bird Observatory.

The gulls serve as an early indication of what is to come. They
stand expectantly on the shore, beaks pointing into the onshore
breeze. They watch and wait. An autumnal fog has cleared, and
though the sunshine is weak, visibility is good.

Some distance from the shore, bull elephant seals ride the rise and
fall of the surf. They arrive here each autumn. It is the season when

the right to breed must be claimed, disputed and then resolved, often at great cost. Elephant seals are formidable beasts. Weighing in at two tonnes, the males or bulls seem invulnerable in the water. Even on land their enormous girth is sufficient to squeeze the life out of anything that happens to get in their way, including on occasion females and pups. Their demeanour seems self-obsessed and all-powerful, invulnerable.

But the gulls know differently; they have been in this situation before, and recognize the signals that have presaged mealtime in the past. They spot an approaching shadow almost before the elephant seals do. This shadow is cast by a mass matching that of the seals themselves but moving with greater speed and purpose.

The gulls take to the air almost as one, moments before one of the bull seals is struck by the shadow – a great white shark. In an eruption of blood-stained froth and frantic thrashing, the crippled victim struggles hopelessly against blood-loss and the inevitable weakening this causes. One and a half kilograms of flesh and blubber have been torn away in the initial assault. The killer circles, content to wait for its prey to succumb to its injuries and bleed to death.

Meanwhile, the gulls are already flocking to the scene to pick at the small scraps of flesh, blubber and skin left by what is a clinical predator, but which also happens to be a very messy eater. While the shark has first option on the huge carcass bobbing on the tide, it will take only crudely executed jawfulls, lacking the oral dexterity to dine efficiently, far less pick its victim clean. Nothing will be wasted though, the gulls will see to that, and they feast even before the seal's ragged remains are washed ashore by the breakers. There are pickings aplenty for each member of the flock, as well as the stragglers attracted by the brief commotion.

This scene, while bringing awe to the watching scientists on the shore at Point Rayes Bird Observatory, provides just one, albeit grand, example of the type of feeding opportunism at which birds excel. These western gulls are demonstrating their ability to take prompt advantage of the situations arising within their range, much as other members of the gull family follow fishing boats for many miles at sea, biding their time until the detritus of the predator (in this case man) is thrown to the tides, and as other gulls have moved inland to take advantage of the muddy banquets left in the wake of a tractor's blades. Why should these gulls do the killing, the fishing or the digging when someone else has unwittingly volunteered?

330

Birds tend to be good at their assigned job. Across the enormous breadth of species that inhabit this earth, virtually every conceivable feeding opportunity presented, in whatever unlikely shape or form, is exploited by one bird species or another. Some display a kind of avian work ethic, while others scrounge, but all have a role to play in the ecological continuum. Many bird species have eclectic tastes and generalized habits, some are opportunistic within narrower parameters, others are almost suicidally specialized. Dependence on the most delicate of habitats and inability to adapt to changing circumstances currently threatens many species, and has precipitated the disappearance of others.

DARWIN'S FINCHES

Where some birds have suffered and even vanished, others have thrived, exhibiting the fundamental dynamics of evolution first identified and proposed by Charles Darwin. Birds of all shapes and sizes can and have adapted themselves to virtually any circumstance in order to secure food.

Darwin's analysis of the behaviour and adaptations of finches in the Galapagos Islands revolutionized our way of looking at the natural world. The processes he identified are ongoing not only on these volcanic islands off the coast of Ecuador, but all over the world. The accumulation of knowledge on the subject is similarly ongoing, as we try to understand the forces that have shaped the many species that constitute the global avian melting pot. From primitive reptilian ancestry, the first creatures recognizable as birds have spread and diverged into thousands of species, from the tiniest hummingbirds of the New World to the towering ostriches of the Old. One of the fundamental influences on the shaping of these species is the need to eat.

Birds fill all available niches, right across the spectrum of feeding opportunities. The comprehensiveness of their evolutionary spread sometimes conjures incongruous, almost unbelievable adaptations, with the most innocuous of birds going to extremes to make a niche their own. Who would have thought, for example, that a finch, ordinarily thought of as a seed-eating bird, could adapt to vampirism? But a 'vampire' is precisely what the sharp-beaked ground finch of the Galapagos has become.

This species is found on many of the Galapagos Islands, and is one of the thirteen species collectively referred to as 'Darwin's finches'. But it is only on an isolated volcanic outcrop called Wolf Island, and a nearby smaller island where water and sustenance are at a premium, that it has turned to parasitism in order to live. In this it has been surprisingly successful. Its hosts and victims are large seabirds such as the masked booby, birds so large in relation to the diminutive finch that it is able to perch on their tails, almost unobserved. From this vantage point it can peck at the rump of its host almost unnoticed, breaking the quills of the tail feathers and sipping the blood that is drawn as a result. The finch is usually ignored as it performs this macabre act, perhaps because it is so small and its toll so negligible to a gannet-sized bird – itself a voracious predator.

It is thought that the sharp-beaked ground finch may have learned to exploit this unlikely source of nutrition from having once filled the role of servant – relieving its hosts of lice and bothersome flies. The marine iguanas of these islands are serviced in this way by mockingbirds, which forage amongst the reptilian sun-worshippers basking at the edge of the waves. Indeed, this source of food is exploited by many different birds across the world – the oxpecker of the African plains is one – and is to the obvious advantage of the other creatures involved, usually large mammals but also potentially dangerous species such as crocodiles. Even these uncompromising giants will gape obligingly to allow the delicate lily trotter to enter their gaping jaws to pick at shreds of flesh lodged in the great reptiles' teeth. A tempting morsel of lily trotter is clearly a secondary priority to dental hygiene, so the crocs are never guilty of breach of contract; although time will tell if the lily trotter, like its Galapagos counterpart, is tempted to diversify and make a profitable sideline out of drinking the blood from crocodile tongues.

The barren, hostile nature of much of the Galapagos archipelago lends itself to survival instincts coming to the fore, and other species have had to be aggressively opportunistic to maintain their foothold in this precarious environment. The hood mockingbird on Espanola is precisely that, a gangster that roves in boisterous parties around the island, alive to any and every weakness that could make its island cohabitants a potential source for a meal. It has also developed a taste for blood in an area where fluids are prized, and will attack injured booby chicks by homing in on their wounds, aggravating them with persistent pecks from all sides, and feasting on the oozing blood.

The sharp-beaked ground finch, meanwhile, has not yet exhausted the booby-as-larder, and in the breeding season will wait until the booby has left its nest unattended before helping itself to an egg. Faced with an egg that is about the same weight as itself, the finch has developed the ingenuity required to break it, using its whole body as a lever and manoeuvring itself into position to flick it against the nearest rock. This may have to be repeated many times before the egg cracks or the owner returns, depending on which happens first. If and when the shell is finally punctured, the enterprising burglar gorges itself on its nutritious and hard-earned prize. For indeed hard-earned it is, since ingenious adaptive behaviour such as this in so small and physiologically ill-equipped a bird takes many years or a special combination of circumstances to come out. The feat embodies more than one trait of resourceful-ness: desperation in a barren landscape; inspiration to recognize a large, white oval shape as food – it is worth bearing in mind that ostrich eggs sometimes prove too much even for lions to negotiate; improvisation to overcome morphological shortcomings – in this case lack of physical strength; and lastly perspiration – although birds do not sweat, the energy expended in securing food and the risks involved must at least balance with the likely rewards of the effort. An egg that equals your own weight can be judged to be worth the effort.

Darwin studied finches on the Galapagos Islands partly because it enabled him, within the limits of one family of birds, to study how changing environmental circumstances elicit behavioural, physio-logical and anatomical changes. The finches found themselves in situations where they had to adapt – or perish. The range of landscapes and variety of feeding opportunities encompassed within the islands have prompted behavioural changes and, ultimately, genetic changes, usually promoted by the geographical isolation of different groups of finches (although it has recently been discovered that different species may arise from a common ancestor where no topographical separation has occurred). Through time, previously related finches have evolved into specific species, quite distinct and sexually incompatible with previous relations.

Studies of Galapagos finches have continued in more recent times. The islands continue to provide an ideal setting for the study of natural selection because they provide small and isolated communities of finches within a variable and changeable habitat. Some of the most creative minds in the bird world learned their trade in the Galapagos ecosystem. Studies of the medium ground finch on the island of Daphne Major in the Galapagos group revealed that these finches subsist on seeds of varying size and hardness. When rainfall is scarce, availability of food is affected. Softer seeds are soon in short supply. This reduced source is quickly depleted by the foraging finches, leaving only the larger, harder seeds. As a result, only birds with bills large enough to crack the outer husks of these seeds can feed with any degree of success, and therefore a greater number of the larger finches with stronger bills survive through the dry years, such as 1977, 1980 and 1982.

A further excellent opportunity to test the theories of natural selection in action was afforded evolutionary biologists on these islands with the 1983 El Niño – a major and sudden climatic upheaval in the Pacific which affected half the world and which led to 1,359 millimetres of rain falling on the Galapagos between December 1982 and July 1983. This created, in microcosm, precisely the type of environmental change in which resident species have to adapt to survive. Researchers reported that after these eight months of unusually heavy rainfall, smaller birds were left with an advantage over larger ones for the two subsequent years.

This conclusion, and those of the earlier studies, have shown that the course of evolution can change, or even reverse, quite dramatically, and indeed is doing so within measurable timescales – as witnessed by today's ornithologists.

It had previously proved very difficult for scientists to actually demonstrate, as opposed to speculate, that the enhancement of differences in body shape or in parts of the body such as beaks can result when more than one species competes for the same food source. Studies of medium ground finches and small ground finches are one of the few good examples to have been found in nature. In most cases, the reasons for the morphological changes have proved inconclusive, since any discernible differences are as likely to have occurred because of differences in food supply. The evidence in the case of these two Galapagos finches, on the other hand, seems incontestable. They co-exist and compete directly with one another on most of the Galapagos Islands, and where they do they differ greatly in beak and body size. But where they occur in isolation from each other their beaks are of intermediate size.

Of course, the Galapagos does not have a monopoly on contemporary evidence of evolution in action. Studies of an African finch, the black-bellied seed-cracker, undertaken in Cameroon in equatorial Africa, produced startling conclusions. This bird shows a wide range of bill size, irrespective of sex, age, body size or geographical origin. It was established that bill size was not yet a factor in the pairing of birds in the breeding season – indeed, large-billed individuals will mate with a small-billed partner – but the species is showing early signs of dividing into two or more, even though there is no geographical boundary between the potential new species: those with large bills and those with small.

Although very rare in the animal kingdom, the benefits of such differences in anatomy within one species are great, and include the reduction of competition between individuals of the same species. The birds are able to exploit both big seeds and small seeds. This promotes speciation and may result in distinct species from the same ancestry. The case of the seedcrackers may represent a very rare example of divergence within a species living in the same geographical location.

Despite this kind of evidence to the contrary, many biologists still insist that speciation can only occur when populations are separated by geographical barriers, although, taking a non-avian example, it is worth noting that single lakes in the Rift Valley have managed to throw up several hundred species of cichlid fish. It seems that there is more to speciation than being separated from the near relations by a mountain or isolated in a lake.

Charles Darwin, visiting the Galapagos in 1835, was first to recognize the dynamic of evolution exhibited by the finches of Galapagos, and he would no doubt have been gratified to know that his ground-breaking and accurate speculation is to this day being backed by conclusive scientific study of the forces as they happen. The finches are a relatively recent example of speciation that has been occurring since the late Jurassic period, about 150 million years ago. Actual scientific evidence of the fact has been accumulating thick and fast in relatively recent times. The discovery of fossil remains of *Archaeopteryx* two years after the publication of *The Origin of Species* gave scientists a pretty accurate idea of the period of time over which the process of genetic and behavioural diversification has been occurring in birds, leaving our modern world its fascinating cornucopia of distinct and idiosyncratic species, each with its own particular role to play and expertise to exhibit within the great global ecosystem.

PLANT EATERS

Darwin noted that one of the finches he encountered on his exploration of the Galapagos Islands was feeding directly on cactus plants. On the face of it there may have seemed no obvious reason why the cactus should have escaped the attentions of the relatively rapidly diverging finch flocks that were colonizing every niche the islands had to offer. But it is one thing to peck at tough, fibrous, relatively non-nutritious plant matter – after all, a lot of hungry birds may sample potential food in this way. It is quite another thing, however, to be able to adapt the body not only to survive the sampling but also to extract from this source sufficient nutriment to subsist on it thereafter.

Birds are thought of, in the main, as seed eaters, insectivores or carnivores; as higher life-forms that depend on a ready source of energy-rich tissue in order to thrive. In actual fact, birds exploit almost every conceivable form of plant tissue (although few are fond of the more primitive plants such as fungi and lichens), and almost 20 per cent of the world's bird species feed principally on nectar. Although this habit is mainly to be found in warmer latitudes, it is not unknown in the more familiar species of the northern hemisphere. Many disillusioned horticulturalists will vouch for the fact that sparrows seem to have developed a taste for early spring bulbs and shoots.

Many birds of northern latitudes will supplement their diet by raiding flowers for nectar, but usually damage the flower and render it incapable of fulfilling its reproductive purpose. Other birds – the bullfinch in particular – have developed a taste for buds. With its short, stubby bill a single bullfinch can strip entire trees of their unopened flowers, wreaking havoc in commercial orchards, and infuriating commercial gardeners. Fruit farmers estimate that one bullfinch can eat half the buds on a pear tree in one day. The trees in their orchards are specially cultivated to produce large buds that swell earlier in the year than wild fruit trees, and the bullfinch is expert at recognizing this nutritious store of growth. As a result, the culling of bullfinches is now permitted in some areas, and the species is paying dearly for its habit of premature harvesting.

The bullfinch's feeding habits are almost parasitic in their consequences, causing lasting damage to some trees, impeding not only their yield in any given season but also their growth over subsequent years. The relationship between bullfinches and fruit tree buds is one-sided and the consumption of buds plays no part in fertilization or distribution in the trees' reproductive cycle. Habits like those of the bullfinch are, not surprisingly, the exception rather than the rule. The relationship between many 'vegetarian' birds and their food-plants is more often mutually beneficial and sometimes complex.

The most northerly bird-pollinated plant so far documented is the crown imperial fritillary, and it is only the blue tit which is nimble enough to cling to the stem and probe discriminately into the flower. The bird 'repays' its source by leaving the flower intact and acting as an agent of pollination. In keeping with other bird-pollinated, or ornithophilous, plants, this fritillary produces 'bird friendly' nectar, containing none of the sucrose that birds have difficulty digesting, and few amino acids. It is clear that this is a specific adaptation aimed at attracting pollinators other than insects.

Although this arrangement is unique in this part of the world, it is widespread elsewhere, and has become a way of life for most hummingbirds. In the jungles of Brazil a plant has recently been discovered with not only the necessary avian enticements, but also an elaborate mechanism to increase the efficiency of the deal. In common with many ornithophilous plants, *Hyptis pauliana* has set out its stall with only hummingbirds in mind. Its shape, colour, lack of scent and special nectar are determined by the needs of birds. This lavish plant knows all about the birds and the bees, but it is only interested in soliciting the former.

Hummingbirds require the high concentrations of sugar contained in nectar to fuel the high metabolic energy requirements of their mode of foraging: hovering amongst flowers for extended periods with up to eighty wing-beats per second. The hummingbird's digestive system has been found to have the highest active glucose transport rate of any vertebrate, and one species, Anna's humming-bird, has a 4.8-gram frame that burns its fuel thirty times faster than humans. Everything about the hummingbird's lifestyle is geared towards maximizing energy efficiency, and its actual feeding behaviour is equally specialized, with minimum time and energy wasted on the wing, and surprisingly long intervals between meals spent immobile, during which the bird may be making room for its next drink.

It is perhaps not surprising that the flowers on which it feeds have also gone to such elaborate lengths to 'advertise' their wares and keep the busy little nectar-sipping allies well informed and supplied.

There can be no unnecessary delay in finding the flower-bound reservoirs of instant energy. Hummingbirds can absorb 97 per cent of the glucose contained in the nectar they consume, and experimental markers have been recorded in the birds' droppings a mere fifteen minutes after consumption.

The flowers visited by hummingbirds contain small, slowly renewed quantities of nectar, ensuring that hummingbirds must visit many flowers, maximizing the potential for cross-fertilization. Clearly, the flowers cannot offer too little nectar or the hummingbird shuttle service might start looking elsewhere. (Hummingbirds, like most birds, are continuously learning and reassessing the profitability of their foraging techniques.) Nor must the flowers produce too much, in which case fewer flowers would be cross-pollinated.

The hummingbird's relationship with *Hyptis* is very delicately balanced and mutually sustaining. When the visitor has probed the nectar supply deep inside its flower, *Hyptis* deploys its secret weapon – a hair trigger hanging from the petals. This causes the stamens to ping against the suitor on the threshold, covering it with adhesive pollen which it will later courier to other, equally alluring, flowers.

Nectar is produced by plants as a deliberate enticement to foraging birds, and the birds are the unwitting agents of plant reproduction. For much of the world's flora, the contract does not end there. Come the autumn, many plants readvertise their wares in various coatings, from sugary, soft and colourful fruits to tough and unwieldy nutshells. In each case, there is a strategy in mind, and birds are willingly enticed to perform their part of the bargain.

Ripened fruits can be regarded as a deliberate offering from plant to bird. As with nectar, the soft, sugary flesh is begging to be eaten – along with its hidden contents. Many birds do not need a second bidding, and will gorge themselves on this rich natural store. Indeed, many birds would not see out the winter months without the sustenance of berry-laden trees. Scandinavian species such as the waxwing are capable of travelling hundreds of miles in voracious flocks, systematically stripping trees such as rowan or mountain ash of their vivid red fruit. The ritual is paralleled in the United States, where flocks from Canada arrive en masse to escape the harsh northern winters. The rowan, meanwhile, is not providing this larder for selfless reasons, and can be guaranteed a return on its hospitality – effective distribution of its seeds across vast areas.

When we think of herbivores, we usually conjure an image of a weighty, ponderous, ruminating farm animal which seems to have to spend all day, every day, chewing and staying still in order to extract all the nutriment it can from a uniform diet of fibrous cellulose. It is not often that birds are thought of in the same way, or as being capable of existing on such a limited, seemingly unbalanced diet. But birds have exploited almost every organic source on the earth, and since leaves are the most abundant form of plant tissue, to have overlooked the potential in leaves would mean a massive, unfilled gap in the world's ecosystems.

Tropical forests contain by far the highest density of different life forms of any habitat, and the most visible, abundant and renewable resource in a tropical forest is the leaf. Not many birds eat them as a rule, but some inevitably do. One such species, the hoatzin, is no ordinary bird though: it can swim and climb trees before it has even grown feathers (see page 25); has claws, like *Archaeopteryx*, on its wings when young; eats green leaves as an adult; and has the stomach of a cow.

Even as an adult the hoatzin is a peculiar-looking creature, an unlikely South American river-dwelling aristocrat with a 20-million-year pedigree. Its behaviour and physique can be regarded as primitive, but the fact of its longevity indicates that it has a winning formula which centres on the eating of green leaves from an enormous variety of plants, snipped off with its scissor-like beak. It prefers young growth, making the digestive process slightly easier, although even young cellulose requires special treatment before it can be broken down. Unlike cows, which have an enlarged hind-gut for fermentation, the hoatzin employs a fore-gut in a manner akin to that in deer and kangaroos. The thick-walled, muscular crop, with its corrugated interior, is greatly enlarged. It accounts for about one tenth of the bird's body weight, and is similar in function to a cow's rumen. The abrasive action of the horny tissue lining the muscular walls begins to physically grind the leaves, while the bacteria in the crop break down the cell-wall cellulose and release the nutrients contained within, mostly energy-rich fatty acids. These are absorbed in the intestines. The lower oesophagus, proventriculus (stomach) and gizzard are small and serve only to produce enzymes that soften and partially break up the leaf material.

The crop itself is divided into two large chambers. This slows down the passage of food so that the bacteria have time to work on the tough plant fibre. Microbes in the fore-gut detoxify any poisons in the leaves before the food is absorbed. A further constriction between the posterior crop chamber and the next chamber, the oesophagus, serves to sift out and hold back any large portions of leaves that have yet to be broken down. Movement is further restricted by the curved and folded nature of the lower part of the oesophagus as it meanders, like a slow-flowing river, into the small gizzard. Microbes in the gut are likely to provide the bird with additional vitamins, minerals, amino acids and other essential nutrients that are not provided by a diet of leaves.

When all is said and done, the passage of food through a hoatzin's digestive tract is a laborious process – slower than in any other known bird. Where ornithologists might wait for fifteen minutes to measure a hummingbird's food retention time, those watching a hoatzin might have to wait for anything from twenty-four to forty-eight hours; at which point the hoatzin will present its socially unacceptable side – the fresh cow-pat smell that has earned it the local nickname of 'stink bird'.

With all these digestive adaptations, the hoatzin has sacrificed some expertise in the air. It can flap sluggishly over distances up to 150 metres at a time, searching the river banks of the Amazon and Orinoco basins for the choicest leaves. Hoatzin landings are an undignified spectacle, as it tends to topple forward because of the imbalance created by its enormous throaty crop, and the fact that it cannot grasp well with its feet. After feeding, the hoatzin tends to perch with its breast bone rested against a branch. A special patch of skin on the breast, known as the resting pad or callus, enables it to do this.

Like domestic ruminants, the hoatzin has to sit around for hours while fermentation takes place, crop visibly churning. In this state it uses up less energy than any other resting bird, and maintains a body temperature of 38°C, facilitating optimal bacterial activity in the crop. On cool mornings it will climb into higher branches in order to absorb extra energizing heat directly from the sun.

That the hoatzin can survive at all, let alone for 20 million years, is something of a mystery to scientists. Its metabolism contradicts conventional laws of nature, which state that small creatures, which lose heat more quickly than those of larger mass, need easily digestible, energy-rich foods in order to maintain an adequate body temperature. That the hoatzin can power its wings – albeit quite feebly – at all is astonishing. Few birds and mammals weighing less than 50 kilograms are able to get anything from leaves, yet the chicken-sized hoatzin, weighing less than 900 grams, lives on them.

But the hoatzin's idiosyncracies are also the secret of its success. It has little competition for its food source, and the adaptations it has had to undergo have not rendered it helpless. Clambering around in dense swamp vegetation makes the stink bird an elusive customer.

Leaf-eating birds are to be found all over the world, from the ostrich on the plains of Africa to the ptarmigan and willow grouse of tundra and taiga. These birds have a large crop and gizzard (unlike the hoatzin) and two large caeca in the hind-gut in order to deal with mainly fibrous foods such as heather, which is poor in nutrients. In contrast with the hoatzin, the fermentation process takes place in a grouse's hind-gut, the preliminary grinding process having taken place in the gizzard.

As with the hoatzin, grouse and ptarmigan are able to live like no other birds. In the winter, they eat parts of plants containing oils that are poisonous to other animals, and thereby survive without competition in the thinner air and colder temperatures at high altitude. In the breeding season, grouse usually supplement their monotonous menu with a greater variety of plants and some invertebrates, enabling them to summon the extra vitality required for raising young.

Birds such as the ostrich and the emu have sacrificed the power of flight in favour of large digestive tracts designed for the digestion of cellulose. Unlike herbivorous mammals, the emu uses bacteria situated in the end of its small intestine, and does not have to retain its food for the extended periods required by sheep and kangaroos to complete the extraction of energy from cellulose: a mere five and a half hours compared with around forty for these mammals. The emu digests a smaller proportion of its fibre than do the mammals. Ostriches and rheas share the mammalian chambers in their hind-guts usually associated with bacterial digestion, while the emu, like the hoatzin, is out on a limb in terms of categorization, but thriving none the less.

One Australian species, the long-billed corella, has lived through profound changes in its habitat, but has made a success of the transformations effected by farming settlers in its native land. At one time it fed on roots, tubers and seeds. Studies in western Victoria have found that more than 90 per cent of the long-billed corella's diet now consists of plant species introduced by European colonists. It has put to good use its ability to feed on plant matter both above and below ground, and has overcome the threat posed to its very existence by the removal of indigenous plant foods, to the point where it is now considered a pest in some farming areas.

Commercially grown grain crops are both attractive and vulnerable to bird predation. They have usually been artificially cultured to produce high yields regardless of the natural defence mechanisms embodied in many wild plants to prevent over-indulgence by predators. Science, however, can help out the unfortunate farmer. Studies carried out in the USA have addressed this problem, and have come up with ways of making species such as the sunflower less 'user-friendly' to seed-eating birds. It has been recommended that droopy, concave flower heads and thin stems make it significantly more difficult for birds to perch on and peck at sunflower seeds and so those are the best to cultivate. In the wild, such modifications can arise by natural selection, the flowers thus formed having an advantage over those more conventionally proportioned. With arable crops, man may have to take the initiative in moulding these adaptations in order to maximize yields.

Since many plants attempt to reproduce themselves without recourse to energy-sapping fruit production, and many birds are adapted specifically to feeding on seeds, we may wonder whether a seed-producing plant stands to gain much from the attentions of avian plunderers, since an exposed seed can be quickly despatched – and rendered useless to the plant in reproduction terms – by a specialist seed-eater. By and large, though, wild-growing plants do not suffer from these attentions, since they are able to produce huge volumes of seeds and, according to the law of averages, some will survive to germinate. As with plant fertilization, birds may play a central role in seed dispersal.

Plants do not always present their seeds on a plate, as it were. Conifers attempt to preserve their seeds in tough cone casings until the time is right for exposing them to the elements – and the plunderers. One of the most curious, but effective, cone-seed extractors is the crossbill – a classic example of the benefits that can arise by chance genetic 'deformity'.

From time to time, birds turn up with weird and wonderful aberrant traits. People often report seeing everyday garden birds like starlings, for example, with hugely distended bills, or even bills with twisted mandibles. Such 'mistakes' in gene copying during reproduction can have roughly three possible consequences: they can debilitate the individual concerned such that it cannot survive to reproduce and the trait is not passed on; they can cause no particular problem or feeding deficiency, in which case the character may or may not be passed on; or they may actually enable that individual to forage more successfully than other members of its species.

Such an evolutionary advantage has befallen the crossbill, which looks like a finch with twisted mandibles. This trait enables the crossbill to prise seeds from tightly shut cones by a very particular method, endlessly repeated. It has the added advantages of a prehensile tongue which takes the seed from within the cone as soon as it is uncovered, and a flexible jaw hinge powered by asymmetric muscles. Indeed, the bill may be crossed in one of two different ways, akin to people's left- or right-handedness. The three European species of crossbill each have slight modifications in bill size according to their favoured cones.

Small flocks of crossbills make their way through the tree-tops in coniferous woodland, wrenching cones from the branches, clasping them against a branch and easing open the tightly-layered outer flakes protecting the seeds within. A tell-tale sign that crossbills are in action is the pattering sound of opened cones dropping onto the forest floor as the flock moves on. Although the crossbill is efficient at this form of predation, it is inevitable that many seeds make it to the soil, where they may be able to germinate and grow.

Small finches have, like the hummingbirds, a high basal metabolic rate and although their method of foraging is less energetic than the rapid wing-beats required in hovering, their seed diet is less energy-rich. Finches often have to spend long periods searching for and consuming seeds, and cannot afford to go about it in a random or haphazard fashion. Goldfinches, like most birds, are fully in tune with their energy requirements, and their way of life is geared towards maximizing the return on their efforts. The goldfinch favours the large seeds of the thistle family, and can consume its daily requirement in less than an hour. When large seeds are in short supply, it may have to spend around thirteen hours a day in order to satisfy its appetite on smaller seeds.

It is clear that birds are capable of exploiting most types of plant tissue, with all the physical and behavioural adaptations that this requires. Plants are capable of producing a great many relatively low-energy seeds, or smaller volumes of energy-rich, readily available fruit. Nuts, meanwhile, can be regarded as something of an intermediate: energy-rich, but requiring a correspondingly greater amount of effort on the part of the predator before they can be consumed. The fact that these seeds are encased in tough, woody shells means that only specialized birds can habitually feed on them. As a result, the relationship between the plants that produce them and the birds that eat them can be an intriguingly complex arrangement, with some trees seeming to exploit certain bird species' capacity to make stockpiles to see them through harsh winters.

STORING THE GOODS

The climate in which a great many of the world's birds live is highly volatile, and those birds which do not migrate in order to ensure a constant source of food and reasonably constant temperatures often have to take steps to ensure that there is also sustenance in times of shortage. Even in the harshest winters birds have to have regular meals, and while they can build up fat reserves in advance of winter, and take steps to minimize energy expenditure and the consequent need to refuel, the quest for food is a perpetual one.

Many species of birds have evolved specialized means of surviving in times of food shortage. Much as humankind is able to plan in advance and use times of plenty to make stockpiles in order to see through the leaner times, some birds have learned to think ahead and cache food. This is a learned technique, specific to some species and absent in the behaviour of others.

The fact that some birds can successfully cache food suggests that they have the ability to do two things: to plan ahead and to remember where the food is hidden. There is no point in food being hidden half-heartedly as it will soon be found by a competitor and lost to the original owner. Similarly, there is no point in secreting food so well that it is later impossible to find.

Studying these feats of avian memory in action is often a simple matter of placing a bag of peanuts in a winter garden and witnessing the activities of the titmice that regularly exploit this source of food. They will often attempt to remove a whole nut, then fly off and stash it in a fissure in a tree. This process is repeated several times, each prize being placed in a different hidey-hole. When the tit is satisfied that it has built up a suitable stockpile, it will then relocate its hidden meals in due course, but sometimes not until hours or even days later. The fact that the food is eventually recovered in this way does not in itself serve as satisfactory evidence that the tits perform feats of memory. It is arguable that by caching food within its neighbourhood a bird is as likely as not to stumble across it again sooner or later, as much by accident as by design.

Recent research, however, has provided evidence that memory does play a significant part in the recovery of .hoarded food. Scientists in Oxford studying marsh tits coated sunflower seeds with a radioactive substance harmless to the birds (since they removed the husks before eating) which enabled the scientists to trace the caches and check on whether and when they were recovered by the tits. To offset the chance that the stores were plundered by other birds or voles and mice, false stores were introduced by the observers, each placed one metre from a hoard established by the birds. In the winter, the hoards were found to be recovered by the birds within a day or two, and the false hoards fairly soon after, suggesting that plundering is common.

It became apparent that the marsh tits had a strategy for counteracting food losses to plunderers. Rather than establish large hoards – placing all of their eggs in one basket, as it were – they distributed their food across a broader range of sites, each about 7 metres from the next. Experiments showed that this was the optimal distance at which seeds could be successfully hoarded: if caches were closer together they were robbed more quickly, and if further apart they were less likely to be found again. The tits had demonstrated the ability to remember where their own caches were, as well as the most efficient method of caching.

Laboratory experiments were undertaken to determine whether sense of smell was a factor in the recovery of seeds by marsh tits, and if the seeds most recently stored by the birds are the ones that they recover first, a behaviour that has been called the 'recency effect'. Evidence was produced that scent was not a factor, since when a bird's caches were removed and placed in nearby holes the bird would still check the original hole (and others besides) before recovering the seed. There was found to be a 'recency effect' of sorts, but it was not marked. The tits were allowed to cache seeds in two batches, and the seeds of the second batch were not necessarily recovered first. Besides remembering where it has stored food, the marsh tit also remembers which sites it has already returned to, and does not waste undue time inspecting sites twice.

Having established that marsh tits have an advanced capacity for memorizing information, the scientists set about finding an explanation for how they achieve it. In birds such as the marsh tit, whose eyes are situated on the side of the head, each eye surveys a different visual field. The marsh tit was observed as it cached its seeds, and it was noted how the bird cocked its head first to one side and then to the other before departing the site, as though it were noting the lie of the land with each eye in turn, perhaps to store visual information in both sides of the brain.

Experiments were set up in which the birds were fitted with an eye patch and then allowed to cache seeds as normal. If the patch was left in place the bird recovered the seeds it had hidden. If the patch was moved to the other eye in the meantime then the bird could not find its cache, providing further evidence that they rely on memory.

Similar but seemingly even more advanced feats of memory are exhibited by Clark's nutcracker, which breeds throughout the western United States and south-western Canada, usually in mixed coniferous forests in mountainous regions. The species often ranges over long distances, outside the breeding season, to more temperate lowland valleys. Towards the end of the summer it harvests the seeds of the piñon pine, a habit to which it is well adapted. It prises the seeds from the cones with its chisel-like bill, filling its sublingual pouch (a pocket under its tongue unique to nutcrackers but similar in principle to the throat crop used by rooks) before flying several miles to its chosen burial sites. These secret locations are often on bare, south-facing slopes where the winter snow cover is not likely to be as deep, and recovery will therefore be easier. Each nutcracker may bury as many as 33,000 piñon pine seeds across a range of sites, each containing four or five seeds. It sees out the severe winter months by revisiting thousands of sites and feasting on the contents. When spring comes round again the young are fed on the resources stored in these caches.

The question of how the birds find so many of their hoards has long intrigued scientists. Until recently, observers of hoarding behaviour doubted that birds could rely solely on memory to make a success of this complex strategy. It seemed improbable that a bird's brain could accommodate so much data: all those sites over distances of many miles and over so long a time-span. Humans have had to develop computer databases in order to store information on this scale.

Different theories were proposed in an attempt to explain how these feats of memory could be achieved. It was thought that perhaps the nutcracker only cached the seeds in a particular type of site, and thereby limited the odds of finding the food in trial-and-error searches. Precisely because of the time lapses and the number of caches involved the Clark's nutcracker is a difficult case to study in the wild. But laboratory studies have found that both Clark's nutcracker and its European relative can remember individual cache sites by reference to nearby objects, and that if these are moved by, say, 20 centimetres, then the nutcrackers' efforts to relocate their caches are also out by 20 centimetres. When snow covers ground previously bare and obscures landmarks the nutcracker's accuracy is affected, although it can still use nearby trees and branches as points of reference. The sense of smell, which is generally poor in birds (other than the kiwi), has been shown to play no significant part in the recovery of seeds.

It is not yet known how many of the 33,000 or so seeds stashed by each Clark's nutcracker are recovered by the hoarder, but it is clear that the piñon pines rely on this as a very effective method of seed-dispersal. Not only are the seeds for any given pine carried off great distances; they are also 'planted' by the nutcracker in an ideal site for germination, under a shallow layer of soil. When the spring comes around, the seed has an ideal opportunity to germinate and sprout, well away from the parent tree. The relationship between the pines and the nutcracker is mutually beneficial, and profoundly influences the natural history of both.

The Clark's nutcracker is just one – albeit the most fastidious example – of several members of the crow family in North America that employ this caching technique. The piñon jay, Steller's jay and the scrub jay also harvest the seeds of a variety of pine species, including the whitebark pine, the south-western white pine and the limber pine; other trees that have evolved to be attractive to foraging birds. The cones that they produce openly advertise the seeds contained within, some fertile and edible, some infertile and inedible.

A fertile pine seed is no longer viable when it has been consumed, and what seems on the face of it to be a suicidal means of reproduction for the tree is actually a central facet of a mutually sustaining relationship. The corvids can rely on the pines for a plentiful supply of food, with the proviso that they take and cache more seeds than they can recover and consume. This is exactly what happens, the nutcrackers frequently burying two or three times more than they could realistically eat. Many may be lost to rodents or decomposition by fungi and bacteria, or to plunder by other birds, although this is rare. But those fertile seeds that are not spoiled or stolen remain viable in the frozen ground throughout the winter and, if not recovered by the particular corvid that buried them, can then germinate in the spring when the temperatures rise and the ground thaws.

Seedlings found growing in clusters can often be attributed to seed caches, and isolated clumps of mature trees offer evidence that caching has been taking place for many years. Pollen analysis suggests that the distribution of pines has undergone major fluctuations since the Pleistocene, unlikely, in the case of the piñon pine, to have been attributable to wind dispersal, given the large, wingless seeds that it produces. It is more likely that birds have spread the seeds. The blue jay is thought to have been the primary agent in the recolonization northward of oak trees – about 350 metres per year – in the wake of the last Ice Age, a process paralleled in Britain by its European cousin. Although squirrels also take and bury acorns and beech mast, they rarely do so beyond the immediate vicinity of the parent tree.

The pines benefit from the feeding habits of all four crow species, although the techniques of each are different. Clark's nutcracker is the most efficient gatherer of seeds, the evolution of its sublingual pouch having enabled it to gather and transport large numbers of seeds in one go. It can carry as many as 90 piñon seeds in its pouch, with no interference in vocalizing, eating or examining other seeds for quality. The nutcracker rejects inedible seeds, taking only ones it recognizes as edible.

Birds studied in the San Francisco Mountains of north-central Arizona were found to use communal caches, often in sites where the snow cover is restricted in wintertime.

The piñon jay shares Clark's nutcracker's sharp, pointed bill, and can therefore access the seeds of green, unripe cones earlier in the season. Steller's and scrub jays cannot, so before the cones have opened they often harass nutcrackers for a share of the spoils.

None of the three jays has a sublingual pouch, although piñon and Steller's do have an expandable oesophagus (throat). The scrub jay uses its bill and mouth, and can only carry five piñon seeds at a time over distances of over half a mile. Although the scrub jay is the least efficient at caching in terms of the quantities it can carry and the distances it covers there is some recent laboratory evidence that this species can and does use bearings taken from the sun in the relocation of caches. Scientists allowed captive jays to cache piñon seeds, then kept them in artificial daylight to disrupt their internal clocks. The birds were then found to search in the wrong places for their seeds. Since this means of navigation is only viable when the sun is visible, it was concluded that landmarks are used when these are available. This may explain how Clark's nutcracker finds the correct location of its caches before using features on the ground to pinpoint the actual site.

The types of location used for caching also vary among the species, providing the pine trees that they service with a comprehensive and wide-ranging distribution network for their seeds. The birds benefit in that they each exploit the seeds in different ways and in different areas, albeit with some overlap.

The breeding cycle of Clark's nutcracker revolves around the pine seeds, and it is among the earliest North American birds to breed. The young are fed almost exclusively on pine seeds, which is unusual in birds, since this narrow diet would not normally provide sufficient protein and fats for the development of the nestlings. The nutcracker has evolved to make do with this situation, and the parents are selective in the type of seeds they bring to the nest, ensuring that they are of the highest quality, rich in fats and proteins. Early breeding also gives the young the advantage of more time in which to gain weight and experience in advance of the autumn. The jays are less reliant on cached seeds, and feed their later broods on a diet principally made up of insects.

Although Clark's nutcracker enjoys the unquestionable benefits of being a food-caching specialist with a uniform diet, there are years when the pine harvest is poor and, like other members of the corvid family, the nutcracker is forced to diversify and become opportunist. In some winters of severe shortage they have been recorded in the Great Plains and the south-western deserts and on the Pacific coast searching for food.

The inter-relationship of these four species with each other and the pine seeds that form part of their diet provides a useful example of gradual changes in behaviour and the shape of parts of the body. The nutcracker is clearly the most specialized in terms of its relationship to the piñon pine in particular, and provides an insight into how this type of feeding specialization can evolve in tandem with other organisms, in this case the piñon pine and its method of seed dispersal. The modifications in the nutcracker – its bill, food-transporting sac and strong, fast flight – have adapted it to more efficient foraging and wide-ranging caching, placing it in a different niche from the jays, which could otherwise have been direct competitors.

Specialization of this kind has costs, and not only for the birds. The pines must invest heavily in large, rich seeds, unprotected in the later stages of the autumn and reliant on foragers not eating them all at once. The dependence of the birds is exposed as a weakness when the seed crop is poor and they are forced to 'erupt' to other areas and other sources of food. Here they face the inevitable competition posed by resident birds. The nutcracker that spends the winter elsewhere will, if it survives, have to raise young without the advantage of its usual stores of seeds, and the chances of breeding success are markedly reduced.

As with all living systems, specialization is beneficial but its sensitivity can also see it penalized. A period of no evolutionary change is never reached, and populations inevitably fluctuate. But, in the long term, as long as at least some of each species are able to survive, the balance is maintained, and remains advantageous to all of the communities that rely upon it.

STOCKING THE MEAT-SAFE

Caching of large prey items also becomes a matter of life and death for some birds of prey that spend the winter in cold climates. Freezing temperatures are a mixed blessing, on the one hand preserving dead tissue that might otherwise decay, on the other hand posing the problem for the hoarder of how to defrost the meal when it comes to retrieve it. The great horned owl of the Americas is known to sit on frozen carcasses in the more northerly parts of its range, thawing them out and consuming them bit by bit.

Sparrowhawks have been observed caching prey between meals, so to speak. One female bird was observed in winter with a jackdaw that it had captured. After plucking and eating some of its kill, it was seen to conceal the remains in some nearby bushes before leaving the area. It was then observed returning for second helpings some time later, and then again after that. In the course of the ensuing days, the sparrowhawk returned to its cache on at least five occasions. It is not surprising that the sparrowhawk took more than one visit to finish off this large prey item.

Birds of prey often show the wherewithal for both concealing food and providing for later meals. They often catch food faster than they can consume it, especially when there are young to feed. Goshawks in California have been observed keeping a larder in the crotch of a tree at a discreet distance from the nest. Smaller raptors are also well used to losing prey to marauding crows, which are attracted to the scene of a raptor's attack by the alarm call of the victim (see pages 153–7). It could be that sparrowhawks which cache food outside the breeding season have experience of losing meals not yet finished and thereby learn that certain spots are safer as storage sites than others.

While some birds of prey will resort to hoarding food, they are by and large fairly inexpert at the technique, and utilize it on an improvisational basis, rather than as a rule. The shrike family, on the other hand, are past masters at the art, and are known in many localities as 'butcher birds'. This horror-story name comes from the fact that it does not simply cache food, it impales it on long thorns, often in full view of the surrounding countryside, creating a macabre little larder stocked with large insects, small reptiles and even other birds. Although the food is out in the open and in full view, it is relatively secure from theft on these makeshift meat hooks. Shrikes are shaped like stocky little hawks, with short blunt wings, hooked bills and long tails. They are active foragers, and even when they are at rest they may be constantly on the lookout for prey from their perch. Perhaps as a result of this, they catch food more quickly than they can devour it, hence the larder. Other functions of a bird's wearing its appetite on its sleeve, as it were, could be to proclaim its occupation of a territory and also to attract a mate to it.

HUNTERS

Speed and surprise are the hallmarks of the falcons and hawks. Kestrels stake out a chunk of territory. Each bird hangs almost motionless above the ground, hovering in wait for a careless vole or a crawling insect. So acute is its daytime vision that the kestrel can spot a beetle in the grass from 30 metres up. Using wings and tail to maintain position, its head remains steady, even if its body is buffeted by crosswinds. And when the time is right it swoops down at 25–31 mph to pounce on the victim before it has had time to escape. But, of all the aerial hunters, the peregrine falcon must be one of the most remarkable.

Most birds of prey use their ability to fly as a special weapon against creatures on the ground or on water, but the peregrine falcon has so perfected the art of flight that it hunts other expert fliers – other birds – in the air.

It does not chase its prey but intercepts it, setting up an ambush in the sky. It waits in the clouds a mile above the ground until, with forward-facing eyes that give it binocular vision eight times more powerful than ours, it spots a passing target, often a wood pigeon, the peregrine's favourite prey. It flies out of the sun, folds back its wings, and plummets.

During the wind-whistling 'stoop', the peregrine reaches 100–150 mph, and seemingly out of nowhere it strikes down on its victim with a single blow, one of the most impressive sights in nature. In a flurry of feathers the talons break the pigeon's neck or back and it tumbles to the ground. The peregrine circles and drops down to retrieve its meal.

Sometimes the peregrine's attack appears half-hearted. It might scatter a flock of pigeons without taking a single bird. This low-intensity skirmish occurs when the predator is responding almost automatically to a visual stimulus like a passing flock of birds. The peregrine is not really hungry at all and stoops without effort. Only when hunger fires the falcon into a high-intensity attack does it pursue its victim to its death.

The peregrine's prey species include over 100 different birds, ranging in size from pipits to geese. In England, the most sought-after targets are pigeons, while in Scotland red grouse are often on the menu, but the bill of fare might include wild duck, waders, song birds, cuckoos, woodpeckers, owls and auks.

Small birds are sometimes snatched in midair, plucked and consumed, and all the while the peregrine flies along in an unhurried manner, using its characteristic series of shallow flaps alternating with glides.

In winter the female or 'falcon' is the dominant hunter and she feeds her life-long partner. She is about 50 centimetres long and, weighing about a kilogram, is a third larger than her mate, known as the 'tiercel'. Her tendency to spend longer at the nest and thus be responsible for defending the home is thought to account for her larger size.

Both sexes possess an alert and watchful head dominated by fierce-looking eyes and a strong hooked bill. The powerful yellow toes are armed with formidable needle-sharp claws. Adult birds have a dark crown and a dark cheek 'moustache'. The white underside is barred with black, the markings more striking in the falcon.

A pair remains together throughout the year, staying close to their territory, unlike younger unattached birds that wander the cliffs and open country in which peregrines live.

During the summer breeding period, chicks may scoff as many as six pigeons a day, so a nest site must have abundant food supplies nearby. The territory is well guarded. Combat can be fatal for an intruder, some non-territory holders being buffetted from territory to territory as they pass through. Aggressive neighbours are tolerated.

Peregrines set up home when about two to three years old. The tiercel may loop the loop and dive on his prospective mate in a mock attack trying to impress her with his aerobatic skill. Freshly caught prey is passed from one to the other in the air and a nervous newly wed might drop it in the sea.

The nest is a shallow scrape on a rocky ledge high on a cliff or crag. In Britain, eggs are laid from March to late April, and both parents share incubation duties for about thirty days. Chicks or 'eyasses' are fed in the nest for forty days, their presence there marked by harsh hecking cries that reverberate around the rocky cliffs.

Young flyers practise their flying skills before leaving home. Nest mates stoop at one another, make mock attacks at rocks and plants, and eventually attempt a few passes at prey. After two months they are ready to take their special place in the world, a masterpiece of aerodynamic design with long sharp wings and a short tail. Today, many birds can expect to live for ten years.

In Britain, peregrines are joined at coastal mudflats – where enormous flocks of wintering waders and ducks gather – by sparrowhawks and merlins. This sometimes presents observers with an excellent opportunity to compare the contrasting hunting and feeding habits of different raptors exploiting prey from the same source and in the same circumstances.

The sparrowhawk's favoured technique is to fly high to spy out the lie of the land and the placement of feeding flocks below. Then it flies down and stalks its prey from the concealment of bushes or trees, until in a final dash from cover it pounces on its chosen victim. In more exposed coastal locations the sparrowhawk may have to modify this slightly. The opportunities for surprise attack are reduced. There is a lack of cover with which to disguise an approach, and the multitude of watchful eyes in a large flock of waders will spot an approaching hawk. If a sparrowhawk does not capture its targeted prey straight away it will soon give up the chase, as it is not cut out for exhausting aerial pursuits. Without the element of surprise its chances of making a kill are greatly hampered. Close-knit flocks (see pages 64–6) make this doubly difficult for marauding raptors, and can prevent them from isolating a particular bird in the midst of a confusion of wings.

The merlin, on the other hand, although smaller, is a much more tenacious customer, capable of pursuing its victims in flight over long distances, following their every evasive twist and turn until the prey is caught, or simply gives in to the attacker through sheer exhaustion. Its diet is not restricted to species smaller than itself, and it will readily tackle medium-sized waders and other shorebirds.

Not all attacks by hawks are successful. Their aerobatic feats are not quite as flawless as many people think. Even a powerful and accomplished flier like the peregrine has to contend with the guile and will to survive of its prey species if it wants to make a successful hunt. Pigeons and ducks, its favoured prey in many parts across its extensive, worldwide range, are no slouches in the air, as careful studies over long periods have testified. Given all the hyperbole and mystique that surrounds the peregrine and its relatives, it may be tempting to assume that they catch prey almost at will. But no predator has it that easy – food must be earned, and there is no such thing as a 100 per cent success rate even for what is widely regarded as the fastest aviator in nature.

In observations made in North America, peregrines were successful in roughly one in ten chases, and about half of the ducks they were preying upon were not seized in mid-air, but on or near the ground or in shallow water. Individual peregrines may have favoured techniques, depending on the habitat in which they hunt, and the successes they have previously achieved, but they must be versatile to survive.

It is often thought that peregrines disable their prey in mid-air as a rule, before returning to collect the victim and finish the job. This strategy, though, would not be as economical as actually clutching the prey first time around, as many catches would be lost on the ground if, for example, they fell into habitat unsuitable for retrieval, such as water or human habitation. There might then be an alternative explanation for apparently successful attacks. It could be that the peregrine watchers were actually witnessing last-minute, and very precise, evasive action by the quarry. Ducks will often drop like stones into the nearest available cover, giving the appearance of having been struck.

Another explanation is that birds used in falconry are likely to employ different hunting styles, and have their quarry flushed from cover by dogs. Wild birds have no such assistance, nor do they usually have accomplices on the ground on hand to retrieve their catch. It could be that young falcons in the wild will knock their prey to the ground rather than risk injury in a mid-air tussle, but they may revise this strategy as soon as they incur the first loss of prey to unforeseen terrestrial circumstances.

That said, there are instances of peregrines exploiting unwitting human 'beaters'. On Vancouver Island in British Columbia, for example, peregrines are known to take advantage of an unlikely ally in the shape of parties of birdwatchers. They associate the approach of these groups with the flushing of ducks from the ponds, and they position themselves accordingly. The ducks, meantime, are also learning and, perceiving a greater threat from the skies above them, they prefer now to stay put. There are other instances of usually timid birds allowing humans to approach to within very short distances when there is a raptor around. Conor Jameson tells of an instance when he made it to within a matter of yards of a wheatear when a sparrowhawk was visibly patrolling over an open moor.

Peregrines too can be persistent, and are not necessarily foiled when intended prey makes it to cover. On the Cote Donana in Spain, a peregrine was observed chasing a magpie into a thorny thicket – apparent safety for the magpie. Instead of staying where it was the magpie attempted to break cover and was promptly snatched in mid-air by its assailant, which had simply bided its time overhead. There is a recorded example from the USA of a panicked dowitcher, under threat from a peregrine, submerging itself in a shallow pool. The peregrine hovered briefly overhead, then plunged in osprey-style, dousing its breast feathers, and lifting its victim clear of this apparently safe refuge.

Individual expertise lends itself to adaptation and specialization, and enables the species to thrive in different habitats across the Old and New Worlds. Prey species too can and do employ different tactics for self-preservation, and the falcons must endeavour to stay one step ahead, acquiring new tricks and constantly updating their hunting repertoire.

The relative safety of nightfall, in so far as diurnal raptors are largely inactive, may partly account for the fact that wildfowl are very active at this time. If this is indeed with a view to avoiding peregrines, it is not necessarily a fool-proof strategy, since some peregrines are now known to be willing to stay up late if hunger necessitates it. Faced with hunting in poor light, they improvise, either gaining height and waiting for the flocks to pass beneath them, or taking advantage of the darkness lower down, concealing themselves against the shadows, then flying upwards towards the silhouetted formations. This may also benefit falcons that are subordinate to other birds in any given territory by day, and, in North America, also serves to minimize losses to plundering buteo hawks and eagles.

It is likely that precisely these kinds of consideration are what prompted owls to 'go underground' and operate after dark. Of course, there is also the consideration that much of an owl's favoured mammalian prey is most active by night, but the same applies to the prey of diurnal raptors, which have never developed the owl's night vision capabilities. It could be that the niche is now filled to such an extent that no other species would be given sufficient time to adapt without succumbing to the night-time competition of the incumbent owls. The peregrine on the other hand is exploiting a prey item – wildfowl – that the owl population does not predate as a rule, and is therefore encountering no competition.

When a peregrine has experienced failures in open pursuit, it can resort to more stealthy surprise attacks. When preying on ducks and waders, it is contending with birds that have an excellent field of view that scans in every direction except down and towards the rear. Experienced falcons make full use of this blind-spot, and will also attack with the glare of the sun at their backs, much as fighter pilots involved in dog fights used to do. It has been established that peregrines have a better ratio of successful chases in the breeding season, which has been explained in terms of the greater urgency of catching prey at that time of the year. On passage in the winter, peregrines can betray their inexperience in their efforts to catch prey, partly because they are in unfamiliar terrain, their prey is often in flocks, or they are immature birds.

In the example of the wintering flocks of waders, it has been acknowledged not only that different raptors hunt in different ways, but that their prey species recognize the different threats each poses, and have learned to take the most appropriate evasive action in the face of these attacks. The success rate of raptors attacking flocks is lower than normal, and the flocks also learn that safety can be found adrift on deeper water.

Raptors are often robbed of their catches by other predators, which explains why hawks and falcons with a fresh kill will arch their wings over their victim in an effort to block any view of it from above. A peregrine can lose out in this way to groups of crows, when its victim is too heavy to carry to a secluded spot. Crows mob as a rule anyway but there is an added bonus if they can make the falcon relinquish its meal. Few birds are above acts of banditry of this kind. Where raptors are concerned, it is the law of the skies. Peregrines in the USA have been observed taking food from merlins and harriers. Northern harriers themselves are known to defend their hunting territories from intrusion by other raptors, but only if these intruders are larger than the harrier itself. Since smaller raptors are free to hunt in the harrier's territory, it has been concluded that the motive behind this discrimination is klepto-parasitism. Harriers will harass smaller raptors only if and when they have made a kill, and by removing larger raptors from the scene they ensure that they are at the top of the hierarchy.

INSECT COLLECTORS

Many people regard the peregrine as the ultimate avian machine, and while there may be a case to be made for this bird, and while what the peregrine excels at may be beyond most other birds, they could all teach the peregrine a few tricks of their own. Many birds catch insect prey on the wing from time to time, but few passerines specialize in the tactic to quite the same extent as the swifts, some of which spend almost their entire lives on the wing, even mating while aloft, and coming down only to nest. The swifts also have a legitimate claim to being the masters of the air, if only because they spend a greater proportion of their time in it than any other creature. Beak agape, the swift must consume huge quantities of insect prey in order to fuel the massive energy requirements of its lifestyle.

The flycatchers are another family of airborne insectivores, except that in their case the launching pad is terra firma, or a perch near to it.

The spotted flycatcher times its return to the northern hemisphere for the breeding season to coincide with temperatures mild enough for larger flying insects to rouse themselves from dormancy and take to the air, for it is from the air that the flycatcher takes them. Although many species of birds will, from time to time, pursue large insects such as butterflies in mid-air dog-fights, only the flycatchers regularly catch prey quickly with this approach. Different species have different tactics, some being prone to return to the perch from which they set off, others alighting on a different vantage point to resume the hunt.

Studies of the hunting behaviour of flycatchers have concluded that they have a distinct preference for larger flies, since these are a greater reward for the exertions of the chase. When insect activity is reduced, as it is when the temperature drops, the flycatcher may have to change its strategy to secure enough food, and may forage in the tree canopy for smaller species.

In common with most birds that come into regular contact with stinging insects such as bees and wasps, flycatchers are careful to remove the sting before attempting to swallow this prey. One bird that specializes in feeding on wasps and bees is the bee-eater, of which there are twenty-four species between Eurasia, Africa and Australia. It often hunts flycatcher-fashion, taking a wide range of winged insects, and nests in ground-based colonies. Within colonies, which may contain up to 23,000 nests in the case of the rosy bee-eater of Africa, there sometimes exists formal social structures, with small clans of three or four pairs pooling their resources and defending their nests and feeding areas on a collective basis.

Some raptors have a taste for insects, and are prepared to undergo exhausting, convoluted chases in order to catch them. Merlins and hobbies, for example, regularly prey on dragonflies. The hobby is even capable of devouring them on the wing, grasping them in its talons, removing the wings and ferrying the succulent parts to its mouth.

The carmine bee-eater of southern and central Africa specializes in group feeding on swarms, usually of bees and locusts, but is also attracted to the site of bush or grass fires, where it takes advantage of the clouds of insects flushed by the smoke and flames. Lack of expertise does not stop less nimble species taking advantage of the sudden appearance of an aerial swarm of ants, for example, which can attract frenzied flocks of gulls, crows and other large birds. Only when there is a great concentration of small insect prey such as ants is it economical for large birds to divert their attention from their more regular prey to catch food on the wing.

GONE FISHING

Across the globe, water is one of the great providers of nutrition for all types of animals, and birds are no exception. Birds go fishing in the deepest ocean and the thinnest trickle on a bare mountainside. They have adapted themselves in a multitude of different ways in order to extract prey from a sub-aquatic environment in which they may not be able to breathe, but have certainly adapted to thrive.

In order to make a success of fishing, birds have to overcome the handicaps that water presents to air-breathers, and the sanctuary that it affords to its inhabitants. Birds must first and foremost be able to see or locate their intended prey, which can appear difficult, especially when the water surface is disturbed. The mastery of this point requires highly advanced eyesight (see Chapter 6), which many fishing birds have. Gannets and their relatives the boobies, for example, are capable of spotting shoals several metres beneath the surface of the sea from considerable heights. They must then gain great momentum and adopt the streamlining of a torpedo in order to plunge to sufficient depth to snatch prey from these shoals. They must also avoid fatal collisions with their daredevil colleagues in a flock. These species are thoroughly expert in every aspect of this strategy.

Other sea fishers, such as sawbills, cormorants and their relative the anhinga, dive from a different starting point, this time on the surface. They are extremely accomplished swimmers, capable of pursuing fish underwater for considerable periods, and are perfectly adapted for doing so. Their feet are set well back on a streamlined body, which does not trap air, as this would reduce speed and restrict movement in the water. The bill is sharply hooked and equipped with a hack-saw-like serrated edge for gripping elusive and often slimy prey, and their bone structure is heavy in comparison with most birds, which are light-boned. This explains the tendency of these birds to swim with only their necks visible above the surface.

In some ways, the cormorant appears to be a bird in transition, as though it were midway through an evolutionary development into a strictly aquatic creature. In fact, the cormorants are birds of ancient lineage, and closely resemble some of the earliest known birds in their habits and in some of their physical traits. The cormorant's wings are not properly adapted to underwater swimming, and are less important in propulsion than the feet. The wings are not oiled and the feathers are loose and thus get very wet, which explains why cormorants and their relatives standing on coastal rocks hanging their wings 'out to dry' are such a familiar sight across the world. In the same way that seals have shed the limbs that their ancestors must have had for use as land-living creatures in favour of more practical flippers, so the cormorants and shags of our coastlines may be on course to lose the use of their wings in favour of more effective paddles. This could only happen in a situation where flightlessness would not be a liability exploited by predators. This, sadly, has often been the case with bird species that have reached a flightless stage in their evolution, as happened to the great auk.

The last great auk in the British Isles was killed by hunters on the island of St Kilda in the Scottish Hebrides around 1840, the only British bird to have been hunted to extinction by man. Flightlessness was only advantageous up to the point where circumstances changed, and predators not previously a factor in the great auk's evolution arrived on the scene.

The Galapagos Islands have been able to sustain a population of flightless cormorants, remote and autonomous enough to survive discovery by humans and the predators, such as rats and cats, they bring with them. Like the dodo and the solitaire, the great auk was not so fortunate.

The European auks that retained their powers of flight and survive, such as puffins, guillemots, murres and razorbills, have adapted to an aquatic life to the extent that they appear ungainly on land, with their stubby flipper-like wings and webbed feet set so far down under the tail that they stand upright – like penguins that have not yet foregone the option of taking off. They spend the majority of their time at sea, feeding on fish, shellfish and plankton. The guillemot can spend over a minute under the waves, and dives to great depths in search of prey.

Other seabirds have adapted in quite different ways to a pelagic life, and have evolved exceptional aerial durability for lengthy periods on the wing, traversing the oceans outside the breeding season. Having the physical adaptations needed for effortless flight, species of petrel such as the fulmar may be less specialized when it comes to fishing. None the less, the fulmar has seized upon the fishing activities of man as a source of food, and since around the turn of the century the fulmar population has spread from St Kilda to encompass almost all of the British coastline.

The strong-flying aerial fishers of the seabird world have benefited from the fishing industry, while the feeding specialists such as the puffin and guillemot have suffered from the competition for sand eels in some areas. Others, such as terns, lose out to larger competitors and have not taken to following boats at sea in the same way as gulls, such as the kittiwake, and different species of petrel have done.

Pelicans often gather in large groups for the purposes of fishing with optimal efficiency, and will form circles, horseshoe shapes or lines above shoals of fish, 'herding' them into cul-de-sacs in which escape routes are cut off. The great white pelican of South America forms this type of co-ordinated flotilla, the birds dipping their enormous bills in unison. The lower part of the bill is capable of distending to hold 10 litres of water, along with whatever fish are swept up in this enormous draught. These pelican gatherings can appear to constitute a co-ordinated strategy, each member of the group benefiting from the contributions of its fellows. The brown pelican is an expert diver and has solved the problem of swallowing water in the course of its fishing forays. Like gannets and boobies, it has evolved special sub-cutaneous air sacs that inflate quickly and enable the bird to resurface before it has to take breath. This padding also serves a shock absorbing function and breaks some of the impact of these high-level sky-dives.

While most airborne fishing birds utilize exceptional eyesight in locating prey, and are adept at snatching it from the water, there is a bird that has a strategy so unusual to behold that some observers reckon its evolutionary origins to be so obscure as to be other-worldly. The skimmer is the 'alien avian', and there are three species between India, Africa and the United States. This bird has remarkable, and quite unique, physical adaptations for a specialized fishing strategy that are not matched in any other creature. Its bill appears to be upside-down, since the lower mandible is so much longer than the upper – almost a third longer – and never stops growing. No other bird has such a bill. Viewed from the front, the bill is so thin as to be almost imperceptible. It has to be thin to slice through the water over which the skimmer hunts, beak agape, ready to snap shut on the first fish it happens to detect.

The approach is not quite as hit and miss as it might at first appear. Each species of skimmer has other adaptations that shorten the odds against actually locating prey in this manner and catching it when initial contact has been made on these high-speed missions. For its size the skimmer has an enormous wingspan, which seems paradoxical in a bird that flies so low over water. These wings allow the skimmer to take full advantage of a phenomenon known in aviation circles as the 'ground effect'. The impediment caused by turbulence is reduced by the trailing wings, while the slipstream from the wings is channelled against the surface of the water and used to give additional lift. Flight efficiency is thereby increased by up to 50 per cent.

The skimmer's head and neck have also had to undergo certain modifications in order to withstand what are effectively high-speed collisions with submerged objects. These objects are not always fish. Each of the bird's movements when such contact is made is designed to reduce the shock effect: the head and shoulders double under at lightning speed to grasp and swallow a catch; the tail fans out to act as a brake; and the wings beat to maintain some momentum and direction. A continually growing beak is essential, since there is much wear and tear associated with skimming.

Skimmers appear to enjoy more success with this unusual approach than mere chance would allow. They are expert at spotting likely fishing spots, and prone to fishing in formation parties. They are even well suited to fishing by moonlight, and are the only birds in the world known to have a vertical-slit pupil such as that possessed by cats, allowing for greater control of the amount of light passing into the eye.

The skimmer must rely to a certain extent on flat-calm water for its fishing technique to be fully effective, but the plucky little dipper thrives where the water is turbulent. The dipper has mastered the art of fishing in fast-flowing mountain streams, in which it is capable of running fully submerged against the swiftest of rapids, searching for insect larvae amongst the boulders. Unlike the cormorants, the dipper dives enwrapped in a cloak of bubbles, a film of air that prevents its feathers from being doused. The force of the current counteracts the buoyancy of the air bubbles and enables the dipper to stay submerged within its silvery air cushion. Staying dry is a crucial factor in its feeding success, as the energy needed to dry out after each foray into a cold mountain stream would render the exercise ineffective. In cold weather, the dipper would almost certainly die if its feathers became saturated. Its ability to find food in this way has given the dipper a niche all of its own in Europe, although like many aquatic species the dipper is susceptible to water pollution, which affects its favoured prey items, and is in decline in some parts of Britain and North America where man-made contaminants have entered rivers.

While continental Europe has no duck species that shares the dipper's habitat as a rule, the Americas are well represented. The torrent duck thrives, dipper-fashion, in the mountain rivers of the Andes, while in North America the strikingly plumaged harlequin duck shares this niche with the American dipper. In its dependence on clean, swift-running water in the breeding season, the harlequin also resembles the blue duck of New Zealand. Having mastered the currents of upland rivers and found a rich store of invertebrate food beneath the rapids, harlequins and their counterparts in other parts of the world are also relatively safe, and can use their 'flumes' to great effect if threatened – simply allowing themselves to be carried away from danger, either borne on the surface or at least partially submerged in the water. Before the young are able to properly negotiate these rivers, the brood is reared in backwater nurseries where, like all duck families, they are vulnerable to predation. If the ducklings survive to adulthood, their ability to thrive on mountain streams will ensure not only a niche with minimal competition, but also a relatively safe haven.

Outside the breeding season, harlequin ducks rejoin the many other species of duck across the world that live on the coast. Like the rushing inland rivers on which they breed, the sea can prove a useful ally, a haven for many species, although often an unpredictable, even hostile, one. To survive off rocky coasts requires certain skills, but if these can be mastered, then the benefits of a rich food store can be won. Like the eiders it closely resembles, the harlequin is an expert sea diver, taking full advantage of the rich pickings on the seabed.

SHORELINES

It is not just seaborne birds that can exploit the rich store provided by the shoreline, and amongst the multitude of flocks that gather at the coast, and the millions of individuals within them, a vast array of feeding techniques, favoured areas and bill shapes and sizes have arisen, perpetually probing, dabbling, sifting and prodding between shallows and high-water mark. No marine invertebrate – from lugworm to sandflea – living in this fluctuating margin between land and sea can be considered safe, since there is a bill for every job on hand.

One of the most familiar birds of the shoreline is the elegant oystercatcher, which congregates in gigantic flocks in front of the tide. Studies of their feeding behaviour have turned up some interesting findings, and what might have been presumed to be a relatively comfortable existence amongst abundant beds of shellfish can actually be a little tricky for the oystercatcher – at least when it is growing up. Oystercatchers are armed with the perfect tool for prising open their tightly clamped prey. Their beaks are long and pointed, and, viewed from the front, are taller than they are wide. This is clearly the ideal shape for opening and eating mussels, razor shells, scallops and the like, but such a tool is no use unless you know how to use it. Scientists watching flocks in action have noted how the first-year birds struggle until they have mastered the feeding art, and they learn their trade from watching the more ex-perienced adults in the flock. The strategies are a lot more complex than they might seem at a glance.

Young birds do not know how to isolate the most likely source of a meal from amongst the thousands of mussels that confront them on the shore. They tend to waste valuable time and energy exploring empty shells, and may get other shells stuck on their beaks, which can be dangerously debilitating. If they are lucky, they may be able to scavenge leftovers or plunder from other birds, and until they learn their trade this may be a necessary last resort.

Later, they may take note of the adults' strategies, such as venturing into shallow water to take mussels that are still slightly open, filtering food from the tide. With a quick stab, the experienced oystercatcher need only then lever the shell open. This can also be done with closed mussels, but may require more persistent jabs of the bill. Sometimes, if the shell has worn slightly thin in the face of the tides, the oystercatcher is able to hammer a hole in the shell without too much difficulty. The secret of success in this approach is to be able to recognize vulnerable shells, and this comes with experience. Oystercatchers are known to tap shells before selecting one that sounds flimsier than the rest, and they may also be able to recognize likely weaknesses by sight. So much tapping and stabbing takes its toll on the narrow beak, and the life-expectancy of the oystercatcher would be a lot less if its beak did not grow continuously throughout its life. A blunted tip can be replaced within two or three weeks. If it is not, the consequences are usually fatal.

Although there are a variety of methods, most individuals have a preferred method and stick to it. There are: stabbers who push the bill between the valves of the mussel; hammerers who smash the beak into one valve; hammerers who consistently smash the dorsal side and others the ventral; and some who break open the left valve and others the right. The preferred method is now known to influence selection of a mate, with like-minded birds pairing off. They may not necessarily, however, be able to pass on the family trade to their offspring since oystercatchers often breed some distance from the shore, and therefore deny their young the chance to witness the shelling technique in action. Pairs that do nest at the water's edge are known to go to great lengths to teach their young how to forage. Oystercatchers are unusual amongst shorebirds in this respect. That the oystercatcher population thrives can be attributed to their versatility as well as their specialization. When times are hard, as they invariably are for birds in their first winter, they can readily turn to probing for worms on mudflats and in fields. They are often forced to do this because, even within the largest, most apparently chaotic flocks, a pecking order exists, and those birds that have yet to reach full maturity at four years are subordinate to the adults in the flock and have fewer rights on the feeding ground.

Alongside the oystercatcher, where land meets sea, a huge variety of different species clamour for space to feed, although competition between species need not be as marked as that within a flock, since these co-existing species have different, non-conflicting appetites and techniques. Most of the world's waders are winter visitors to the coast. As it was for early nomadic peoples, the seashore, though often harsh, is a reliable source of rich food, and the habitats there are reasonably constant. While further inland the waterways and marshes may be frozen solid and therefore impenetrable to a wader's beak, the ocean's winds and currents are mild by comparison. Some families, like the relatively short-necked and stubby-billed plovers, are well suited to remaining at the shore in the breeding season, laying their eggs out of reach of the summer tides amongst the rocks and pebbles that are also their feeding grounds. Some, like the crab plover, are adapted to a more limited diet on the warmer seas of the Middle East and Africa.

A related species, the turnstone, has a beak that could be described as 'snub-nosed', and a habit of looking for food under shoreline debris, hence its name. Turnstones on the Pribilof Islands in the Bering Sea have been known to take advantage of the swarms of flies attracted to fur seal carcasses. Then there are the sandpipers and their relatives, with intermediate-sized bills, suited to probing in the softer sections closer to low tide, and the phalaropes, the only waders that habitually swim. The red-necked phalarope is known to use a strange 'twirling' technique when feeding. It is usually the female that is to be witnessed behaving in this way, using her mobility on the water to spin and pirouette in pursuit of insects on small Hebridean lochans, while the male incubates the eggs. Although classed with the waders, the phalaropes spend most of the year at sea.

Inland, freshwater lakes, ponds and rivers have become the naturalized habitat of many species of passerine, which have adapted to specialize in the rich foodstore that freshwater provides. The many species of kingfishers belong to an order of birds that includes species as diverse in habits and appearance as the hornbills and bee-eaters. The kingfishers are the anglers of the clan, specialist 'plungers' that fish from a perch or hover over still or slow-moving waters before dropping head-first to grasp small fish beneath the surface.

Other species, such as wagtails and pipits, frequent water, but are not fishers nor even strictly speaking aquatic. They are opportunists around the water's edge, where they take advantage of the large numbers of insects that are trapped by water's treacherous surface, as well as invertebrate life washed ashore from the riverbed. They simply pick these casualties off the surface and from the shore. In summer they also feast on the swarms of insects that gather above rivers, while in winter the food provided by aquatic habitats can provide sanctuary for insectivorous species from all but the most severe of weather.

FISHING RAPTORS

Besides being masters of the air and of aerial hunting and feeding, some birds of prey have evolved to exploit aquatic habitats and the sources of food these provide. Some, such as the widespread black kite, have concentrated particularly on scavenging around bodies of water, with a particular taste for fish carrion. They even share the same niche as gulls in certain ports, preying on the waste products thrown overboard from fishing boats, and perching on the masts of these boats much as gulls are more commonly associated with doing.

Most families of raptors also have their fishing specialist. Hawks, kites, eagles and owls all have representatives that live almost exclusively on live fish caught in water.

Where the black kite is an opportunist, adept at snatching debilitated fish from on or around water but not wholly dependent on this, the osprey is a master of its craft. It is the most specialized of all raptors when it comes to catching fish, and belongs to a family (*Pandionidae*) of which it is the sole member, owing to its unique features: phsyical adaptations for catching fish in water. These features include large, strong legs and feet, long curved talons of equal length, short spines on its soles for extra grip, a reversible outer toe, and a large oil gland with which to manicure its plumage, which it does in regular and prolonged preening sessions. The osprey occurs right across the northern hemisphere, and winters in the south, always keeping within reach of water. The osprey can take other types of prey, but usually only in exceptional circumstances.

To catch its supper, the osprey swoops down out of the sky and plunges into the water, talons first. Grabbing the fish just below the surface it struggles back into the air with the victim firmly hooked. Returning to a perch or back to the nest to feed its young, it holds the fish torpedo-fashion, that is, head first, in order to reduce drag.

Africa's resident fish-eating eagle fishes a little more elegantly than the osprey, snatching fish from near the surface of the large expanses of water which it usually frequents, or plunging fully to capture fish in deeper water. The snatching method involves a flight from a perch of no more than 27–46 metres, which usually ends in a successful catch. The entire event lasts no longer than 30 seconds: an almost effortless way of obtaining a meal. Unlike the osprey however, the African fish eagle can turn its hand to other prey and hunting tactics. In some East African rift valley lakes, fish-eagles are now denied fish and have turned to flamingos instead. They are adept at snatching this unusual prey from the midst of a cloud of pink flapping shapes.

The African fish eagle is as elegantly plumaged as that famous symbol of the United States – the bald eagle. This eagle has long been in decline over much of its range, although a healthy population has been maintained in the north-west, from which large winter migrations southward became a famous event. These movements had also become a major tourist attraction, since in any autumn the eagles could be relied upon to congregate in huge numbers at salmon spawning grounds such as that in Glacier National Park, Montana. At this time of year thousands of salmon arrived to spawn, and then to die, leaving the eagles with a banquet of easy pickings from the shallow creek. Now, however, the party may be over for eagles and spectators alike, as the salmon numbers have dwindled to a tiny fraction of previous years. The reason for the decline is something of an ecological mystery, but the consequences could be dire for the eagles on their long journey south to the warmer climes of states such as Utah and Idaho.

There is some dispute as to the exact reason for the disappearance of the salmon, but it is thought that the introduction of the tiny oppossum shrimp, which feeds on the same zooplankton as the salmon, may be the main cause. Ironically, these shrimps were introduced as a source of food for the salmon, which themselves were introduced in the early 1900s. Since that time, the bald eagles had come to rely on this source of food for sustenance on the long flight south. Immature birds may now suffer badly in the sudden absence of a once reliable picnic spot.

As recently as 1976, 30,000 people visited the scene, where it had been reported a few days earlier that 639 eagles had been counted in a single day on one two-and-a-half mile stretch of McDonald Creek. Unless the salmon can be reintroduced, a great loss to both eagles and humans may have been incurred.

FISHING OWLS

It is perhaps not surprising, given the large number of diurnal raptors that have made a success out of catching and eating fish, that there are also many species of owls that have fared similarly.

The adaptability of certain owls is exhibited by the most familiar of European owls – the tawny. The tawny owl is a general feeder, taking as large a range of food prey as diurnal birds of prey such as the buzzard, and capable of hunting in dense woodland in a similar way to the goshawk. It will readily eat fish washed ashore, and is capable of capturing live prey from water, using its remarkable night vision and powerful claws to good effect.

Two giants of the world's owls, the Eurasian eagle owl and the North American great horned owl, are similarly eclectic in their taste, and have been recorded hovering over water in search of fish prey, which is also eaten in the form of carrion on the shore. Where these owls take whatever is available, some owl species, such as Blakiston's fish owl, have become more specialized. Blakiston's is a true fishing owl – larger even than the taxonomically similar eagle owl – living in the secluded forests of east Asia, and hunting by walking in shallow water and on river banks, leaving characteristic trails as it does so. It catches fish of considerable size, as well as mammals up to the size of cats and small dogs. In winter it congregates in small groups at the best fishing sites, such as rapids and non-freezing springs, much as fishing eagles have to do in the harsher northerly parts of their range. It is thought that this may contain the answer to the question of why this owl has not extended its range into parts of southern Asia and North America which have no resident fishing owls, as it loses out in competition with diurnal sea eagle species such as Steller's, which it meets at its winter havens on rocky east Asian islands. Large birds like these are also vulnerable to hunters in such aggregations.

Although there are many species of fishing owl in different parts of the world, there remain large geographical areas notable for the absence of any owl exploiting the aquatic niches available, such as on the lakes and rivers of the American tropics. Again, the reason for this apparent gap could be the owl's ecological subordinance in the face of competition from other species unrelated to it except in similarity of prey. Alternatively, it could be that evolution has yet to fill all the planet's available niches.

PIRATES

Birds, like everything else within the plant and animal kingdoms, are involved in a perpetual struggle for food, against both the elements and the other constituents of their environment. There are a great many instances in the course of these struggles of direct competition for food, often resulting in a confrontation that usually results in the strongest taking the prize. The early bird only gets the worm if the slightly later bird doesn't arrive in time and with the means to rob it. Some species of birds, having found themselves on to a good thing as far as the food resources of their territory are concerned, go to extraordinary lengths to defend it from intruders, even those belonging to other species.

One such bird is the bell miner of south-eastern Australia, which defends communal territories against other species, even when there is an apparent surfeit of food available. Mistle thrushes are similarly belligerent in the locality of laden berry trees, while prolonged disputes can be witnessed at any bird table, where rights to a sudden high concentration of food are the subject of endless, and often fierce, negotiations. It often seems that the most energetic defenders of the food spend more time posturing than actually eating, and may be losing out. Birds have to be careful to get the balance of eating and defending right, and at a bird table they may find their efforts to defend the food rendered futile by the sheer number of competitors attracted to the scene. Communal defence strategies are therefore much more efficient and beneficial to a species.

The taking of food from other birds is practised by many species at one time or another. African fish eagles are not always the magnificent monarchs of the sky that we often so romantically portray. They rob pied kingfishers, hammerkops, pelicans and those giants of the heron world, the man-high goliath heron. This enormous bird wades out to depths that cannot be reached by other herons, where it stabs at fish with its enormous bill. It gets the biggest fish, and the fish eagle knows that. Fish eagles also hijack ospreys, other fish eagles and even their own young. Mates have even been known to rob their partners.

Joining the fishing-eagle raiding parties are tawny and steppe eagles. They have developed the habit of following European and maribou storks that are themselves following the misfortunes of burrowing mole rats. The mole rats are excavated by tractor-drawn ploughs, and no sooner has a stork gulped down a rat than a tawny eagle dives down to pirate the prey. The tawny eagles maximize their impact by barking loudly.

Species making a living out of thievery or who habitually use the tactic are known as 'kleptoparasites'. Examples of it can be seen any time that bread or scraps are found by a flock of gulls. Far from observing an orderly 'first come first served' protocol, the flock will indulge in raucous chases as any gull with a beakfull of food is harangued by the others. If it drops the bread, another will swoop to pick it up, and the process continues until the bread has been wolfed down and is out of sight. Gulls of the same species are as likely to observe this ritual as gulls of two or more different species, and crows will often become involved in the skirmishes.

Studies of kelptoparasitism by common gulls or black-headed gulls undertaken at a refuse tip in Cork showed that the common gulls preferred to leave all the foraging to their smaller relatives, then to try to relieve them of their food when this was too large to consume in one go. It was discovered that the resultant chases had only a 25 per cent chance of success if one common gull maintained the pursuit, rising to 75 per cent success if five or more birds were involved in chasing. The actual success rate this represented for each individual in the chasing pack was of course divisible by the number in the chasing pack, since a surrendered catch could only be claimed by one of the common gulls, and the others would not benefit from the robbery. Thus this example of kleptoparasitism does not seem to have been particularly cost-effective, in the sense of effort being rewarded, for any individual within the community of common gulls, and the fact that they did not resort to foraging for their own food from the rubbish dump indicates that they may have simply been supplementing their diet of earthworms from neighbouring farmland.

Studies of black-headed gulls parasitizing plovers also found that individual success was diminished with each additional gull joining the chasing pack, even though the chance of the bounty materializing increased. Arctic skuas, on the other hand, have been found to benefit from co-operation between a chasing pair resulting in greater benefits for each individual. For the skua family, parasitism is a way of life, and even individual birds will persist with the tactic, robbing a succession of hapless seabirds of their hard-earned catch.

Gulls and crows are notorious robbers of hawks and falcons, and will sometimes form 'snatch squads' to deprive an otherwise formidable customer of its catch. Since the strategy obviously works, it is perhaps not surprising that some species have resorted to piracy as a way of life, and not just an occasional habit arising only in certain circumstances.

Although the tactic seems unscrupulous, it is difficult not to admire the aerial dexterity of the aptly named frigate bird, a majestic man of war of tropical and sub-tropical waters. It is highly specialized for life over the high seas, with a skeletal structure that is light even by birds' standards. The frigate bird's wing area is greater in relation to body weight than in any other bird and the wings are deeply cambered, which, in tandem with the gracefully forked tail, allows for perfect balance and effortless manoeuvrability in the air. The feet are so reduced in size that they are of no use for swimming, and the plumage is not fully waterproof. This sacrifice is more than compensated for, since the frigate bird does not have to settle on water in order to procure its food from this source, preferring to snatch morsels from the surface with millimetre precision and without pausing to break speed. When food is not available from the waves it can readily switch its attention to other sources.

In places like the Galapagos Islands, two of the world's five species of frigate bird – the great and the magnificent – slot in alongside the boobies, sharing the same stretches of coastline, but differing sufficiently in their role within it to co-exist in relative harmony. The booby is an accomplished aeronaut, but next to the swashbuckling frigates it appears little more than pedestrian, and is sometimes robbed by its nimble neighbour with such alacrity that it is powerless to take preventive action beyond indignant scolding. Frigates have, for example, been known to snatch food as it is being passed from an adult booby to its offspring. Such a theft requires immaculate timing, as there is no margin for error between the bills of its much heftier victims. Frigates even steal from their own kind in this fashion. Although they are more than capable of foraging for themselves, they often nest in the midst of a colony of other species providing close-hand opportunities for parasitism.

The most common procedure for parasitism by frigates is to chase a bird such as a booby in a small band, often pulling at the tail or wings of the victim and even sometimes driving it into the sea until it has regurgitated its catch. Since the catch is not visible until it has been surrendered in this way, the frigates may often be chasing a lost cause, and even when there is a prize, only one of the band is able to claim it. Such a hunting technique is clearly only viable for a bird that does not have to expend too much energy employing it, and must only serve as a supplement to a broader dietary intake.

Parasitism only works if it does not ultimately exhaust the reserves of the victim. Young frigates must learn to feed in more than one way, such as forage-feeding many miles out to sea. It takes a considerable period of time before fledged frigate birds learn how to feed themselves and become independent of their parents – such is the price of their specialization.

HUNTING PARTNERS

Frigate birds practising kleptoparasitism in groups are one example of something that seems on the face of it to be co-operative hunting in birds. There are other examples of it, some of which may have a better claim to embodying the true spirit of co-operation, as opposed to a loose group of individuals happening to find themselves in pursuit of the same prey, but ostensibly in it for their own benefit, rather than that of the group as a whole.

In the breeding season, pairs of hawks and falcons are often seen attacking the same prey, and will share the spoils of the hunt. While it is true that their chances of making a kill are increased by dual involvement, this is not strictly speaking co-operative hunting, as each hawk is likely to be trying to make the catch, rather than deploying itself as a foil for the other to make the strike.

It is probably force of circumstance that leads a species like the Eleonora's falcon to hunt in groups. Being amongst the most ecologically specialized of falcons, large concentrations of these birds breed in late summer on Mediterranean islands, their egg-laying timed to coincide with the throughflow of autumn migrants across wide expanses of water, where they are vulnerable to attack. At these times, groups of Eleonora's falcons gather, with individuals taking up position at various vantage points in the sky up to 1000 metres, presenting a formidable barrier through which passage migrants must pass in order to reach their wintering grounds. Running the gauntlet of the falcons' colonial breeding territory sometimes involves prolonged chases involving two or more assailants over considerable distances. This hunting strategy is effective, and it is estimated that as many as one in 600 small birds migrating across these stretches of the Mediterranean may fall prey to Eleonora's falcons.

At other times, small flocks of falcons may gather where there is an abundance of insects, much as flocks of black kites gather near towns and waterways, where pickings are rich. This type of social gathering is not typical of many raptors, although the ones that practise it are simply responding to the presence of others of their kind, interpreting it as a sign of food for the taking. Each bird benefits to the extent that it is led to a source of food, and the presence of the others increases an individual's chance of securing a meal, although it is not helped by the other individuals beyond that. Vultures benefit from gregarious habits, and seem able to interpret the behaviour of their fellows, often at great distances, if prey has been sighted. Some fruit-eating species of tropical forests will loudly proclaim to other members of the same species that they have found a tree laden with food. If the favour is returned at a later date, then this strategy could be seen to be working to the benefit of the community as a whole in a habitat where finding food amongst dense foliage can sometimes prove problematic.

In so far as the rewards for collective hunting provide a meal for more than one of the group members, the behaviour of Harris hawks is relevant. This species has been observed in New Mexico hunting in groups in order to capture rabbits and hares: prey that are ordinarily too large and too speedy for them to take when hunting alone. Groups of four to six increase their chances of capturing this elusive prey by a variety of means, depending on how the hunt unfolds. The group will chase a rabbit, taking turns to lunge at it, or attack it from different directions at the same time, often simply to prevent its escape rather than in an effort to kill it. This approach relies upon a degree of mutual understanding of the means and ends of the hunt, but perhaps the most intriguing evidence of forethought and cunning occurs if and when the rabbit or hare takes refuge in cover.

The hawks then employ what scientists have called the 'flush and ambush' technique, whereby one hawk walks into the cover in order to flush the refugee. It is a reasonably safe assumption that this is the hawk's intention, since it has no chance of making the kill itself in such circumstances, and may if anything be exposing itself to a certain level of personal risk if at close quarters with a cornered hare, which may weigh anything up to three times as much as a Harris hawk and is armed with a powerful set of hind legs. The hare is likely to bolt, and thereby afford the rest of the hunting group another opportunity to strike.

It is this fact of differentiated role-playing within the group that distinguishes the co-operative hunting of the Harris hawks from the social hunting of other raptors such as the Eleonora's falcon. It is thought that the Harris hawks have been able to develop these tactics as they are non-migratory and therefore have relatively stable social groups that are together all year round.

HUNTERS ON THE GROUND

Where Harris hawks find themselves having occasionally to return to ground level in search of prey in the deserts of the American south-west, another, more legendary, species has made it a way of life. Not many people think of the roadrunner as a member of the cuckoo clan, but that is precisely what it is, having taken to a more terrestrial existence at a time when it became expedient to do so. It is thought that its forebears may have lived on easily accessible fruits and insects, and that foraging on the wing became as impractical as shopping by plane.

The roadrunner has since acquired a more catholic palate, as well as a more specialized hunting repertoire, and, like the tiny predatory theropod dinosaurs, has made an art of its bipedality. It is now the sprinter of the cuckoo family, able to run at up to 15 mph over large areas of arid terrain; and also able as a result to exploit prey species that are out of the reach of predators in the skies overhead, since most desert creatures avoid leaving the safety of ground cover too far behind them. The roadrunner has come down to the same level as these reptiles, small animals and invertebrates, and has evolved to match the timing of their movements. It has a particular penchant for catching the fleet-of-foot whiptail lizards that prove too elusive for most other predators.

On the plains of Africa, the snake-catching specialist is another long-legged, almost stork-like bird of prey that has opted for a ground-based strategy. The secretary bird uses its long, bare legs to grapple with deadly snakes, keeping its body out of reach of the jaws in the course of its struggles with these often sizeable reptiles and killing its victims by administering blows with its claws until it has subdued them sufficiently to administer a death-blow to the head.

In both species, the legs are highly adapted to life lived on the ground, where flying ability is a secondary consideration for successful hunting, but not sacrificed to the extent that the bird becomes vulnerable.

SCAVENGERS

Within the eternal cycle of life in the natural world, where nothing that dies goes to waste, and the misfortune of one creature is invariably life-enhancing for another, birds are numbered amongst natures morticians. Most people think of vultures spiralling overhead when scavenging birds are mentioned, but they are just one of numerous groups of birds that have a taste for the detritus of nature and, within this, man in particular has in the past been a great provider.

For the griffon vulture, however, the provision has also been taken away, and changes in the rural make-up of some parts of Europe have had a deleterious effect on the resident populations. Until the 1950s, the Pyrenean vulture population was able to co-exist harmoniously with the farming community, and benefited from the carrion found on livestock farms. When the laws were changed on the French side, and it was ordered that dead animals should be disposed of rather than left for nature to recycle, the repercussions were severe, and the vultures began to die out.

The 'pastoral ecosystem' of the western Pyrenees has evolved over at least 4,000 years, since man first brought livestock to the mountains, and the land previously roamed by large wild animals was adopted by domestic creatures, providing the vultures with, if anything, a readier supply of food. They became dependent on the activities of shepherds, and in turn the farms relied upon the vultures to clean up decaying carcasses. Nowadays, the balance is more precarious, and reintroduction programmes are under way in certain parts of France in order to stabilize the populations, and ensure that the vultures are not lost.

Even carcasses left in the vicinity of villages are picked clean by a succession of scavengers. First ravens venture down, in turn attracting the shy Egyptian vulture, kites, eagles and latterly the griffons. They will dispose of all the flesh in around an hour of noisy activity and frenzied clamour.

Griffons are resident throughout the year, and are possessed of a unique energy-conserving metabolism which sees them through the bitterest of winters high in the mountains. The Egyptian vulture is a summer visitor to Europe, and returns to Africa in the winter. It is an eclectic scavenger, perhaps taking the principle of scavenging to its logical extreme in some of its habits. It is known to be partial to lion's dung, for example, although it does not partake of the dung of other large predators, such as wild dogs and hyenas. This fussiness has been traced to the fact that lion dung is more nutritious, since the lion has a shorter gut and does not extract as much of the nutrients from its food as the other carnivores.

Genetic analysis has shown that the turkey vultures of the New World are actually more closely related to storks than to the vultures of Eurasia and Africa. They are distributed throughout the Americas, across a wide range of landscapes, including urban situations. Much of their utility has been put down to their energy efficiency, crucial for a bird that relies heavily on fate in finding food, and often has to go for days on end without eating. They have an internal 'thermostat' which they turn down at night to reduce metabolic energy loss, and use the sunlight of early morning to recharge their cooled organs.

When they do eat, they are not fussy about the size of carcass that they visit, and will descend to pick a mouse from the roadside. They are light-framed and broad-winged, enabling them to soar for long periods with minimum effort, but perhaps their most effective secret weapon, and a development that makes them almost unique amongst birds, is their acute sense of smell. Engineers in the United States are aided by vultures in locating leaks in gas pipes, by pumping strong-smelling gases through the pipes and noting where the vultures gather.

Another adaptation of turkey vultures that sets them apart from other birds is their capacity to eat the most putrefied of animal tissue. They are immune to many bacterial toxins, notably botulism, and thrive on carcasses that might poison any other creature. The digestive waste disposal system is so effective that the vulture happily defecates on its own legs, since its droppings are an antiseptic coating which will protect those bare limbs from the possible infections lurking in its prey. The bald head is also vulnerable to these bacteria, but the absence of feathers exposes any unwelcome microbes to the sanitizing rays of the sun. With all this in mind, it is odd to think of a turkey vulture being sick, but they often are – in response to stressful situations. Regurgitating their last meal serves one or two useful functions: reducing bodyweight for optimum manoeuvrability, or deterring an assailant in a way that puts even the infamous skunk in the shade.

FINDING FOOD AND USING TOOLS

While many birds are able to spot and recognize prey on sight, many others have to go to great lengths to uncover it. They therefore have to know how to recognize not, in the first instance, the prey itself, but the place where they are likely to find it. This usually requires physical adaptations, with beaks and claws acting as tools, as well as organs by which prey is caught and consumed. The classic example is the woodpecker, a family with representatives across the globe, wherever there are trees, and even cacti. Woodpeckers are perfectly suited to their role, and are more likely to be seen clinging to the face of a vertical trunk than perched in more orthodox bird fashion. They are equipped for this purpose with strongly curved claws and with toes that are splayed in different directions to facilitate a firmer grip.

European woodpeckers tend to be sedentary, which means that they must be able to change their diet in accordance with the changing seasons. In summer they are largely insectivorous, feeding largely on caterpillars gleaned from the canopy of their woodland homes. In the winter, when there are neither leaves nor caterpillars to be found and insects are dormant, they resort to foraging for their prey in hidden cavities, listening for the tiniest sound of grubs wriggling in their chambers or insects twitching behind the bark. In order to be successful at excavating this invertebrate prey from its winter chambers woodpeckers have to do a lot of drilling, and have specially reinforced skulls to absorb the shock this entails, and powerful neck muscles for vigorous hammering (see Chapter 4). A further weapon in the woodpecker's armoury is its long, snaking tongue, which enables it to reach wood-boring insects and larvae from the deepest chambers. The tongue is part of an elaborate mechanism, known as a hyoid, that is tucked neatly round the skull, enabling the tongue to extend up to four times the length of the woodpecker's beak. This apparatus also comes in handy for wood-peckers that feed on ant hills, as the American flickers habitually do. These species have adhesive tongues that also neutralize the acidic stings of indignant ants.

The woodpecker's chiselling bill can also be put to good use during the nut harvest. The acorn woodpecker of North America specializes in finding and opening acorns, and forms co-operatives which collect and stash them. The acorns are wedged into holes in the trunks and limbs of the oak, usually so tightly that only a woodpecker can dislodge them. Large caches can therefore be accumulated, and the breeding success of the collective the following spring depends on how many acorns they have pooled the previous autumn.

The woodpeckers are an ancient family, now reaping the rewards of millions of years of natural selection that have bequeathed to them all the tools they require in their physical make-up.

Other species are not so well endowed, but this has not prevented them from finding their own means of excavating prey from tight crevices. The Galapagos finches have, within their number, one species that has learned the technique. Lacking the woodpecker's chisel bill, muscular neck and protruding tongue, the woodpecker finch employs thin twigs or cactus spines to get at its food – true tools. Some individuals are better at the job than others, and some may even modify their chosen implement if initially unsuccessful, or discard it and try again with a new one. They may even keep a particularly well suited one and hold on to it between meals.

The American brown-headed nuthatch is another species that uses tools to compensate for its physical limitations. In its case, the device is bark scales, which it uses as an 'extra corporeal limb' – the term used by scientists to categorize actual tool-using in non-human animals – to lever other pieces of bark scale off trunks that it is examining for insect prey.

The regular occurrence of such behaviour across a species is very rare in the bird world, although reports of individual birds such as blue tits and blackbirds using sticks do arise. The orange-winged sittellas of Australia have been seen to insert pieces of wood into cavities containing insect larvae, the tool held first in the beak and then by the feet while the tasty morsel is consumed. In Tanzania, grey flycatchers fish for termites with grass stems in the manner of chimpanzees.

It is perhaps not surprising that there is a record from the resourceful crow family. The white-winged chough has been witnessed breaking into freshwater mussels using part of the open shell of another mussel as a hammer. These observations were first made at the Hattah Lakes National Park in Victoria, Australia, and subsequent reports from New South Wales record this species as adopting other strategies – albeit inexpertly – such as using the hammer as a missile and using other solid objects as anvils.

The green heron is a tool-user. It is an angler, and catches fish with an artificial lure. The bird breaks off small twigs and throws them onto the water in such a way that they resemble insects in distress. Any fish that comes to investigate the potential meal becomes a meal itself; the heron strikes fast and grabs the fish before it can return to hiding. Some individuals use feathers instead of sticks: the ultimate avian flyfisher.

The black heron uses a sunshade. It runs along in shallow water, stops, spreads its wings over its head like a parasol and remains still for up to a minute. It is thought the wings act as a sunshield under which the bird can spot any fish.

When the often tricky business of securing food is complete, birds may yet find that their food is not in a state of readiness for consumption. As with the raw ingredients of a meal, some preparation may have to go into it before eating may begin.

We may witness food preparation of a kind by birds if we throw dry bread onto a duck pond. It appears that wildfowl deliberately saturate the bread on the surface, crushing it up into a soggy mush before swallowing. This simply ensures that the food slips down readily, without catching in the gullet. Reports of birds 'washing' their food are also now quite regular. Marabou storks are widely accepted as using a deliberate sanitation technique before eating dung beetles, but reports of other species dousing prey before eating it are borderline cases, and the use of water may be as much for added lubrication and moistening as for cleanliness.

It is common for blackbirds and their allies to spit out the seeds from certain types of fruit before consuming the sugary surround. Specialist snail eaters such as song thrushes and the Everglade kite with its winkle-picker beak are fastidious about removing the albumen gland from snails. Some birds are known to wipe slugs clean of their unpleasant tasting slime before attempting to swallow them, and the same applies to the irritant hairs that are designed to protect certain types of caterpillar.

Many raptors leave untouched certain parts of a larger item, such as entrails, feet and the larger bones, feeding mainly on the flesh of their victims. Owls, meanwhile, have a tendency to swallow prey whole, since they do not digest the more fibrous parts and regurgitate these as pellets.

Birds which eat wasps may be running the risk of being stung in the throat which, even if it did not kill the bird directly, might cause it to suffocate due to the swelling that would probably result. If birds are to make a success of feeding on potentially hazardous prey, they either have to learn the right strategy from others, or hope that they get a second chance to learn from a first-time mistake. In the case of the bee-eater the removal of wasp and bee stings before consumption may be second nature, or the birds' partial immunity to the stings may help to protect them from one or two unpleasant – though not fatal – experiences. Interestingly, birds such as flycatchers can become so familiar with the exact make-up of their prey that they are not fooled by the attempts of species such as the hoverfly to look like a stinging insect, and do not attempt to remove a sting that is not there.

Other birds have to learn to recognize objects that are not yet ready to be eaten as potential food sources. Shellfish and nuts fall into this category. Nuts, for example, may not look much different from a small knot of hard wood, although the contents are very nutritious. Learning to distinguish the two requires experience, to make the connection between object and meal, or a demonstration of how the edible centre can be accessed.

Just as eagles must remove feathers from bird prey, so other species must treat their food. Most fish-eaters have to learn to swallow fish head first, or risk choking on abrasive scales. Some species of thrush have learned to smash snail shells against a hard surface before claiming the soft flesh inside; although, interestingly, similar species that share their habitats never do.

The same applies in East Africa, where the Egyptian vulture, long famed for its ability to break into ostrich eggs using stones as missiles, is still the only bird recorded doing this. There has been some controversy about the origin of this behaviour, some scientists claiming that the skill must be learned, and citing as evidence the fact that a captive bred vulture shows no inclination to break into an ostrich egg. Subsequent observations have shown that there does appear to be an instinctive urge in young vultures to project stones with their bills. The trigger need not be the witnessing of an actual stoning by another bird but simply a hint of what the egg contains. Such hints are likely to be commonplace in the wild, except in years when ostrich breeding is limited, in which case some young vultures might never establish the link. It is thought that the vultures' apparently innate tendency to throw objects such as smaller eggs may have prompted the habit of breaking ostrich eggs to develop. An ostrich egg is too big to throw but is still recognizable as an egg. The hungry vulture, used to throwing smaller eggs and gaining a meal as a result, will thus throw smaller, often egg-like stones at the shell until it breaks. The fact that other opportunistic birds have not picked up on the habit suggests that the vultures have the extra dexterity needed before it can be done successfully. (There are unconfirmed reports from Australia of the black-breasted buzzard dropping stones onto clutches of emu eggs, but this, for the moment, is a figment of Aboriginal folklore rather than scientific observation.)

Another vulture that makes its living from a very particular type of food also goes to impressive lengths, or rather heights, to access it. This bird is the lammergeier, or bearded vulture, of which there remains a small European population, mainly in the Pyrenees, besides healthier populations in Asia and East Africa. This vulture is subordinate to larger species at carcases, but it does not necessarily lose out, since it has an appetite for the bits that even these other scavengers overlook. Confronted with the gleaming bones of a carcase picked clean, it will swallow bones whole, but its speciality is to take the larger bones in its talons, fly to great heights over the rocky landscape, and drop them onto suitably hard surfaces far below. In this way the lammergeier satisfies much of its nutritional requirements, and certainly all of the calcium requirement that is important in the development of its young.

Studies of South African vultures found that the incidence of bone deformity in young vultures was high in areas where the parent birds were unable to provide their offspring with sufficient calcium. Such areas were found to be ones bereft of hyenas, which are able to break the bones of carcases, and provide fragments for secondary scavengers such as vultures. Without the hyenas to break into the bone marrow for them, these vultures were unable to rear their chicks on a sufficiently calcium-rich diet. This discovery should enable scientists to save the threatened Cape vulture by providing them with specially fragmented bones, on which they readily feed. The lammergeier, as long as it has bones to crush, need never require human assistance in this way, and when it feels like a bit of fresh meat it is able to turn its attention to live prey, such as tortoises, which it prepares in much the same way as its bone-marrow starter.

Birds learn to recognize, Pavlovian fashion, certain variables within their territories, and associate them with food even if these stimuli are not themselves food. Many birds exploit factors such as livestock, large wild animals, marching army ants and fires, much as game hunters use beaters, as something that flushes prey from its protective environment. In tropical forests, a parade of ants on the forest floor means rich pickings for the birds in the canopy, and they will gather around the procession to pick up the terrestrial creatures fleeing in the path of the unflinching ants (see Chapter 3). On the African plains, it is customary to see large grazing animals accompanied by an avian entourage, often including bee-eaters, thriving on the insects that are both attracted and disturbed from the grass by the presence of a large animal. Kestrels are often amongst those species that pick up the insects and other small creatures fleeing in the face of a brush fire.

Gulls are renowned opportunists, but some have learned a few considered tricks for bringing prey their way. Common gulls, for example, associate heavy rain with the presence of earthworms on the surface of fields. When there is no rain, seagulls sometimes simulate the sound of rainfall by pattering their feet. This fools the earthworms into rising instinctively to the surface – as they do when it rains – to avoid drowning. Birds really have, it seems, thought of everything.

9

LIVING WITH PEOPLE

IN THE HOT ARID BUSH OF THE SUDAN AND NORTHERN KENYA SOURCES of calorie-rich food are few and far between. Even so, there is a bird which has found an unusual supply of food there and it exploits it in an unusual way. The bird is the greater or black-throated honey-guide. It is a small (20 centimetres long), fairly drab bird which is not easily noticed by predators. It has keen eyesight and a highly tuned sense of smell. And it needs these, for its unique diet is as scarce as it is precious. The honeyguide is a specialist consumer of bees' wax and larvae. Wild bee colonies are scattered randomly throughout the bush and, in more arid areas, may be many miles apart. Honeyguides follow bee activity and can smell out colonies.

But, having discovered the huge food cache, the honeyguide can go no further without help. It is simply not powerful enough to overcome sentry bees or break its way into the colony. The local bees are after all the same type that were introduced to South

America and escaped from a bee breeding farm in Brazil, causing panic amongst local people. To the rest of the world they became known as 'killer bees', but to the honeyguide they are the producers of essential food supplies. To get at the honey combs, however, the bird needs powerful bee-proof, honey-loving partners. These tend to be 6 feet tall and technologically advanced enough to pacify angry bees with smoke. What is more, man adores honey but does not eat honeyguides.

The honeyguide's human helpers are the Boran people of Kenya. The Boran claim, quite legitimately it turns out, that the behaviour of the honeyguides tells them not only in which direction the bee colony is to be found, but also how far away it is. The honeyguide also demonstrates awareness of many colonies that are in its territory, and if the first one it betrays is not excavated it will quickly redirect the Boran to another.

Once a honeyguide has located a bees' nest, it perches on an obvious calling perch, such as a fence post or dead branch near a human trail, and gives a distinctive 'weet-er' advertisement call. This, it hopes, will attract a helper. In arid areas man himself is scarce and the bird may have to call for several weeks before finding a willing accomplice. When a likely candidate approaches the honeyguide becomes agitated and changes to a chattering 'ke-ke-ke-ke-ke-ke' call. This machine-gun-like rattle is unmistakable and never fails to attract the attention of passers-by. Local people have been familiar with this call for probably many thousands of years, possibly since both man and honeyguide first evolved. Both parties can now look forward to the feast in store.

The honeyguide flies a few yards ahead of its helper and continues to give its excitable call. As the man approaches, the bird flies off again and calls, gradually guiding its partner to the colony. Honeyguides have been reported leading people several miles from the pick-up point, straight to an active colony. At the destination, the bird perches and waits whilst its human partner kindles a small fire, using smoke to stupify the lethal bees. After half an hour or so, the honey combs can be breached and the honey is collected in pots or cups made from woven fan palm leaves. Man takes only the honey. Whilst undoubtedly delicious, honey is not the most valuable part of the haul.

Bees wax has a much higher calorific value – loathed by the fashion-conscious, but preferred by most survival-conscious animals. As a honeyguide can only eat a limited volume, high calorific wax is more practical than comparatively low-calorie honey. Birds not only need calories for fuel, they also need protein for body repair and growth. Extracted from the wax cells, bee larvae are possibly the ultimate high-protein, high-carbohydrate bird-sized growth food.

Over the millennia a division of labour as well as a division of resources has evolved. The birds find the bees, and guide the man, who alone can make the spoils available. Then the man removes the honey, leaving the wax and larvae on nearby branches or platforms for the honeyguide. No-one knows how this unique symbiotic relationship first evolved. It has had around 20,000 years to develop, although the changing human world may mean that it will soon be a thing of the past – the Boran can get their honey from the supermarket. If this is the case, the honeyguide may still have other willing mammalian associates such as the honey badger or the baboon, assuming that these animals can 'read' the cues and are scrupulous about leaving aside the honeyguide's share of the spoils after the bee's nest has been plundered.

SPORT OF KINGS AND COMMONERS

Honeyguides, it could be argued, were the instigators and leaders of these mutually beneficial food raids. But, with superior intellect, it did not take man very long to realize the potential of turning the table on another group of birds for their mutual benefit.

The art of falconry was developed in central Asia. Whilst falconry evokes images of medieval heraldry and the sport of nobility, this merely represents a late Western European manifestation. Falconry did not develop first as a sport but as a means of securing meat in a harsh, unpredictable landscape where early livestock husbandry was not to be relied on. And in any case, in the harsh semi-desert regions of central Asia, India and the Middle East, livestock husbandry was often not sustainable; other sources of protein-rich food, and the means of acquiring it, were sought.

Life is hard for falcons too. Night temperatures are surprisingly cold in most arid areas and the birds can only surivive a few days without food. If consecutive hunts prove unsuccessful, a falcon may perish within a week. In such a harsh and unforgiving environment these wild hunters were tempted by the promise of easy pickings. So the basis for falconry was that the birds could be, at least in part, trained to accept human handlers. Man guaranteed a daily food supply and protected his own birds. In return the falcons were carried to the places where they stood the best chance of securing quarry which, in turn, they were forced to share with their handler.

Men trained falcons because they were the most reliable means locally of securing meat. The bond between man and bird is based on food. Whilst domesticated dogs work for their handlers out of love, loyalty and an eagerness to please, falcons do not. Falcons will only hunt if they are hungry. Man soon learned to detect the most subtle changes in his falcon's weight and moods. Lean and keen birds are hungry enough to hunt and kill bustards, grouse and hares. Well fed ones are not. The birds must be fed enough to ensure their health and survival, whilst not blunting their keenness to work.

The first written accounts of trained birds of prey being used for hunting were from Japan in AD 244, but it is thought that the origins of falconry go back more than 4,000 years. Ever since those beginnings in the Far East the peregrine has been the falconer's greatest prize. Speed, air supremacy and beauty combine to make it a bird fit for princes, although in Britain during the Middle Ages the people also commonly flew birds. It was only the rich who could afford to have their pictures painted doing it.

The birds most commonly used in falconry are grouped into three types: 'broad-wings' or eagles, 'short-wings' or hawks and 'long-wings' or falcons, like the peregrine. Falconry has its own vocabulary to describe the birds, their behaviour and the equipment used by the falconer.

The female peregrine only is known as the 'falcon' and the male the 'tiercel' on account of its being a third the size of the female or the third egg in a clutch to hatch, depending on which story you believe. Similarly, the female names – gyr falcon, saker, lanner, merlin and sparrowhawk – are matched by the male names – jerkin, sakret, lanneret, jack-merlin and musket.

Birds taken from the nest are known as 'eyasses', those taken from the wild in their first year are 'passagers' or 'passage-hawks', and adult birds are 'haggards'. After its first moult in captivity the bird is 'intermewed'. So, 'an intermewed eyass peregrine tiercel' is a male peregrine, more than one year old which was obtained by the falconer as a chick.

In many countries today it is illegal to take birds from the wild. Only captive birds can be used in falconry. Nevertheless there is an illegal international trade and poachers raid nests to obtain eggs and young birds. In Italy, for example, the number of breeding peregrines was reduced to just 350 pairs in the 1980s because of egg collecting for falconry.

Once trapped on migration or taken from the nest, hungry birds are held captive and gradually persuaded to accept their handler and fly to the falconer in return for food. Later the birds are flown free to perfect their flight and hunting strength whilst being recalled for food. Ultimately the fed but hungry birds are taken to hunt for themselves. They are taken to areas where game may be found and human beaters or canine flushers may even be used to force ground-dwelling game into view. The birds are then 'cast off' or launched at their quarry.

If successful in grounding a bustard or other game a falcon does not return to its handler as a dog might. Falcons are not that subservient. They are hunting for themselves. The birds at once start to break into the quarry, from which the falconer must lure them with alternative morsels or else physically remove them. Larger hawks and eagles are powerful, often single-minded pred-ators, and the rescuing of the quarry for the pot may not always be such a simple matter. Once extracted, the bird may be flown at further game if its appetite is keen.

Traditional falconry could prove a positive benefit to the birds involved. The falcons were trapped or taken in late autumn and used to hunt through winter. At this time many of the birds would otherwise have to risk the hazards of migration to distant wintering grounds. Trained falcons were guaranteed a daily food supply through the winter which ensured their survival until the spring breeding season. With the arrival of spring, life became easier for the falconers, and the birds were released back into the wild. During the spring and summer, meat was readily available and the falcons were just an unwarranted drain on the meat supply and so were forced to fend for themselves. In this way, man had meat through the winter and the falcons similarly survived this period of hardship and may even have had a weight and early arrival advantage on their spring breeding grounds.

With the development of civilization, foods could be more reliably grown or bred. Falcons were no longer needed to provide meat for the table. The wealthy élite now had the time to appreciate the birds' aesthetic beauty. Falcon worship developed in the Nile valley some 3000 years BC. The birds were protected as deities and their precious remains carefully mummified. However, as with sacred ibises, the number of mummified falcon bodies recovered from temples far exceeds the number of cadavers which could be legitimately stumbled upon. Presumably it was an act of some religious significance to go to the expense of preserving the falcon corpse. Only the wealthy could afford such acts of piety, devotion and ostentation. Less affluent, and less religiously inclined traders must have made a reasonable livelihood by procuring fresh 'naturally deceased' falcon corpses for the gentry.

Increasingly through history it is the nobility which is associated with birds of prey. Strict codes of conduct evolved in Medieval times. These ensured that only the social élite had the right to fly and hence be associated with the powers of the most impressive raptors. Emperors alone could exercise the right to hunt wolves with eagles.

Eagles do not naturally risk hunting so dangerous an animal as a wolf. Young eagles were trained to be fearless, all-conquering hunters from an early age. Fledglings were at first allowed to kill harmless prey. As they grew, they were presented with larger and larger, but always defenceless or disabled, quarry. Their training sessions were fixed so that however disproportionate in size the tendered prey was, the eagle always managed to overcome it. The eagles' natural instincts were simply encouraged to develop further in the absence of natural checks by failure. Such golden and imperial eagles were fearsome hunters. Imprinted in this way, they knew no fear of man or beast and could be successfully flown at a man or wolf for sport. Genghis Khan was a particular devotee of this exclusive sport.

Whilst falconry flourished until the late seventeeth century, the small numbers removed from the wild had little effect on the wild population. By the late seventeenth century game birds could more easily be downed by the use of new shot-firing blunderbusses, and falconry waned. The enclosures acts diminished the range of open spaces available to falconers and the sport of shooting began to lead men to view raptors as competitors. As they began to shoot birds for the table, so the natural predators were also hunted, as vermin. With the artificial raising of native and exotic game birds in Victorian times, effective poisoning, trapping and shooting of all European raptors increasingly brought many species close to extinction.

Whilst sea eagles, goshawks and black kites all disappeared at one time from the British Isles, falconers and their age-old skills have gone some way to restoring the score. In the late 1950s, escaped falconers' goshawks, imported from Scandinavia, recolonized an area of the Midlands. Since then the birds have successfully radiated outwards to re-populate much of England and Wales. White-tailed sea eagles from Scandinavia have been deliberately and carefully released on the Scottish island of Rhum. Since the early 1980s the introduced birds have matured and now breed successfully after an absence of a century.

FISHING CORMORANTS

Falcons are not the only hunting birds whose skills have been adapted by man. For many thousands of years Chinese fishermen have used trained cormorants to fish from boats. Cormorants are highly successful at fishing in rich waters and can satisfy their own needs in as little as half an hour a day. The Chinese have historically used this expertise to their own advantage. The birds are leashed by a removable ring around their necks to the sides of small fishing boats equipped with perches. Typically, each fisherman works ten to twenty birds at a time. The birds jump back onto the perches to which they are tethered but are disabled from swallowing their catch by the neck ring. The fisherman then simply has to take the fish from his birds' beaks. In this manner the healthy but hungry birds can be used for many hours a day. At dusk each bird receives a fair share of the catch as its pay.

In some regions the cormorants are allowed to eat every tenth fish they catch and, it seems, cormorants can count. If the neck ring is not removed on the tenth dive, the cormorant will refuse to dive.

Night fishing is particularly successful. Lamps are slung around the slowly rowed boats. Though they are naturally diurnal these bright lights enable the domesticated cormorants to dive for the fish that are attracted by them. Night fishing is in fact much preferred to day fishing, which is less effective in cloudy river waters.

Cormorant fishing was so obviously successful that it was outlawed when the Peoples Republic of China was declared, although the burgeoning population and the myriad forms of intensive fish netting and trapping probably had more to do with declining fish stocks than trained cormorants. However, in several remote parts of China, especially in rural mangrove or estuarine regions, cormorant fishing is still practised today.

*   *   *

While Old World oriental cormorants are deprived of nine out of ten fish they catch, in the mid-western USA, New World cormorants are exacting a contemporary revenge.

In the 1970s, cotton growing was replaced by catfish farming over much of the Mississippi Delta. Today about 100,000 acres of land are devoted to catfish breeding. Unfortunately for the farmers, New Orleans gourmets and Lousiana housewives are not the only folk who appreciate traditional southern cuisine. Up till the early 1970s the cormorant population had declined through the combined effects of pollution, pesticide use and habitat destruction. In that decade a turning point was reached and the population began to recover. Since the mid-1970s, cormorants returning from their northern breeding grounds have started to winter around the Delta catfish pools. When the land was devoted to cotton, the birds were almost unheard of. Until the farmers lured them astray from their ancestral breeding grounds in Florida and the Caribbean, cormorants did not find January in the Mississippi at all appealing. On any winter evening around the Delta, over 35,000 cormorants now fly back to their roosts with a cargo of over 9,000 kilograms of fresh catfish, which would have a market value in excess of $20,000 if it were not marinating in cormorant stomach juices.

The cormorant's name literally translates as 'the crow of the sea' and they have received a bad press since Chaucer's time. Then they were synonomous with gluttony. Shakespeare heaped abuse on them as devourers of life. Later loan sharks and usurers became known as 'money-cormorants'. Recently the notorious Khmer Rouge deaths squads were known as 'the cormorants'. Now southern farmers regard them as the plague sent by God to replace the cotton boll weavil.

The fact that cormorants make their raids look easy probably does not help. In the period of a couple of minutes, the birds fly in at 50 mph, dive effortlessly under the water and catch a basket or more of fish each before quickly making off. They don't even leave enough time for a man to run for his shotgun.

Deep ponds are no protection. The catfish are not safe from a bird which can dive to 25 metres for over a minute. Luckily for the birds, man has catered for their every whim. The pools are rarely more than 2 metres deep and at feeding time boil with up to 175,000 cramped catfish. On average each cormorant takes only a single 10–20-second dive to secure a gulletful. They have even adapted to improve their efficiency. Perhaps taking a leaf out of the pelican's fishing manual, cormorants gang up to drive the catfish into shallow corners where they don't even need to get their tailfeathers wet. By the time the farm hands arrive on the scene armed with shotguns and pyrotechnic 'bird-bangers' the birds have left their roosts, or moved two ponds further down the road.

Man even caters for a healthy balanced diet. Shrimp farmers make sure the birds do not suffer from calcium deficiency by 'donating' to the cormorants up to $25,000 worth of shrimp per farm week! In severe cases, raiding has only stopped when the shrimp pools have been drained.

Farmers see themselves as besieged. Almost everything has been tried to discourage or destroy the birds. Radio-controlled model aircraft were displayed to scare the birds by diving down into the pillaging flocks. Initial experiments seemed promising. On seeing the dive-bomber descending towards them, the birds immediately sought refuge by diving the last 4.5 metres into the pond for safety. And it was true that not all of the birds managed to surface with a catfish in their beaks. But the cormorants were quick to learn that the planes were a threat not actually backed up by talons or shot, and within days became quite blase. They became less disposed to vacate airspace for the planes, which then crashed into them. The cormorants survived, the planes spun and broke up on hitting the pond.

Superior intellect is not to be easily vaniquished. Butane cannons which periodically boomed out blanks were sited around the pools in the late 1970s. These not only allowed the birds to time and compare their diving feats, but also were soon adapted as convenient look-out points: from the raised cannons it was very much easier to spot the perfect prey whilst keeping an eye out for farmers.

In the Mark II version of the cannons they were adapted to shoot a man-in-a-box out of a converted 55-gallon oildrum with a dull bang. This not only helped rob farmers of sleep but gave the cormorants and the national TV networks something to giggle about.

Perhaps the ultimate de luxe model among cormorant deterrents is the 'air-crow'. This, not inexpensive, device uses a fairground array of revolving strobelights, inflatable plastic arms, shotguns and loud noises up to 130 decibels – above the human pain barrier! It probably seemed foolproof on paper, but the most valuable function it serves is to let flocks from miles around know where the most valuable stocks are.

To rub salt into the farmers' wounds, cormorants have been protected under the US Migratory Bird Treaty Act since 1972. Perhaps it is just coincidence that this precisely corresponds to the time when the cormorants learned to modify their winter vacation plans. The US Fish and Wildlife Service (USFWS) will issue licences for farmers to kill up to 200 cormorants a year but the application procedure is daunting. Anyway, culling 200 cormorants out of a roost of 10,000 is of little use. The birds roost in tupelo and cypress swamps only accessible by boat. Every tree for hundreds of metres will support 50–60 cormorants where a decade or so ago there were none.

The cormorant's ability to adapt to new opportunities shows a flexibility towards timeless migration patterns. Its ability to exploit other species – ourselves – has enabled it to recoup its former losses. This is a time when natural wetlands are being drained, and developed for agriculture. Entire populations of some species of waterfowl are attracted to the shrimp and catfish pools which now replace traditional wetlands. Partly because of this the USFWS is less willing to grant cormorant-culling permits which often result in field hands blasting away at anything that flies or swims. As large-scale aquaculture operations are expensive and run by wealthy businessmen, these powerful individuals have been actively lobbying Congress for help.

Federal intervention hinged on whether or not the cormorant population was a new menace of gigantic proportions. Here ornithologists stepped into the fray in an effort to objectively report 'the truth' to increasingly enlivened conservationists and farmers. Over the past 100 years over 125 research papers reported that cormorants living elsewhere have a preference for alewives, sticklebacks and sculpin. These staples have no economic significance and are preferred even where valuable salmon fingerlings are stocked. Nevertheless both US and Canadian fisheries managers played safe and in ignorance culled neighbouring roosts of up to 2,000 cormorants at a time. The conservationists cited these unnecessary killings as evidence that cormorants around catfish pools should be left unharmed and the law unchanged.

In the Mississippi catfish pools, cormorants were undoubtedly a commercial problem. Catfish here constituted 64 per cent of the birds' diet. Farmers estimated their losses at over $3,000,000 a year.

This figure was nearly doubled when the $2,100,000 or more spent on cartridges, butane and the like was taken into account.

Whilst significant, catfish losses to birds accounted for only 7 per cent of overall losses; 70 per cent was due to disease, and 10 per cent to oxygen depletion. Neither of these factors was so obviously galling as black aerial sneak-thieves snatching your profit from right under your nose! The cormorant population was also growing at the remarkable rate of 15–63 per cent a year. Nothing, it seemed, died for want of a little hospitality in the Mississippi Delta.

The late 1980s saw a period of hasty pool building. These were mostly giant, high-cost 500-acre pool assemblages laid out like cormorant runways. Shortly afterwards researchers effectively solved the cormorant problem. The solution costs just $13 an acre and it is as easy as pie. Cormorants need 30–36 metres of open water to run flapping over in order to get airborne. Narrow pool design, combined with wires stretched at 10-metre intervals and perpendicular to the prevailing wind, prevents the birds from taking off. No take off, no landing, no feeding. The result: bumper catfish harvest and record-breaking jambalayas.

The same research has unexpectedly highlighted a larger and more disturbing problem. The cormorants breed at the Great Lakes, which contain 20 per cent of the world's supply of fresh water. The lake system is really a series of inland seas with inlets but no outlet. It takes about fifteen years to achieve a single turnover of lake water. Though banned as carcinogens in 1976, polychlorinated biphenyls (PCBs) and other organic compounds used as heat exchangers, lubricants and hundreds of other products, are still present and accumulating in the lakes. The monitoring of PCBs and other compounds in cormorant blood and embryo samples has highlighted disturbing flaws in previously used monitoring techniques.

At each stage in the food chain contaminants become concentrated. Small fish eat lots of contaminated plankton and larger fish eat lots of smaller fish. By the time the apex predators, like cormorants, arrive and eat their fill the poisons are present in stored fats in the birds' bodies at unbelievably high levels. At the Lakes, the cormorants have been found to have concentrated these toxins at 25 million times the levels found in water. And infertility and embryonic deformation typifying PCB and dioxin-type poisoning are increasingly recorded.

Parallel research on bald eagles and mink corroborate these

findings. Women consuming PCB-contaminated fish around Lake Michigan have been shown to give birth to children with small head size and impaired neuromuscular development. Public health authorities have now advised against eating any fish caught in the Great Lakes. The cormorant findings indicate the urgent need for a multi-billion dollar clean-up operation. If and when the information is acted upon, the catfish farmers' problems will look like very small beer indeed.

RAVENING HORDES

American cormorants illustrate how large-scale monocultures act as irresistible magnets for birds which share our own tastes. Changing land use can lead to a change in seasonal migratory, reproductive and feeding behaviour. In the cornbelt of Kentucky and Tennessee the opportunistic behaviour of red-winged blackbirds is rather less than appreciated. The USFWS estimates the blackbird population to be constant at 550 million, double that of the US citizenry. In spring the birds migrate to Canada and the northern US states, where they disperse to breed. Their offspring are raised on a diet of weed seeds and insects, including many species of crop pests. In autumn they return to the warmer southern states where groups coalesce to form enormous super-flocks. A single 30-acre copse can support individual roosts of 5 million birds. A recent survey of seventy-one Louisiana roosts counted 77 million blackbirds. In recent times these enormous swarms of birds have successfully modified their roosting preferences as well as their diets.

Crowding branches for warmth is not as effective as wind-proofed roosts on buildings. During the expansion of settlements in the 1960s designer towns like Columbia, Maryland sprang up. Here eaves, ledges, air-vents and a multitude of 'construction errors' combined to provide radically new, bird-tailored roosts in formerly open land. Each night, millions of birds move into small towns to roost, chatter and defecate. The filth, pungent ammoniac stench and noise are intolerable for most townsfolk.

Recent advances in farming have endeavoured to do their best to offer the birds a range of delicious, previously unavailable food stuffs. US cattle are railed or trucked miles to pre-slaughter feed lots to increase their weight. These intensive corn and pellet feeding stations have a similar effect on blackbirds, which take up to 10 per cent of the feed. New juicer varieties of maize have been developed to grow as far north as Ohio. Avoiding a migration hop across Lake Erie, the birds fly over these thoughtfully proffered crops in autumn, just as they ripen. After the rigours of breeding and the post-nuptial moult, the birds are only too keen to alter their plans to make the most of the corn crop. Aside from their eating the cobs, opening the husks makes the ripening heads vulnerable to rotting and moulds. Much more of the crop is ruined than is actually consumed by the birds. The damage is valued at $5–15 million per annum.

Local warming has been proposed as the explanation for the change in the birds' habits. The real reason is the birds' flexible response to recent changes in farming practices. Monocultures stimulate plagues of insect pests which the birds valuably destroy. Combine harvesters waste about 10 per cent of the crop, which is left scattered to attract the birds. Farmers also now plant winter wheat so late that it is perfectly sprouted by the time blackbirds reach the fields. Sprouted seeds are, of course, another of the birds' favourites. In the marshes in which the birds once roosted, rice is now cultivated. This makes for a useful addition to the corn, cattle feed and alfalfa diet.

Overall, blackbirds and the starlings and grackles which flock with them consume only 0.1–0.5 per cent of the US corn crop. Individual farmers, however, can be hit severely. For most farmers who decided to switch to corn production under migration routes the solution was to be found in bird control. Changing crops, to soya bean production for example, is far simpler but goes against the grain of frontier-taming farmers.

Regional blackbird opposition groups were formed. A group called 'Bye-bye Blackbirds' was formed by Ohio farmers and began to lobby Congress. What was needed was something that caused more widespread disgust than crop damage. The right angle was provided by a disease, histoplasmosis, for which the birds could be blamed. Histoplasmosis is a respiratory disease endemic to Kentucky, Tennessee and the Mississippi River valley. It is carried by inhalation of windborne spores of *Histoplasma capsulatum*, a fungus prevalent in rural areas where livestock manure is used as a fertilizer. Between 70 and 90 per cent of the population contract the cold or flu-like disease, which often passes undiagnosed. Lightning is a far greater local killer.

Birds rarely carry the disease, but the fungus does grow in the deep piles of droppings which accumulate below major roosts. This line was used by the farmers to force action and led to the first large culls by the army at Fort Campbell, Tennessee, in 1975. To permit culling, state governors were required to issue health hazard notification to roost sites. This was easily accomplished, and half of the 3–million–bird roost was culled by Tergitol spraying near the airport and living quarters of the fort. Greater success was later achieved by thinning the grove in which the birds roosted. Towns mounted their own campaigns and sprayed with more enthusiasm than planning. Typically 80–90 per cent of the birds killed were starlings or grackles, the rest comprising cowbirds, blackbirds and others. Most of the blackbirds got away.

Hysteria was successfully cultivated under the histoplasmosis banner, and in the later 1970s towns organized bird sentries to be ready with riot guns and cracker shells to fend off opportunistic flocks. They proved easier to dissuade initially than to eventually dislodge from their firmly established roosts. Alarmed by the 'kill the birds' policy, wildlife conservation groups sought to curb the increasingly widespread 'control' powers. Any agreements that were obtained lasted only for the matter of weeks it took for the birds to readopt former roosts. Locals quickly developed a loathing of all things feathered as well as of their protectors. 'Disease-ridden birds' replaced 'migrating flocks' in the local media. The argument over bird behaviour, agricultural practice and age old local maladies moved with equal vehemence into the Senate. Unheard-of legislative procedures introduced and passed overnight by an empty Senate removed the remaining obstacles in the way of the 'shoot-em-spray-em' lobby. The bill negated the National Environmental Policy Act and the Federal Environmental Policy Act. A busy weekend followed.

A lethal organo-phosphate insecticide called Fenthion was 'passed' for immediate deployment by pasting notes on the drums. Normally used to control mosquitoes, the poison was sprayed at 100 times its legal rate. It did not kill many blackbirds. The helicopter raids were rather poorly directed. Instead the pest controllers successfully culled songbirds, blue jays, cardinals and others. Raptors, feeding on their poisoned corpses, were also killed. Environmental agencies questioned why the Agriculture Department was 'experimenting' with poisons closely related to nerve gas. If it had rained, the run-off into local water supplies would have relegated all bird problems to the Minor League. Freed from frustrating controls, many residents were more interested in exacting revenge and getting even than in curbing local pest problems. One county judge even handed out 7,000 12-gauge shells to volunteers. The shooters did not succeed in making any discernible impression on the roosts. But they did probably feel much better for it.

Other unusual compounds were desperately tried. Avitol is a slow-acting 'fright-producing chemical' poison. When the blackbirds eat poisoned grain nothing happens for the first 5 minutes. Then the bird's nervous system is affected, causing it to fly out of control, become blinded, and scream helplessly, behaviour that is quite effective in scaring the rest of the flock away. This technique involves poisoning one grain per hundred and is effective at this low level. Careful baiting reduces the unwanted killing of incidental species.

Cleanliness can also bring the birds closer to God. Detergents sprayed on the roosts when night temperatures are set to fall induce hypothermia. During rain, the detergent washes away insulating oils in the birds' plumage. When the temperature falls below 4°C, the birds can no longer maintain their body temperature and so freeze.

Although red-winged blackbirds are the main problem species, the introduced European starling contributes substantially to the enormous flocks, and it is in North America because it was introduced deliberately and irresponsibly. In 1890 Eugene Scheifflin, fond of their comical gait and urban adaptability introduced eighty European starlings to Central Park, New York. The birds proved quite popular and another forty were later added. The birds spread over most of the country under the hospitality of their hosts. In 1954 a colony of 500 birds in Vancouver, British Columbia, rose to 25,000 in just over four years. These super-flocks cannot be supported by a permanent food supply and the birds' behaviour changed. They began to rove from farm to farm, joining flocks of blackbirds, cowbirds and grackles, to exploit locally abundant food supplies before moving on. The birds have evolved the locust-perfected ability to breed and turn into roving flocks to support enhanced populations.

Now, after several decades of spraying, poisoning and shooting, the blackbird section of the flocks is estimated to be constant at 550 million, exactly as it was in the 1940s. The dynamics and solutions of the problem have become a little clearer. Despite the cries of 'new plagues' the population has not risen, it has merely adapted its behaviour to make the most of recent changes in agriculture. For most of the year, the birds are highly beneficial to agriculture. Dispersed to breed on their northern breeding gounds, they perform millions of dollars worth of service by consuming countless tons of weed seeds and insect pests. Unfortunately this good work goes largely unreported and is confined to the extreme northern USA and Canada.

On migrating south the tired birds are effectively lured astray by the recently introduced new crops. The damage they do is more obvious and annoying than far more important losses due to other causes, such as harvesting techniques, rodents and disease. Culling their numbers is in fact often counter productive. Each year half the birds die during the winter, mostly due to the limited food resources. Though this is counter-intuitive, culling a small percentage actually leaves just enough food to see far more birds than usual through the winter. In fact, adding even more birds is more effective than culling. The birds then rapidly use up available supplies and a greater percentage die of starvation.

Despite the ingenuity, diversity of techniques and expense spent on trying to cull the birds, such measures have had no overall effect. Relief for affected farmers can in fact be quite easily achieved. Making natural roosts less suitable has a pronounced effect on the flocks' sedentary/migratory behaviour. Copses can be removed and favourite trees felled. Making dwellings less suitable as roost sites is often relatively easy to accomplish. But the most important area of relief lies in food provisioning for the birds. In the areas where cultivation has once more swung away from late-sown winter wheat or late-ripening maize, the blackbirds are no longer a problem. Minor changes to the variety of the crop grown or the timing of agricultural practices can have a major effect on bird movements and damage. The birds will then continue their migration south (to areas where harvesting has been completed for many weeks) to their ancestral swamp roosts. Such modifications in practice are less expensive than control attempts and would probably also have a beneficial effect on local blood pressures!

QUELEA QUELEA

Even though changes in blackbird behaviour can be locally damaging, they are rarely, if ever, life-threatening. This is not the case over much of sub-saharan Africa, where a tiny weaver bird, the red-billed quelea (see Chapter 2) can devastate crops. Rainfall is seasonal throughout much of the continent, allowing only a single crop to be grown. The success of this annual harvest is therefore of paramount importance to rural communities, which have no recourse to social welfare and often lack even the communication system necessary to request assistance.

The quelea are highly gregarious seed-eaters which are always encountered in flocks ranging from a few dozen to many millions. Distinct flocks may come together and coalesce or fragment into small units. The core of any flock's range is its roosting site. These are normally trees protected by swamps or actually growing in water. The roost is daily divided up by a dispersal system in which several huge groups each fly out to different potential feeding sites. In this manner the birds daily fan out to cover several hundreds of square miles. In addition, as resources such as ripe fields are distributed unevenly, some groups will happen upon richer feeding grounds than others. The following day, less fortunate birds apparently take heed of the successful members' eagerness to return to their bounty and follow them. The flock size is therefore adjusted to meet the food resources available. Farms ravaged by a hundred thousand birds one day may be devastated by a million or more the next.

In the wet season natural foods are usually abundant. As the dry season approaches and crops ripen, food becomes scarce and patchily distributed. Flock size then becomes progressively larger as birds unite to search for food. The roosts never harm natural vegetation enough to cause permanent damage. If the food supply dwindles, the flock leaves the roost in search of new pastures. Moving from site to site they become nomadic. Marked flocks have been recorded as travelling from South Africa as far as Malawi, a distance of a thousand miles.

In the wet season the birds stop migrating to nest in large numbers at suitable breeding sites. Pairs are monogamous and become territorial. Moist riverine, lacustrine or swamp areas are selected for breeding as they better ensure the water and food supply necessary for raising a brood. Fresh green grass is used to weave the nest (see Chapter 7) and the young are raised on unripened seeds and insects.

Counting the number of tiny quelea nests in dense thorny acacia, overhanging mosquito-infested swamps, is difficult. Estimates in Senegal average 500–600 nests per tree. Most sites are about 125 acres and contain 500,000 nests. Not infrequent 500-acre colonies support 10 million nests – equivalent to 47 million birds at fledging! In rich farming areas such roosts may be only a few miles apart. Most of tropical Africa is flat and even the largest colonies are virtually impossible to find except by accident. When attempts are made to fire nests of large colonies, the quelea respond by fragmenting the colony into many smaller, undetectable sub-units. Their combined numbers, of course, remain the same.

The nests take only a few days to build. Three eggs are laid which hatch in fourteen days. Two weeks later the young leave the nest. Breeding is highly synchronized within a colony. If a flock has, say, 5 million birds when it arrives, it can select a site, breed and depart as 12-million strong within a month. Remarkably 87 per cent of babies fledge and colonies are almost impossible to detect and cull within their short nesting residency. The birds breed using true hit-and-run guerilla tactics, never stopping to raise a second brood at any one site. Quelea usually breed only once a year. This is because the entire 10-million-square mile range is inadequate to support the total population of adults with even a single season's young. The populations are enormous, pegged at the carrying capacity of the entire continent.

The birds' natural diet consists largely of seeds picked off the ground. Food plants include the wild relatives and ancestors of contemporary crops such as rice and millet. The wild grasses grow during the wet season, set seed and die. Then no more natural seed is produced for another nine months. Farmers irrigating their fields do grow further crops and thus offer the only food available once all the wild seeds have been gleaned. Initially, the birds fly in small flocks more or less evenly over the land. As the dry season progresses seed becomes scarce and the flocks coalesce to forage on richer alluvial ground. This is precisely the area which is irrigated and farmed. With hunger, the birds become less selective about the type of seed eaten. Super-flocks wheel towards fresh feeding sites. The birds in the rear quicken their flight to surge forwards to be the first to feed. Depending on region, their natural food may all be consumed by the end of the dry season or at the start of the rains.

At this point the birds are forced to turn their attention to whatever substitutes are available. These are most frequently millet and guinea corn. Devastated plantations of rice and wheat are secondary but are more vociferously reported, as such schemes are normally government- or agency-run. Contrary to popular belief, quelea do not prefer cultivated crops to natural foods. Where natural grass seed is abundant, adjacent fields are left unscathed. This is one of the birds' great strengths. They are able to support their huge numbers in remote areas well away from human agriculture. Even when flocks do swarm into crop areas and completely destroy them, the birds rarely rely on them for all their food. Even in swarm-damage years, birds culled in the field have only 20 per cent cultivated corn in their gizzards. In times of severe hardship this figure can rise to 62 per cent. Over most of Africa the birds rely on natural grasses for 90–100 per cent of their diet. However, what are relatively minor contributions from agriculture can have locally devastating effects. Farmers rely for their survival on their annual harvest. This ripens at the time of greatest vulnerability to bird damage at the precise moment when natural supplies dwindle. The quelea's sheer weight of numbers can also cause severe mechanical damage to non-food crops such as cotton.

There are no reliable figures even attempting to estimate the extent of damage caused by quelea. All that can be reliably said is that the flocks do cause considerable damage to crops and can locally devastate harvests in an unpredictable manner. In some areas they make cereal cultivation effectively impossible and may routinely ruin crops in areas of marginal profitability. Virtually nothing is known about the distribution and migration patterns of quelea in the twenty-five or so states in which they are abundant. They can only be located with difficulty for the month each year that they settle to breed. They breed during the wet season, when it is often impossible to survey anything by air or road until the rains recede and fuel, aeroplanes and vehicles can again be moved. Ringing and radiotelemetry are being tried to make sense of the birds' unpredictable movements. A better understanding of popu- lation dynamics is essential if they are not to further aggravate the already worsening agricultural picture in lands already stricken by famine.

In South Africa in the late 1950s, 400 million quelea were killed by spraying from aircraft. This seemed to bring the problem under control until 1962/63 when over 600 million birds again invaded farms from surrounding bush. A few years later the population was the largest on record, resulting in over 100 million birds being culled over a three-month period. It became apparent that the money spent on ill-researched 'control programmes' was largely wasted and even led to a direct increase in the quelea numbers! As with the red-winged blackbirds, half the population dies annually after breeding, to recoup its numbers in the subsequent year cycle. If millions of pounds are spent in culling the enormous post-fledgling population, which is responsible for crop damage, then this represents only those birds which were to die anyway. In fact very much less than half the population could expect to be culled. If a quarter of the birds are killed, all of the remaining three-quarters may be able to survive on the available food supply, and thus produce increased numbers in the next season. Again, if we could actually *add* birds, the population would mostly starve to death.

Control methods over most of Africa are at the local village level and are non-destructive. The crops are vulnerable for a very long time as the birds eat unripened as well as ripe corn. The fields are constantly guarded by women or children, often from raised observation platforms. When the flocks are sighted a hue and cry is raised and rattles, drums and shouts are used to dissuade the birds. In fact the poor subsistence farmers who still comprise the vast majority of African peoples are effectively powerless to affect the birds' behaviour. Frantically wheeling, hungry flocks of up to 10 million birds are not deterred by a little noise for very long. It is difficult enough to hear anything above the birds' own clamour. At best, dedicated bands of farmers might succeed in driving the birds from one field only to watch them descend into the next.

In pre-independence times considerable sums of money could be allocated to quelea control. In the River Senegal valley, teams using explosives culled 80 million birds in five months almost annually in the late 1950s and early 1960s. The fact that 'controls' were annual gives some idea as to the programme's effectiveness. There are many practicable ways of culling quelea. Poisons, explosives, hand-held flame-throwers and even napalm – incendiary bombs which cover several acres with burning phosphorous – launched from aircraft are all deployed.

Despite the time and effort and technical advancement of all the control measures, it is now largely accepted that quelea are uncontrollable. Their population probably stands at 10 thousand million to 100 thousand million. The upper end of this estimate is equivalent to twenty quelea for every man, woman and child on earth – the human population is 5 billion. Whereas there are two blackbirds per American, there are 200 quelea per African. Killing quelea around farms only vacates that area's resources for other flocks from surrounding natural 'reservoirs'. At best, only local relief can be attempted. This may produce a valuable respite to enable the crops to ripen and be harvested. Alternatively, local success simply forces the birds to travel short distances and predate less well defended farms elsewhere. Given the birds' mobility, this could be at 100 metres or 1,000 miles distance.

In areas where crops are grown intensively, such as government plantations, it may be economic to cull birds, but the cost of killing each quelea must still be less than the value of the produce it destroys. Modern bird-scaring devices are really no more effective than traditional techniques. It may be possible to develop some 'quelea resistance' within crops or alternatively to reschedule farming practices so as to harvest cereals before the supply of wild quelea food is exhausted. A variety of techniques will need to be developed and locally tailored before there can be any attempt to benefit the continent as a whole. To date, the guerilla-raiding quelea have the upper hand. With almost military precision they stop to breed, depart before being spotted, then migrate unpredictably as nomads. Man's fields are devastated in hit-and-run lightning raids. The quelea is certainly one species whose flexible behaviour has benefited enormously by adapting to a changing environment in order to exploit man's endeavours. For the moment we can do nothing to stop them.

IN THE WAKE OF CIVILIZATION

The evolution of some species of birds is so closely tied to our own that they cannot live without us. These species are not crop pests or parasites but are termed 'commensals'. They are defined as simply 'feeding at the same table'. Modern man gradually switched from hunting and gathering unreliable foods to sedentary agriculture about 12,000 years ago in the Middle East. Wild ancestors of modern grains were cultivated each spring. Ancestors of the house sparrow originally fed on scattered grasses which were patchily distributed over wide areas. With the development of agriculture, huge volumes of seeds were produced in small fields. This concentrated food supply was very much appreciated by the sparrows, which gained the additional advantage of nesting alongside the fields in houses. The nests were built in gaps between pieces of masonry, where they were virtually impregnable. With an abundant food supply furnished by man, the birds could afford to reap the benefits of living in flocks, so predation rates fell and populations rose.

Agriculture gradually spread east and west and the birds followed. Their rate of expansion and evolution was hastened by a remarkable change in the sparrows' breeding biology. Most birds can only breed at a specific time each year, as food, even in the tropics, is abundant only for a brief period. Even in winter sparrows could find ample spilt or discarded food around villages. Their nests were also warmer than natural sites, thus reducing their daily calorific requirement and acting as winter incubators. Breeding all year round, their numbers increased rapidly and their biology became finely attuned to this commensal lifestyle.

Sparrow flock size (see Chapter 2) is relatively small at ten to fifty individuals. Even this has evolved to suit the patterns of food made available by man. Operating at this size, all flock members should receive a share of a spilt handful of grain or even the crust of a sandwich. Solitary birds are less able to spot these uneven resources and are more liable to be spotted themselves by a sparrowhawk. Man's use of the horse for transport ideally suited the birds who foraged around their grain troughs and spillages. Sparrows expanded their range many fold to reach the British Isles around 2400 BC. This represents up to 8,000 generations of sparrows to the present day but only 140 generations of man. An idea of how far the sparrow has evolved to fill its niche may be gleaned by imagining how far man has developed in the same period!

Farming in Britain had a negligible impact until about the eighth century BC when practices had improved sufficiently for the human population to rise. The sparrow population started to increase in about the first century BC when enough land was cultivated to produce surpluses. This freed some people from farming so that towns and ultimately cities grew up. This suited the sparrow admirably as the larger towns were mostly freed of predators and at any time there would always be some spillage, bakery, grain store or horse feed available to them. The birds cause little real damage and have long been accepted as a likeable aspect of our communal living.

For well over a century now, many people have felt that cities are too far removed from the countryside and living things and actually encourage sparrows with deliberate feeding. Most city dwellers look favourably upon sparrows. They are a reminder of our ability to survive often appalling conditions with cheeky perseverance. They are now so much a part of the fabric of our civilization that new cities cannot be founded without them. Sparrows have been deliberately introduced to most of the new lands colonized by Europeans as a homely reminder and companion in strange lands. As a commensal, the sparrow is the avian equivalent of the house mouse.

The other familiar commensal is the feral pigeon. The town pigeon's rural ancestors were the rock doves which still nest on many sea cliffs. These birds soon learnt to benefit from wasteful agricultural practices and were less despised than wood pigeons which pluck germinating corn seeds from newly sown fields. The pigeons spread into Britain with Neolithic agriculturalists and soon traded cliff edges for building ledges. Pigeon numbers boomed with the development of cities throughout Eurasia. Pigeons nest under railway bridges, on building ledges, viaducts and derelict structures. Docks and warehouses act as magnets, and huge numbers can accumulate. Typically, most feral pigeons live on buildings and forage for food scraps in streets and squares. Again, as few of the pigeons' competitors can tolerate our cities, the birds learn to solicit handouts from people and many congregate at traditional feeding sites. Pigeons, more than sparrows, have lost their fear of man and will perch excitedly on heads and arms to secure grain offered from the hand. Office or factory workers are often only too pleased to pay a tithe of sandwich crusts to be cheered by milling birds at lunchtime.

Pigeons, though, have become a problem species in many cities. They can transmit cryptococcus and histoplasmosis, although hard evidence showing that they originate cases of infection in humans is scarce. There is, however, evidence demonstrating the spread of ornithesis by pigeons in fifteen countries. Two thirds of Parisian pigeons have been shown to be infected with the disease, which is usually only associated with pigeon fanciers, however, and is not as virulent as the form transmitted by parrots.

Fouling is a more serious problem. On historical stone buildings pigeon droppings accumulate and eat into the rock. Ledges, details and gargoyles are all gradually eroded away. The environmental managers of most European and American cities recognize a need to reduce the population of feral pigeons. Having evolved to depend solely on man for their daily bread, pigeons are fairly simple to poison, trap or shoot. The main problem is not a problem of bird behaviour or cunning but of human interference. People like pigeons. They brighten our cities and, along with sparrows, may be the only wild creatures for miles. Hence baiting and netting generally take place at dawn so as to pass unnoticed. Efforts are made to 'educate' the public to understand the necessity for the control policy.

Once numbers have been reduced, action can be taken to repair structural damage and prevent re-invasion. Important and vulnerable buildings are cleaned, and ornamental ledges, windows and other pigeon-preferred nest sites are screened off with fine wire mesh. In many cities, food is abundant and is not a population-limiting factor. Thus preventing the re-adoption of former roosts has a marked effect in controlling numbers. Where poisoning or trapping alone is used, birds quickly immigrate to refill the vacated niche. When 1,300 pigeons out of a total population of 2,500 were removed from one London site, it took only two weeks for the population to return to 2,500. The next attempt also removed 1,300 birds. Four weeks later the population had risen to 2,900 birds, a net rise of 400! Other studies involving the virtual annihilation of entire colonies frequently report the discovery of much larger colonies when the sites are revisited a year later. It is far better to deny access to food supplies around docks and granaries or prevent roost access in cities than it is to attempt basic culling.

The greatest admirers of pigeons are those devotees, including Charles Darwin, who have bred dozens of different varieties since at least medieval times. The variety of man-made pigeon races helped to formulate Darwin's concept of how nature might selectively alter successive generations. Selective breeding can select for behaviour as well as appearance. The ancestral rock doves had to forage far inland to collect a full crop for their young. On returning to the cliff face they needed the ability to find their own nest amongst hundreds of identical ones. From their innate ability to use the earth's magnetic field (see Chapter 3), planes of polarized light, smell and visual cues to navigate, fanciers have developed the homing pigeon. These skills combined with fitness, fast flight and great powers of endurance to produce modern racing pigeons.

These birds can be released over a thousand miles away to fly straight back to their lofts. But the race is not over when the racer returns to the loft roof. The bird must then be caught and a running clock stopped by inserting a special ring from its leg. Tales of brilliant racers taking hours to capture from loft roofs are legion. To persuade the birds down from the roof, man has promoted another aspect of pigeon behaviour by careful experiment and breeding. Doves bred for sheer promiscuous sex appeal are used to lure the racer down from the roof. The sexier the dove, the sooner the racer can be caught and the race clock stopped.

Racing and sex-luring behaviour are obvious features to promulgate. Other traits are less obviously useful or even desirable. Tumbler pigeons fly upwards until a given height is reached. The birds then have a mental black-out and tumble earthwards, recovering just before impact. The beauty lies, apparently, in the form and grace of the tumbling descent.

COMPETITORS FOR THE SKIES

Normally man does not seek to alter birds' behaviour by breeding, but they can nevertheless rapidly respond to changes in habitat that we create for them. Since the 1940s, airfields have become very popular habitats. Birds are attracted to them to seek food, shelter and open roosting sites, and even to breed. The short grass around the runway provides abundant insect food, particularly when invertebrates are forced to the surface by take-off vibrations. The areas receive little human disturbance, and gulls, oystercatchers and lapwings will even breed on them. Over the large area of most modern airfields, effective scaring techniques have proved hard to develop. Bangers, pyrotechnics and amplified bird distress calls have all been tried. The problem is that, as with the noise of jet engines, the birds soon become familiar with them. Trained falcons or eagle owls are used with great effect on many airfields the world over. The fear of those raptors is innate and the habituation of prey species to their predators is unlikely. At night or in poor visibility, however, they are unfortunately unusable.

Bird strike is a serious problem and has resulted in tragic crashes with the loss of many lives as well as of civil and military aircraft. As with crop pest control, killing or scaring produces only limited and temporary relief. To keep a species population below the carrying capacity of the environment is very difficult. The current approach to the problem involves attempting to make the airfield less attractive or else creating a more suitable alternative close by.

Ornithologists were instrumental in the success of Auckland's new International Airport. Initial investigation involved assessing whether birds used the existing airstrip because it was the most suitable area or because it was simply the only available spot. Simple management changes, such as modifying the grass height, can be very effective. If the problem species prefers long grass it is regularly mown short or vice versa. Given the specificity of most birds' feeding techniques, this alone proves successful in some cases. Many birds have difficulty in spreading their wings to land or to take off in long grass, which also affects their vision and sense of security. In Auckland long grass has been an effective deterrent. Elsewhere long grass might encourage small land mammals and lead to even worse problems. Almost annually, Vancouver Airport has to catch, remove and release around 150 short-eared owls and snowy owls which move in each winter to hunt for mice.

Spraying with insecticide works in some places. It reduces insect populations and, with their decline, reduces bird strike frequency. In Britain, where ground-roosting gulls are a major problem, this would have little value. Geese, especially amongst waterfowl, may visit airfields to graze. Experiments have shown that if geese are the problem, less palatable grass species might replace existing ones. In Holland lucerne is grown instead of grass as it is unattractive to most birds. But in southern England lucerne draws wood pigeons to feast from miles around. Where birds are concerned, they always seem to have the last word.

The most thoroughly studied airport in the world is the US base on Midway Island, ancestral home of several species of albatrosses. Aircraft collisions with albatrosses stood at 300–400 per year and almost every conceivable approach, including culling, has been tried to reduce the problem. Fire, bulldozers, sterilants and barbiturates have all been tried and have failed. The 7,000 black-footed and 70,000 Laysan albatrosses might finally win the day. The US Navy has several times been forced to abandon flying completely. It seems quite possible that the Navy, beaten by the island's original occupants, will seek local alternatives for their airbase.

Generally, though, airport problems are not insoluble. The overriding factor is that a thorough investigation of the local geography and bird species should be conducted, preferably before construction begins. Armed with this knowledge the problems of bird collision can be greatly reduced.

ADAPTABLE BIRDS

Many generalist birds have learned to take advantage of man's wastefulness. Possibly the world's largest concentration of gulls is that found every day scavenging over the Fresh Kills infill on New York's Staten Island. The waste from the city is so colossal that the island grows skywards by several metres each month. The gulls have fresh supplies delivered daily by barge and spread for them by giant bulldozers.

In the tropics the scene is repeated by vultures scavenging on the tips outside Karachi, Bogota and Mexico City. Here the poor, the dispossessed and young children forage alongside vultures as their direct competitors. Other vultures, caracaras and corvids have learnt to exploit man's motorways. In Europe whole populations of rooks exist which derive most of their diet from insects that have collided with cars and other road kills gleaned along motorway verges. Boldness is favoured as many birds vie to be the first to snatch some new tit-bit from between the paths of streaming cars. Foolhardiness or poor judgement results in the tarmac-pureed individual being recycled by its kin.

Sewerage plants and open sewers are considerably less dangerous sites, and insectivorous birds the world over exploit the rich pickings to be had there. Wagtails, rollers, pygmy kingfishers, swifts and swallows all benefit from the insects breeding in human waste. It is certainly one means of recycling matter straight back into the food chain.

These examples are all unusual in that they illustrate the small number of species which have modified their behaviour to exploit the environment as altered by man. Most birds have highly specialized niches requiring specialized diets and environments. These species, the majority of the world's birds, cannot adapt to the drastic changes we wreak. When we drain the marshes, cut the forests and build cities or monocultures in their stead, they simply retreat or disappear. There are, however, a few examples in which specialists have apparently unknowingly identified and exploited a new 'artificial' niche.

One such is the black redstart of northern Europe. This wagtail-like insectivore is a relatively shy bird, associated with European cliffs and rock faces. It is also one of the very few birds to have markedly benefited from the Second World War and the Blitz in particular. The black redstart has been occasionally recorded as a rare straggler in Britain since 1829. One isolated nest was built in 1845 and then again in 1909. In the 1920s several pairs nested on the south coast and then on the Palace of Engineering at Wembley. Occasional birds reminded scientists of their presence by singing from the Natural History Museum in Kensington. Progress was painfully slow. What the birds needed was millions of tons of rock to be assembled as cliffs or scree slopes in quiet corners of the south of England. This work began in earnest in 1940 with the heavy bombing of cities during the Blitz. Cliffs, scree slopes and derelict buildings sprang up overnight as rubble-filled bomb sites where houses once stood. Bomb sites are dangerous places best avoided by people. Weed colonization and poor wartime sanitation provided the redstarts with bumper crops of insects and quiet hunting grounds. It was as if a tenth of London had suddenly been miraculously transformed for the sole purpose of attracting black redstarts.

The bombers did not succeed in winning the war, but they did enable the redstarts to radiate out from their occasional forays to the coast to occupy southern England. The spread of the redstarts reads like the bombing plan of the war. First the birds took central London while rearguards from the continent occupied Dover, Ramsgate, Rochester, Gillingham and other military strategic targets. Non-breeding scout males were soon recorded from Plymouth, Bristol, Birmingham and Liverpool. The redstarts were succeeding where the Nazis had failed.

Similar bombing elsewhere in Europe encouraged other expansions northwards and eastwards. One pair arriving at a strange northern town even successfully nested amongst the artificial rocks of the polar bear exhibit at Cologne zoo!

The redstarts are continuing their expansion by adapting to former industrial sites and derelict inner city areas. Without man to supply their daily food, even pigeons and sparrows might not be able to eke out a living in such places. It is pleasing to see that a wild cliff-living specialist such as the black redstart can successfully adapt to exploit these niches.

THE MILK RUN

There are ever-fewer places in the developed world where birds are not affected in their everyday lives by the influence of humans. In many cases, these effects are detrimental to natural habitats and therefore to the well-being of birds. But in other cases birds are adapting their behaviour to exploit the environment that humans are changing, and some, like the magpie, have never looked back, finding life safer in towns than in many rural areas, where they have a history of persecution.

Few birds have taken as well to the sprawling urban landscapes across the globe as the magpie, of which there are thirteen races very similar in appearance and habits to the thriving resident population in Britain. It is more widely distributed than any other crow, bar the raven. Many people argue that the magpie is doing too well, at the expense of other species. It is notorious for its depredations on other garden birds, whose eggs and fledglings it has a knack of finding and raiding.

The magpie, like most members of the crow family, is an intelligent and inquisitive bird, examining any and every potential feeding opportunity presented to it in any situation, including our towns and cities. It is nowadays the 'artful dodger' of the urban environment, always on the move in its dapper, conspicuous outfit, doing deals to secure meals, apparently aware of all that is going on around it.

The reason for its success as a plunderer of other birds' nests may lie in its alertness to situations around it, and its willingness to learn new tricks. It is aware of the behaviour of other birds, and will watch them as they ferry to and from a nest-site, picking up the tell-tale signals that will lead it to the nest. Magpies are content to bide their time until a wood pigeon leaves its nest unguarded, even just for a moment, before raiding the contents. They have even been witnessed catching small birds in flight. This awareness and versatility may account for the relatively recent reports of magpies plundering milk from doorsteps, a habit that had previously been the preserve of the dexterous blue and great tits. It seems now that magpies are exploiting this free source of nourishment in increasing numbers, although, lacking the finesse of the tit family, they are prone to making more of a nuisance of themselves in the act, even knocking the bottles over in their efforts to balance on narrow lids. (They might also be spreading disease. It is thought that magpies are responsible for the increasing incidence of certain bacterial infections in humans in several parts of Britain, such as South Wales.) The first reports of tits pecking at milk bottle tops to get at the cream were made in the early 1930s. The fact that the habit is now almost universal has provided an excellent example, literally 'on our own doorstep', of the passing on of learned behaviour between individuals in a population. The fact that magpies have learned the trick too shows that birds are capable of mimicking other species, albeit clumsily, in an effort to feed. The behaviour is a fairly logical extension of these species' habits in natural environments, where they have to be equally alert to 'hidden' sources of food. Tits will hammer at loose bark to investigate nooks and crannies that might contain grubs or insects. Bottle tops may present a recognizable source of successful foraging.

We need only watch the efforts of greenfinches, and sometimes even robins, to emulate the dexterous blue tit on the bird table assault course to realize that birds are adaptable. Bird tables are another meal ticket provided by humans for an ever-increasing number of different bird species. According to survey results produced by the British Trust for Ornithology's Garden Bird Feeding Survey, which has now run for twenty years, more and more unusual species are venturing into gardens in an effort to find sustenance in the cold winter months.

A spotted redshank, a rare marshland wader which is normally migratory, has been recorded at a bird table in Norfolk, feeding on pork fat, while another record, this time in Devon, had a turnstone picking at scraps in the garden. A wide variety of species will turn to household hand-outs when desperation necessitates it, including shy birds of the open fields such as redwings, fieldfares, reed buntings and yellowhammers. Normally insectivorous species, such as the blackcap, have been seen overwintering in these islands (they are usually migratory) and will visit gardens to mingle with the more familiar residents such as starlings, robins, chaffinches and sparrows.

The example of the blackcap indicates that there are sometimes no hard and fast rules where migration is concerned, and if the climate remains mild enough then certain individual birds may modify their behaviour accordingly. In the same way, the weather conditions affect how far birds will have to travel in order to secure a regular supply of food, and the survival rate of any species may depend on the degree to which it can change its habits in the face of shortage or the need to move from regular feeding haunts because of exposure to factors such as wind chill. This affects many wading birds in hard winters when mudflats and coastal fields are exposed to the elements.

Many birds depend on the magnanimity of householders to see

them through the colder snaps, and many people go out of their way to cater for the different food requirements of the various visitors. In this way the pattern is likely to be maintained, and more species encouraged to use this as a standard part of their dietary intake. In the harshest winters bird tables assume great importance, and hunger will bring the rarest and shyest of species to within yards of our back windows. The more dire the need for food, the greater the risks that birds are prepared to take in order to secure a meal. In early 1987, the severe weather saw numbers of certain species visiting gardens hit their peak in the records. Jackdaw, black-headed gull, great spotted woodpecker, brambling, bullfinch, reed bunting, goldfinch, siskin, coal tit, tree sparrow, sparrowhawk and jay all visited in unprecedented numbers.

Bird tables and feeders, however, can be dangerous places, for the frantic activity around the food scraps can attract the attention of the hunters. The birds of Warsaw, Illinois, for instance, are wary of bird tables. Many chickadees, house sparrows, mourning doves and pigeons live through the North American winter with the help of free hand-outs from local backyard feeders, but a few must pay the ultimate price for the survival of their fellow birds. Some are taken by the resident cat, snakes get a few, and one pet dog was credited with a dozen or so kills; but by far the greatest number of losses are from attacks by hawks. Hawks, particularly sharp-shinned hawks and Cooper's hawks, have discovered that bird tables in suburban gardens are a mecca for small birds and therefore a promising hunting ground for hungry raptors. Indeed in a survey conducted by Cornell University, New York, it was found that about 77 per cent of attacks on bird table birds were by opportunistic birds of prey.

Over a quarter of the incidents involve sharp-shinned hawks. They sit and watch from nearby trees and then swoop in across the gardens, snatching an unfortunate victim from the ground or directly from the bird table. The small birds flee in all directions, some seeking refuge in bushes and shrubs. But they are not safe for long. The hawks reach into the bushes and grab at the fluttering birds. One hawk was seen to trap a sparrow against a window pane, while another chased a flock of small birds into a lake, grabbed one and held it below the surface until it drowned.

HERBACEOUS BORDERS AND
HARD SHOULDERS

The sparrowhawk in Europe is becoming an ever more familiar sight, and not just in the remote countryside. Populations are bouncing back after the banning of persistent pesticides, such as DDT and dieldrin, and sparrowhawks are now numbered amongst the most notable examples of birds that are adapting readily to the changing environment. As mankind advances on the countryside, sparrowhawks are in the forefront of the counter-advance.

The sparrowhawk had never been noted for its taste for carrion of any kind, but one observer has reported seeing one feasting on the remains of a Christmas roast in a back yard! In another, larger garden the owner could only tot up the death toll as visiting hawks picked off every dove in his new cote. The hunters used the lie of the garden as a narrow corridor through which to launch these surprise assaults, although the doves – not as predator-conscious as their wild relations – made comparatively straightforward quarry.

One of the sparrowhawk's favoured hunting techniques (see Chapter 8) involves soaring high above its territory to spot likely prey, often a gathering of small birds. The hawk will then descend to a lower level for the purposes of attack, and thereby remain hidden from view until just before an attempted strike. Small flocks of birds such as that gathered around a bird table make ideal targets, and the sparrowhawk seems to have discovered this source of food with a vengeance.

Not only are sparrowhawks becoming an increasingly familiar feature of the urban landscape, they are even advancing on our most densely populated cities. Most cities provide a rich source of avian prey, and at all times of the year, unlike some woodland haunts. Starlings and pigeons are numerous, and there are plenty of nesting sites in parks and large gardens. In Edinburgh, for example, there are around fifteen pairs of sparrowhawks currently breeding within the city limits. They are now a familiar sight, not just in parks but also over the busiest of the city's streets, where they can be seen on reconnaissance – soaring, using the sides of buildings in much the same way as they use hedgerows in rural areas for the low-level surprise attacks at which they excel, 'jumping' suddenly up and over onto groups of prey species on the other side of walls and buildings.

Although the terrain is different, the sparrowhawk has simply had to improvise. Cities have familiar prey species and suitable breeding sites. What the sparrowhawk has had to overcome is its shyness around humans. Pressure on the food supply in its more traditional habitats has necessitated this, and by now new generations of sparrowhawks born and bred in cities will be well used to the close proximity of the hardware of urbanization. They will have known nothing else.

A longer-standing associate of urban development across Eurasia is the adaptable kestrel, a familiar sight around towns and cities, especially in the vicinity of major roads. The kestrel's hovering presence is a familiar sight in other parts of the world, from the Americas to the East Indies and Australia, where relatives of the European kestrel are making a similar success of the changing landscape beneath them. Habitual hovering is just one of the features of these small falcons that is diagnostic of most of the family members, but the kestrel is versatile, and has adjusted to life in a variety of habitats with some, such as the Madagascan kestrel, now adapted to hunting in dense forests.

The European kestrel feeds on a variety of prey species, and will take almost anything that it is able to kill. It is therefore adapted to hunting in several different ways, and to making the most of opportunities afforded by the activity of man. Fenland farmers have reported that kestrels regularly follow beet and potato harvesters to pick off the fleeing rats and mice disturbed by the activity in the fields. They are also known to follow ploughs in much the same way as gulls do, reaping the rich supply of exposed earthworms and insects left in the wake of the tractor. The habit of hovering, and its willingness to hunt from perches such as telegraph poles and pylons, have made the kestrel perfectly suited to one niche that it has made its own, exploiting the unlikely site of rich pickings by the roadside, where the vibrations of passing traffic bring invertebrates to the surface. The embankments and verges alongside the road are also preserved in their unkempt state, and are therefore a good habitat for mice and voles, as well as for wild flowers and the insects they attract.

Because of its resourcefulness, the kestrel has become Britain's most common raptor, not least because these roadside habitats encompass thousands of miles in total. Overall 1,700 miles of motorway have been built since 1958 in the UK alone, with 21,420 acres of associated grassy verge created as a result. Motorway verges, where people are not permitted to stop or picnic, have become strips of unofficial nature reserve. Here, mice and other small rodents thrive undisturbed by the plagues of automobiles and juggernauts thundering past on the black tarmac or grey concrete surface – and where there is prey, there come the predators, and the hovering kestrel is king.

The kestrel has even made itself at home in the busiest of cities, London playing host to 337 breeding pairs in 1977, at least seven of which had set up residence right in the heart of the city. This adaptability to both urban and agricultural landscapes, where the kestrel's hunting technique and diet differ but its success has been the same, accounts for its widespread status. In rural areas small mammals make up the greater part of its favoured diet, while cities provide ample supplies of sparrows and starlings. A strong flier, the kestrel will readily travel several miles to rich feeding grounds on the outskirts of cities.

The kestrel's feeding technique is uniquely specialized. Like most birds of prey, it has exceptionally keen eyesight, allowing it to spot the tiniest of movements in long grass up to 60 metres below. It has eyes set forward on its head, giving it the binocular vision typical of most birds of prey, providing them with a wider angle of vision which enables them to judge distances with great precision. The kestrel has a 150-degree field of vision, over the middle of which both eyes view the same field, giving it a three-dimensional image within a narrow field.

Other specializations have rendered the kestrel capable of prolonged bouts of effortless hovering flight, even in turbulent conditions, making it perfectly suited to the choppy air above busy roads. As it hovers, although its wings may be beating extremely rapidly, it has to ensure that it keeps its head absolutely still, to enable it to focus at long range. If prey is spotted, the kestrel swoops, often pausing in mid-dive to readjust its position before pouncing. Small birds are usually caught in flight, while less mobile prey can be caught on the ground after a short run. A less energetic method of hunting often employed by the kestrel involves sitting motionless on a roadside post or pylon. Roads also provide a constant supply of titbits in the shape of other creatures killed by the traffic, although the kestrel is not known for feeding on carrion.

This is more likely to be a source of food for carrion crows, rooks and gulls, other species which have thrived on the progress of human development. Although many raptors rely on carrion as a source of food, particularly in the winter, there is no species in Britain that has filled the type of niche occupied by kites in other

European countries, where they often flock, much as seagulls do in Britain, in the neighbourhood of towns, and scavenge from rubbish tips and other places where there are scraps of food, particularly by rivers. Red kites were once widespread in this country until persecution by those interested in shooting game birds wiped out all but an isolated pocket in Wales. And while the black kite has been showing a north-westward expansion of its range in Europe, and the number of sightings in Britain is increasing, it is highly unlikely that it will establish itself in this part of the world as a scavenger, since the modern-day city offers less rich pickings than those of yesteryear.

Another bird that is making a success of the move from the wilds into the big cities is the peregrine falcon. More than most birds, the peregrine is associated with remote wilderness areas, places far from human interference where it can be master of all it surveys. But in some cities, from Los Angeles to Dundee, pairs are exchanging rocky cliffs for high-rise buildings as launching pads for their aerial sorties. Again, the pentiful supply of pigeons in particular makes this change of habitat all the easier for the peregrine.

POISONED BIRDS – ENVIRONMENTAL INDICATORS

Some environmental changes brought about by modern man have almost ended in disaster for certain species of birds. Their decline, however, has helped man to realize what impact his activities are having on the natural world. Birds have become important indicator species, warning of environmental upset and serious misuse of the planet.

Peregrines were amongst the birds of prey worst affected by the use of agricultural pesticides in Europe and North America, until the ban on their use in developed countries. The more remote parts of Scotland were the last remaining stronghold of the British population by the 1960s. The recent renaissance of the peregrine has led to its recolonization of many of its former haunts, as well as more urban areas. It may one day regain its status as 'the world's most successful flying bird', as it was once described, because it had a stable and apparently unassailable population worldwide. The bird has become a rather different symbol since then, such that Tom J. Cade, who studied the peregrine at Cornell University in the

1970s, has called it 'a unique biological monitor of the quality of the world's environments', reflecting in its status and numbers the health of the global ecosystem of which it has traditionally been at the head.

Peregrines are apex predators. This means that they are at the top of their food chain. Nothing eats peregrines, but peregrines eat birds that eat seeds. In the 1950s agricultural crops were sprayed with pesticides and seeds were contaminated with chemicals that remain active for many years. DDT, a chemical used to kill insect pests, was one culprit. It coated the seeds eaten by pigeons and the other seed-eating birds relished by peregrines. Gradually the poisons built up in the bodies of the prey and then, because they are the next link in the food chain, in the bodies of the peregrines. And at each stage the poisons were concentrated. The result was catastrophic.

DDT affects the way the body uses calcium, so the eggs laid by females had abnormally thin shells. They cracked or did not hatch properly, so birds failed to breed. It also caused nervous disorders in adult birds, which sometimes crashed to the ground, unable to pull out of a stoop. During that time many birds were found barely alive, lying on their backs clawing aimlessly at the sky. Populations collapsed across the entire northern hemisphere and the species was close to extinction. North America took the brunt of the damage with no breeding birds in eastern USA, and 90 per cent gone from the western states.

It was the decline in peregrine populations that alerted the world to the dangers from agrochemicals and the bird has become a symbol of concern for the environment. By the 1970s, a ban on some poisons resulted in a recovery of some populations and today over 1,000 pairs are breeding in the British Isles alone. But this has not been the end of the story. An even more insidious danger has appeared.

Birds of prey, like peregrines, hunting along sea cliffs and taking seabirds that have been gorging on seafood are beginning to turn up with very high levels of pollutants, such as DDT and dieldrin, even though the substances have been banned or drastically reduced. It seems that the chemicals have been washed off the fields, into rivers and thence to the sea. Here they enter the marine food chain, first taken up by plankton which are eaten by small marine invertebrates, which are eaten by small fish, which are eaten by larger fish, which are eaten by fulmars or guillemots, which in turn are caught by peregrines. And it has taken not several years but several decades for the poisons to build up in the coastal food chain. What were thought to be yesterday's problems have reappeared today.

There is, however, a silver lining to the pesticide cloud. On recovering from the ravages of organo-phosphate poisoning, raptors such as the peregrine falcon, as we have seen, have adapted even to city life. As man increasingly isolates himself from the living world, the sight of falcons or even sparrows in our cities help us to modify our own behaviour towards these adaptable colonists. The fact that peregrines have shown that they are willing to share the same haunts as man indicates their willingness to adapt to a world that may be changing around them, and is an encouraging sign that these changes need not be detrimental.

Like many raptors, peregrines are prepared to lead a nomadic existence outside of the breeding season, and will follow wintering flocks to the coast from their regular haunts. It is as a result of this ability to roam over large areas that they discover cities as bountiful feeding areas. Young birds, forced to leave the area in which they were raised, often come to be resident in cities after their first summer.

The news of building populations of peregrines in recent years has not been greeted with wholehearted delight by all bird lovers. There is one section of the bird-keeping fraternity that is positively hostile. Pigeons are a peregrine's favourite food, making pigeon fanciers their greatest enemy. Pigeons in long-distance races are intercepted by peregrines, and the more peregrines there are, the fewer pigeons return to their home lofts. Fanciers spend enormous sums of money on prize pigeons, and they do all they can to thwart the peregrines, including battering their chicks to death in the nest.

This is not the first time that peregrines have been deliberately killed. During the Second World War, RAF Sunderland flying boats tracking German U-boats in the Atlantic Ocean maintained radio silence, but could still get their messages back to base using carrier pigeons. To ensure the pigeons' safe return with the vital despatches, 600 peregrines were slaughtered.

EXTINCTION IS FOR EVER

The peregrine, sparrowhawk, and white-tailed sea eagle warned humankind that it was mistreating the planet, and for that privilege they almost paid the ultimate price. Each of these species was on the brink of extinction. Others have not been so lucky. September 1914 not only marked the death of the last passenger pigeon but also the final days of the Carolina parakeet. Like the pigeon, the parakeet fell foul of the guns, a target for sport, food and feathers. In the early 1930s, the heath hen of the dry, open lands of New England was shot in its thousands and was exterminated by 1932. Eskimo curlews, which migrated in huge flocks from breeding grounds in the Canadian tundra to wintering sites on the Argentinian Campos, were intercepted at roosting and refuelling stops en route and massacred in their millions. A bird that was almost as numerous as the passenger pigeon was finally acknowledged as extinct in 1970. And so the list of casualties goes on.

It has been estimated that there have been in excess of 150,000 species of birds living on the earth at one time or another, the greatest number having flown, walked or swum during the Pliocene between 5 and 1.5 million years ago. Today less than 9,000 known species survive, only 6 per cent. The rest are extinct.

Extinction is a rather curious phenomenon – an inevitability, some would say. Species last no more than 4 million years at the most. Like a gambler at a casino they eventually go broke. They either die out and disappear altogether, like the dinosaurs of the Cretaceous, or they change into something else, like the smaller dinosaurs which evolved into birds. The process is continuous, and sometimes episodic. There are large-scale mass extinctions every 26 million years, when enormous numbers of species are wiped out by some cataclysmic event such as an asteroid colliding with earth or a mighty volcanic eruption which blankets the earth with dust.

Some species – the generalists and opportunists – can cope with everything nature has to throw at them. They tend to be small, to breed quickly, occupy ecological niches which are newly formed and temporary, and die young. Others – the specialists – are more vulnerable to change. They tend to be larger birds which live in more stable, established habitats where the food supply is reliable. They breed late in life and live longer.

The ubiquitous European house sparrow is clearly a generalist, able to take advantage of anything going including the debris left by man. It requires very little living space, breeds at one year old and could easily die before the next breeding season. It is, however, highly successful as a species and is now found all over the world. The Californian condor, on the other hand, is a specialist. It needs a lot of space, and must find suitable carcasses on which to feed, but it lives in a region where the wilderness has been destroyed, dead animals are few, and those that are available are often laced with poisons. It is big, does not breed for the first time until five years old, and thereafter lays its single, vulnerable egg every other year. If anything happens to the offspring, then recovery of that population takes a long time. Chicks are few and far between. The species is therefore highly vulnerable to change and, indeed, is now extinct in the wild.

The demise of the Californian condor, though, is not due to some great climatic change, geological upheaval or cosmic collision. It lost in an environmental confrontation with a species that has come to dominate the planet – man. Interestingly, during the last 10,000 years – a time when man began to influence events – the extinction of birds parallels that of mammals. About sixty-seven species of mammals and twenty-two of birds became extinct, of which thirty-two of mammals and ten of birds disappeared just as man arrived on the scene. Were the birds dependent on the large mammals that man was slaughtering? Did man kill both mammals and small birds? Are the two estimates merely coincidence? More research and more fossil finds might one day reveal the answer, but it does seem that what the changing climate, ice sheets and multifarious geological or celestial events had not previously eliminated, man is now doing his best to finish off.

Furthermore, birds living on islands have been some of the first to go. The moas of New Zealand, for example, were despatched by the invading Polynesian peoples – the Maoris – who arrived in AD 1350. Excavations in ancient Maori encampments reveal that the birds were killed for food and their bones were used to make hunting and cooking utensils and ornaments. Introduced rats and dogs finished off what the invaders had started. It is thought that the last moa died just a hundred years before Captain Cook first visited the islands, although there are reports of some smaller birds still living after his visit in 1769.

Sailors visiting Madagascar in the eighteenth century found the local people using elephant bird eggs as containers. Over-collecting and forest burning quickly exterminated these giant birds. By 1700, the last ones disappeared: what was a new and exciting species to western science was exterminated before anybody had a chance to study it.

Since 1600, nine out of ten of all birds that have become extinct have lived on islands. As 'civilization' from the west spread across the world, island birds came under threat. The dodo of Mauritius and the Rodriguez solitaire – large, flightless relatives of the pigeons and doves – were killed off during the seventeenth and eighteenth centuries. The solitaire was good for eating and, despite a fair turn of speed, was easily caught and made ready for the pot. The dodo was less appetizing (Dutchman Jacob Corneiszoon van Neck, the bird's discoverer, named it 'walghvogel' meaning 'nauseous bird') but it had no defence against the dogs, cats, monkeys, rats, pigs and goats that destroyed the forest and ate dodo eggs. The species was quickly wiped out. By 1681, the last dodo had gone.

There is some evidence to suggest that the dodo itself was not the only loss at that time. The bird ate the nuts of the Calvaria Major tree. The seeds passed through the bird's gut, were softened and then expelled at the other end. The tree, it seemed, relied on the bird to process its seeds, for no seed germinated after 1681 and no new Calvaria tree grew. Only a few 300-year-old trees survived to the present. That is, until 1977, when an ecologist from the USA took some Calvaria nuts, fed them to turkeys, and planted the seeds the birds defecated. Of ten seeds planted, three germinated, and the first new Calvaria trees for 300 years started to grow.

In the northern hemisphere another episode of mindless extermination took place. The great auk – a large, 1-metre-high, flightless, penguin-like seabird – was found to be good eating and, on its breeding colonies, was easy to catch. In 1534, the French sea captain Jacques Cartier landed on Funk Island, near Newfoundland, and took away boat-loads of auks from the largest colony that existed at that time. Others followed suit; the prospect of fresh poultry to vary a monotonous maritime diet was irresistible. Local settlers raided the colonies and boiled down the birds for oil. Their bones made needles and their meat was preserved for the lean winter months. By the end of the nineteenth century all the surviving auks had flown. They abandoned Funk Island and went to the volcanic island of Geirfuglasker, off the Icelandic coast. Unfortunately, Geirfuglasker erupted and vanished beneath the waves, taking its auk population with it.

By 1844, the great auk was thought to be extinct and an Icelandic merchant offered a cash prize to anyone who could find a specimen. Fisherman Vilhjalmur Hakonarsson took up the challenge and went exploring. He had an inkling that there could be survivors on the tiny island of Eldey off the south-western tip of Iceland. And he was right; two birds were nesting there – the last pair in the world, and they had just laid an egg. Hakonarsson killed the parents and in the confusion trod on the egg, and the great auk went into the history books.

In more recent times, with conservation and bird preservation very much on the agenda, it is, perhaps, surprising to find that things still go wrong, and that, even today, we sometimes help birds over the brink instead of saving them. The dusky seaside sparrow is a case in point.

This species once lived in the saltmarshes around Cape Canaveral on the Atlantic coast of the USA. It was restricted in its distribution but there was a healthy population. Its primary food was the seeds from cordgrass, but the grass was gradually being replaced by cattle pasture. The construction of the space centre and the various mosquito control programmes introduced for the comfort and health of the staff further reduced the sparrow populations, so that by 1968, when the Cape's rockets had carried men to the moon, the population was down to just a thousand individuals. Alarm bells rang, and the US Fish and Wildlife Service was persuaded to buy up the remaining wild cordgrass habitat and create the St John's National Wildlife Refuge. Unfortunately, the birds were already on their way out, and the last female died in 1976. In 1980, five males were caught and brought into captivity, and an extensive search of the area in 1981 revealed that the species was finally extinct in the wild. But there was a last ditch attempt to bring the species back to life. It was decided to start a breeding programme in which the males would be cross-bred with another closely related sub-species and then in-bred to produce hybrids with 96.9 per cent dusky seaside sparrow genes. When enough of these hybrids were bred to form a sizeable flock they could be released back into what remained of their former habitat – at least, that was the theory.

The programme was started and the surviving males bred successfully with the females of the other sub-species. The last pure dusky died in 1987, leaving its hybrid offspring – one male and four females. Then, under mysterious circumstances, the hybrids died. Depending on what version you believe they either died from a palm frond crashing into their enclosure, or escaped through holes that appeared in their cage, or succumbed to disease. But whatever the reason, all the resources of such diverse bodies as the US branch of the International Council for Bird Preservation, the Wildlife Preservation Trust, the Florida Audubon Society and Disney World could not save the birds. Due to foul means or fair, the dusky seaside sparrow is no more. It joins Steller's spectacled cormorant (extinct in 1850), the Bonin night heron (1879), the Madagascar serpent eagle (1950), the Rodriguez parrot (1800), the Seychelles parakeet (1881), the Cuban red macaw (1864), the Norfolk Island kaka (1851), the Wake Island rail (1945), the Mauritius red rail (1680), the Laysan rail (1944), the Hawaiian 0–0 (1934), the Lord Howe Island flycatcher (1920), the white mascarene starling (1880), the New Zealand quail (1868), the pink-headed duck (1942), the Auckland Island merganser (1910), the American ivory-billed woodpecker (1972) and a host of others on the role call of vanished birds.

There are, however, nearly 9,000 species left and we, as trustees of the planet, must ensure that conditions are right for these birds to survive and thrive. In 1970, conservationist Guy Mountfort drew attention to the fact that recently extinct or endangered bird species attracted little attention from researchers. That situation is slowly changing, and the 13 per cent of living birds that are considered to be the world's threatened species – about 1,100 species of birds in all – are a little less likely to join the 100 or so types of birds known to have become extinct in recent historical times, since AD 1600.

Of the survivors, most birds today are only still here either because they are sufficiently specialized to have successfully carved out and maintained a unique niche in the face of competition, or because they are opportunistic enough to take advantage of what is on offer. In the main, though, species have evolved over millions of years to exploit a very narrow range of foodstuffs, habitats and environmental parameters. When we destroy or modify traditional habitats, we are altering the playing field on which the birds evolved to play. Many species, including the giant thunderbird, dodo and dusky seaside sparrow, have already lost the battle to withstand change. The rates at which other species are declining indicate that, despite our best efforts, ever more species are almost certain to join the passenger pigeon and the giant auk as museum curios.

Close investigation of bird behaviour does offer several strands of hope. Of paramount importance is the need to know what birds do, how they do it and why, if we are ever to begin to understand what their survival depends upon. With this knowledge, and with increased awareness and concern from the human population, many species can be saved. Furthermore, detailed study shows just how adaptable and resourceful some species of birds can actually be. A few species continue to thrive despite everything we can throw at them. Others, like the feral pigeon, have evolved so closely with us that they cannot live without us. For some time now, people have argued that the reliance is mutual. Without birds to charm our ears and our eyes the world would be a very dull place. Who could imagine a world without the spectacle of a vast flock of pink flamingos, the humour of a group of penguin waiters or clown-like puffins, the breathtaking aerobatic display of frigate birds, the bizarre colours and shapes of pelican or toucan bills, or the wonderful songs of blackbirds and thrushes in a dawn chorus? Only by studying the private lives of birds can we learn to understand them better and hopefully thereby to help them better to maintain their position in a world where natural living space is shrinking, food is less easy to obtain and man-made poisons threaten all living things including ourselves.

BIBLIOGRAPHY

Chapter 1   LEGACY OF THE DINOSAURS

Beardsley, Tim (1986). Fossil bird shakes evolutionary hypotheses, *Nature* 322:677.

Cracraft, Joel (1988). Early evolution of birds, *Nature* 331:389–390.

Feduccia, Alan and Harrison Tordoff (1979). Feather asymmetry. *Science* 203:1021.

Goslow Jr, G.E., K.P. Dial and F.A. Jenkins Jr (1990). 'Bird Flight: Insights and Complications', *Bioscience* 40:108–115.

Gould, Stephen Jay (1986). The *Archaeopteryx* Flap, In 'This View of Life', *Natural History* 9/86, pp16–25.

Houck, Marilyn A., Jacques A. Gauthier, and Richard E. Straus (1990). 'Allometric Scaling in the Earliest Fossil Bird', *Science* 247:195–198.

Houde, Peter and Storrs L. Olson (1981). 'Paleognathus Carinate Birds from the Early Tertiary of North America', *Science* 214:1236–7.

Houde, Peter (1986). Ostrich ancestors found in the Northern Hemisphere suggest new hypothesis of ratite origins, *Nature* 324:563–5.

Howgate, Michael (1985). Back to the trees for *Archaeopteryx* in Bavaria. Report on the International *Archaeopteryx* Conference 1984, *Nature* 313:435–6.

Huxley, Thomas Henry (1868). Remarks upon *Archaeopteryx lithographica*. *Proceedings of the Royal Society of London*, pp 243–248.

Molnar, R.E. (1986). An enantiornithine bird from the Lower Cretaceous of Queensland, Australia. *Nature* 322:736–8.

Nachtigall, Werner (1988). Long non-stop flights using their own wings. German Research: *Reports of the DFG* 3/88, pp19–22.

Necker, Reinhold (1985). Filoplumes. *Journal of Comparative Physiology* 156:391.

Owen, Richard (1863). On the *Archaeopteryx* of von Meyer, with a description of the fossil remains of a long-tailed species, from the Lithographic Slate of Solenhofen. *Philosophical Transactions of the Royal Society of London*, pp33–47.

Roodyn, L. (1985). An avian water-repellent proposed. *Nature* 317:581.

Sanz, J.L., J.F. Bonaparte and A. Lacasa (1988). Unusual Early Cretaceous birds from Spain. *Nature* 331:433–5.

Sereno, Paul C. and Rao Chenggang (1992). Early Evolution of Avian Flight and perching: New Evidence from the Lower Cretaceous of China. *Science* 255:845–848.

Simmons, K.E.L. (1986). *The Sunning Behaviour of Birds*. The Bristol Ornithological Club.

Thulborn, Tony (1985). Cladistics and *Archaeopteryx*. *Zoological Journal of the Linnean Society* 82:119

Van Dam, C.P. (1987). Efficiency characteristic of crescent-shaped wings and caudal fins. *Nature* 325:435–7.

Wellnhofer, Peter (1988). A New Specimen of *Archaeopteryx*. *Science* 240:1790–1792.

Wellnhofer, Peter (1990). *Archaeopteryx*. *Scientific American* May 1990, pp42–49.

Chapter 2   BIRDS OF A FEATHER

Anonymous (1883). Ginnheim raven battle. *American Naturalist* 17:897.

Anonymous (1984). Starling flocks plague city. *Daily Telegraph*, 5 September.

Anonymous (1985). Suburb attack by birds. *Sunday Telegraph*, 24 March.

Anonymous (1985). Scores of birds die in suicide attack. *The Times*, 15 November.

Baker, Sherry. Vultures of Gettysburg in Anti-matter, *Omni* (date unknown).

Barnard, Chris (1979). Sparrow flocking. *New Scientist*, 13 September 1979 pp818–820, and *BBC Wildlife*, December 1983, pp90–93.

Bertram, Brian (1980). Ostrich head bobbing. *Animal Behaviour* 28:278.

Birkhead, Tim and Keith Clarkson (1985). Magpie flocks. *Behaviour* vol. 94.

Bourne, Nicholas (1622). The wonderful battle of starlings, fought at the city of Cork, Ireland, 12 & 14 October 1621. British Library.

Brown, Charles R. (1986). Cliff swallow colonies as information centres. *Science* 234:83–85.

Brown, Charles, R., Mary Bomberger Brown, and Martin L. Shaffer (1991). Food-sharing signals among socially foraging cliff swallows. *Animal Behaviour* 42:551–564.

Bruemmer, Fred (1989). Island of Murres. *Canadian Geographic* Oct/Nov, pp45–51.

Caraco, Thomas, Steven Martindale, H. Ronald Pulliam (1980). Flocks and predators. *Nature* 285:400–401.

Catton, Chris (1986). Why female pheasants join social circles. *BBC Wildlife*, July, pp325.

Elgar, Mark A. (1986). House sparows establish foraging flocks by giving chirrup calls if the resources are divisible. *Animal Behaviour* 34:169–174.

Gaston, Tony (1987). Seabird Citadels of the Arctic. *Natural History* 4/87, pp54–59.

Hoelzel, Rus, Eleanor Dorsey, and Jonathan Stern (1989). The foraging specializations of individual minke whales. *Animal Behaviour* 38:786–794.

Hogstedt, Goran. (1983). Screaming starlings. *American Naturalist* 121:562.

Lendrem, Dennis (1983). A safer life for the peeking duck. *New Scientist*, 24 February, pp514–515.

Michell, John and Robert J.M. Rickard (1982). *Living Wonders: mysteries and curiosities of the animal world.* Thames and Hudson.

Munn, Charles A. (1984). Birds of a different feather also flock together. *Natural History* 11/84, pp34–42.

Munn, Charles A. (1986). Birds that 'cry wolf'. *Nature* 319:143–145.

Peach, W.J., T.S.H. Gibson, J.A. Fowler (1987). Starling huddles. *Bird Study* 34:37–38.

Potts, Wayne K. (1984). The chorus-line hypothesis of manoeuvre coordination in avian flocks. *Nature* 309:344–345.

Rabenold, Patricia Parker (1987). Recruitment to food in black vultures: evidence for following from communal roosts. *Animal Behaviour* 35:1775–1785.

Renton, Katherine (1990a). Balancing acts. *BBC Wildlife*, March, pp146.

Renton, Katerhine (1990b). Manu – A Macaw's-eye View. *BBC Wildlife*, October, pp684–90.

Rohwer, Sievart (1983). Screaming starlings. *American Midland Naturalist* 96:418.

Roper, Tim (1986). Badges of status in avian societies. *New Scientist*, 6 February, pp38–40.

Summers, Ron, Graham Westlake, Chris Feare (1987). Starling roost hierarchy. *Ibis* 129:96.

Weatherhead, Patrick (1985). The birds' communal connection. *Natural History* 2/85, pp35–40.

Whitfield, D. Philip (1986) Plumage variability and territoriality in breeding turnstone: status signalling or individual recognition? *Animal Behaviour* 34:1471–1482.

Whitfield, D. Philip (1988). The social significance of plumage variability in wintering turnstone. *Animal Behaviour* 36:408–415.

Chapter 3   ACROSS THE WORLD

Aidley, D.J. (1981). *Animal Migration*. Cambridge.

Able, K.P. (1982a). Field studies of avian nocturnal migratory orientation I. Interaction of sun, wind and stars as directional cues. *Animal Behaviour* 30:761–767.

Able, K.P., V.P. Bingman, P. Kerlinger, and W. Gergits (1982b). Field studies of avian nocturnal migratory orientation II. Experimental manipulation of orientation in white-throated sparrows *Zonotrichia albicollis* released aloft. *Animal Behaviour* 30:768–773.

Able, K.P. and M.A. Able (1990). Calibration of the magnetic compass of a migratory bird by celestial rotation. *Nature* 347:378–380.

Alerstam, T. and G. Hogstedt (1983). The role of the geomagnetic field in the development of birds' compass sense. *Nature* 306:463–465.

Anonymous (1979). The tissue that brings pigeons home. *New Scientist*, 23 August, pp589.

Anonymous (1985). Bedtime for Bewick's. *BBC Wildlife*, March, pp101.

Anonymous (1987). Lancelot the swan drops out after 23 years. *Daily Telegraph*, 5 January.

Anonymous (1987). Making Whoopers. *Natural History* 8/87, pp84.

Baker, R. (1980). *The Mysteries of Migration*. MacDonald, London.

Bairlein, F. (1987). Fat fuels the birds on their trans-Saharan flights. German Research: *Reports of the DFG* 2/87:15–17.

Beason, R.C. and J.E. Nichols (1984). Magnetic orientation and magnetically sensitive material in a transequatorial migratory bird. *Nature* 309:151–153.

Berthold, P. (1988). Blackcap migration. *Journal of Evolution Biology* 1:195–209.

Campbell, B. and Lack, E. eds. (1985). *A Dictionary of Birds*, T & A.D. Poyser.

Cloudsley-Thompson, J. (1978). *Animal Migration*. Orbis, London.

Cooper, G.S. (1988). Goose hits jet's nose cone at 33,000ft. *Daily Telegraph*, 16 November.

Claypole, E.W. (1881), Hitchhiking birds. *Nature* 24 February.

Cramp, Stanley et al (1977). *Handbook of the Birds of Europe, the Middle East and North Africa*, vol. I. Oxford.

Elkins, N. (1983). *Weather and Bird Behaviour*. T & A.D. Poyser.

Emlen, S. (1975). The stellar-orientation system of a migratory bird. *Scientific American* Fall, pp102–111.

Flegg, J. (1986). *Birdlife*. Pelham.

Greenwood, Jeremy J.D. (1990). Changing migration behaviour. *Nature* 345:209–210.

Griffin, D.R. (1976). The audibility of frog choruses to migrating birds. *Animal Behaviour* 24:421–427.

Gwinner, E., and W. Wiltschko (1978). Endogenously controlled changes in migratory direction of the garden warbler *Sylvia borin*. *Journal of Comparative Physiology* 125:267–273.

Helbig, A.J. (1991). Dusk orientation of migratory European robins *Erithacus rubecula*: the role of sun-related directional information. *Animal Behaviour* 41:313–322.

Hill, John A. (1987). Unlucky albatross. *The Times*, 16 June.

Hiscock, J. (1990). Capistrano is forced to swallow its pride. *Daily Telegraph*, 26 March.

Holgate, M.W. (ed) (1971). The seabird wreck in the Irish Sea, autumn 1969. The Natural Environment Research Council, Publications Series C, No. 4.

Jarman, C. (1972). *Atlas of Animal Migration*. Heineman.

Joyce, Christopher (1986). Food for flight in Deleware Bay. *New Scientist*, 9 October, pp34–36.

Katz, Y.B., (1985). Sunset and the orientation of European robins *Erithacus rubecula*. *Animal Behaviour* 33:825–828.

Krapu, G.L. and J. Eldridge (1984). Crane River. *Natural History* 1/84:69–74.

Martin, B. (1987). *World Birds*. Guinness.

Mead, C. (1983). *Bird Migration*. Country Life Books, Feltham, Middlesex.

Michell, J., and R. Richard (1982). *Living Wonders*. Thames and Hudson, London.

Moore, F.R. (1985). Integration of environmental stimuli in the migratory orientation of the savannah sparrow *Passerculus sandwhichensis*. *Animal Behaviour* 33:657–663.

Moore, F.R., and J.B. Phillips (1988). Sunset, skylight polarization and the migratory orientation of yellow-rumped warblers *Dendroica coronata*. *Animal Behaviour* 36:1770–1778.

Myers, J.P. (1986). Sex and gluttony on Delaware Bay. *Natural History* 5/86:69–76.

Petterson, J., R. Sandberg, and T. Alerstam (1991). Orientation of robins *Erithacus rubecula* in a vertical magnetic field. *Animal Behaviour* 41:533–536.

Rae, John (1881). Hitchhiking birds. *Nature* 3 March.

Rees, Eileen C. (1989). Consistency in the timing of migration for the individual Bewick's swans. *Animal Behaviour* 38:384–393.

Rees, Eileen C. (1987). Conflict of choice within pairs of Bewick's swans regarding their migratory movement to and from the wintering ground. *Animal Behaviour* 35:1685–1693.

Sandberg, R., J. Petterson, and T. Alerstam (1988). Why do migrating robins *Erithacus rubecula* captured at two nearby stop-over sites orient differently? *Animal Behaviour* 36:865–876.

Stanley, E. (1865). *Familiar History of Birds.*

Stoddard, P.K., J.E. Marsden and T.C. Williams (1983). Computer simulation of autumnal bird migration over the western North Atlantic. *Animal Behaviour* 31:173–180.

Takahaski, J. and M. Menaker (1984). Pineal gland. *Journal of Comparative Physiology* 154:435.

Waldvogel, J.A., J.B. Phillips and A.I. Brown (1988). Changes in short-term deflector loft effect are linked to the sun compass of homing pigeons. *Animal Behaviour* 36:150–158.

White, G. (1788). *Natural History of Selborne.*

Williams, J.M. (1984). That divine impulse. *The Living Bird Quarterly*, Fall, pp8–12.

Williams, T.C. and J.M. Williams (1978). An oceanic mass migration of land birds. *Scientific American* 10/1978, pp138–145.

Chapter 4 SOUND SENSE

Boswall, Jeffrey (1983). The language of birds. *Proceedings of the Royal Institute* 55:249–303.

Brenowitz, E.A. (1982). Long-range communication of a species identity by song in the red-winged blackbird. *Behavioural Ecology and Sociobiology* 10:29–38.

Bright, Michael (1984). *Animal Language.* BBC Books/Cornell University Press.

Brooke, M. de L. (1978). Sexual differences in the voice and individual vocal recognition in the Manx shearwater. *Animal Behaviour* 26:622–9.

Brown, Charles (1982). Owls and alarm calls. *Zeitschrift für Tierpsychologie* 59:338.

Catchpole, Clive K. (1979). *Vocal Communication in Birds.* Studies in Biology no. 115. Edward Arnold.

Comfort, Nathaniel (1991). From Bird Song to the Philosophy of Life. *The Living Bird Quarterly*, Summer, pp26–29.

Daniels, Denver, Jason Heath and Wendy Rawson (1984). A declaration of intent in the kittiwake gull. *Animal Behaviour* 32:1151–1156.

Date, E.M., R.E. Lemon, D.M. Weary, and A.K. Richter (1991). Species identity by birdsong: discrete or additive information? *Animal Behaviour* 41:111–120.

Davies, N.B. (1980). Calling as an ownership convention on pied wagtail territories. *Animal Behaviour* 29:529–534.

Evans, Roger M. (1990). Vocal regulation of temperature by avian embryos: a laboratory study with pipped eggs of the American white pelican. *Animal Behaviour* 40:969–79.

Gurney, Mark E., and Masakazu Konishi (1980). Hormone-Induced Sexual Differentiation of Brain and Behaviour in Zebra Finches. *Science* 208:1380–2.

Hauser, Marc (1988). Superb starlings and vervets. *Behaviour* 105:187–201.

Konishi, Masakazu and Eric Knudsen (1979). The Oilbird: Hearing and Echolocation. *Science* 204:425–7.

Kroodsma, Donald E. and Edward H. Miller (1982). *Acoustic Communication in Birds*, vols I and II, Academic Press.

Marler, Peter, Susan Peters, Gregory F. Ball, Alfred M. Duffy Jr, and John C. Wingfield (1988). The role of sex steroids in the acquisition and production of birdsong. *Nature* 336:770–2.

McKinney, Frank (1990). Duck quacking. *Wildfowl* 41:92–8.

Mead, Chris (1984). Robins. *BBC Wildlife*, December, pp578–579.

Mundinger, Paul C. (1970). Vocal imitation and individual recognition of finch calls. *Science* 168:480–482.

Nowicki, Stephen (1987). Vocal tract resonances in oscine bird sound production: evidence from birdsongs in a helium atmosphere. *Nature* 325:53–55.

Orton, D.A. (1985). Light on the language of owls in the dark. *The Field*, 8 June, pp43–4.

Ratcliffe, L. and R. Weisman (1987). Phrase order recognition by brown-headed cowbirds. *Animal Behaviour* 35:1260–1262.

Richards, Douglas G. (1981). Alerting and message components in songs of rufous-sided towhees. *Behaviour* 76:223–249.

Sebeok, Thomas A. (ed) (1977). *How Animals Communicate*. Indiana University Press.

Thorpe, W.H. (1973). Bird vocalizations as systems of communication. *Journal of the Bombay Natural History Society* 71:2–13.

White, Sheila J., R.E.C. White, and W.H. Thorpe (1970). Acoustic Basis for Individual Recognition by Voice in the Gannet. *Nature* 225:1156–8.

Zimmer, Ute (1982). Chiffchaff heart rate. *Journal of Comparative Ethology* 58:25.

Chapter 5   SOLOS, DUETS AND CHORUSES

Baker, Myron Charles, Kimberley J. Spitler-Nabors, and Dana C. Bradley (1981). Early Experience Determines Song Dialect Responsiveness of Female Sparrows. *Science* 214:819–21.

Baker, Myron Charles, Tore K. Bjerke, Helene U. Lampe and Yngve O. Espmark (1987). Sexual response of female yellowhammers to differences in regional song dialects and repertoire size. *Animal Behaviour* 35:395–401.

Barrington, Daines (1773). Experiments and Observations of the Singing of Birds. *The Philosophical Transactions of the Royal Society of London*.

Breitwisch, R. and G.H. Whitesides (1987). Directionality of singing and non-singing behaviour of mated and unmated northern mockingbirds. *Animal Behaviour* 35:331.

Breitwisch, Randall (1989). Who Listens to the Mockingbird? *Natural History* 6/89, pp6–13.

Bright, Michael (1984). *Animal Language*. BBC Books/Cornell University Press.

Catchpole, Clive (1981). Why do birds sing? *New Scientist*, 2 April, pp29–31.

Chilton, Glen (1991). Observations on a 264-Year-Old Ornithologist. *The Living Bird Quarterly*. Summer, pp10–13.

Clayton, N.S. (1987). Song tutor choice in zebra finches. *Animal Behaviour* 35:714–721.

Cuthill, Innes and William MacDonald (1991). Blackbirds and the dawn chorus. *Behavioural Ecology and Sociobiology* 26:209.

Dobkin, David S. (1979). Functional and evolutionary relationships of vocal copying phenomena in birds. *Zeitschrift für Tierpsychologie* 50:348–363.

Eales, Lucy A. (1985). Song learning in zebra finches: some effects of song model availability on what is learned and when. *Animal Behaviour* 33:1293–1300.

Eriksson, Dag. and Lars Wallin (1986). Flycatcher song. *Behavioural Ecology and Sociobiology* 19:297.

Godard, Renee (1991). Long-term memory of individual neighbours in a migratory songbird. *Nature* 350:228–9.

Gottlander, Karin (1987). Variation in the song rate of the male pied flycatcher: causes and consequences. *Animal Behaviour* 35:1037–1043.

Hall-Craggs, Joan (1976). Errors in song-phrase performance by blackbirds. *Biophon* 2:6–7.

Horn, Andy (1988). Report of presentation to the Association for the Study of Animal Behaviour on meadowlark song. *BBC Wildlife*, September, pp468.

Kacelnik, Alejandro (1979). The foraging efficiency of great tits in relation to light intensity. *Animal Behaviour* 27:237–241.

Kelsey, Martin. G. (1991). A Well-travelled Warbler's Repertoire. *Natural History* 4/91, pp6–10.

King, Andrew P., and Meredith J. West (1983). Epigenesis of cowbird song – A joint endeavour of males and females. *Nature* 305:704–5.

Kling, J.W., and Joan Stevenson-Hinde (1977). Development of song and reinforcing effects of song in female chaffinches. *Animal Behaviour* 25:215–220.

Krebs, John R. (1977). The significance of song repertoires: the Beau Geste hypothesis. *Animal Behaviour* 25:475–478.

Krebs, John R., Ruth Ashcroft and Karl van Orsdol (1981). Song matching in the great tit. *Animal Behaviour* 29:918–923.

Kroodsma, Donald E., and Roberta Pickert (1980). Environmentally dependent senstitive periods for avian vocal learning. *Nature* 288:477–9.

Kroodsma, Don (1983). Marsh Wrenditions. *Natural History* 9/83, pp43–47.

Kroodsma, Don (1989). What, Where, and Why Warblers Warble. *Natural History* 5/89, pp51–58.

Mace, Ruth (1986). Importance of female behaviour in the dawn chorus. *Animal Behaviour* 34:621–22.

Mace, Ruth (1987). The dawn chorus in the great tit is directly related to female fertility. *Nature* 330:745–746.

McGregor, P.K., and J.R. Krebs. Mating and song types in the great tit. *Nature* 297:60–1.

Marler, Peter and Susan Peters (1981). Sparrows Learn Adult Song and More from Memory. *Science* 213:780–2.

Marler, Peter, Susan Peters, Gregory F. Ball, Alfred M. Duffy Jr, and John C. Wingfield (1988). The role of sex steroids in the acquisition and production of birdsong. *Nature* 336:770–2.

Mead, Chris (1984). Robins. *BBC Wildlife*, December, pp578–579.

Payne, Robert B. (1981). Song learning and social interaction in indigo buntings. *Animal Behaviour* 29:688–697.

Rothstein, Stephen and Robert Fleischer (1986). *Cowbird Dialects*. Condor.

Searcy, William A. and Peter Marler (1981). A test for responsiveness to song structure and programming in female sparrows. *Science* 213:926–928.

Searcy, William A. and E.A. Brenowitz (1988). Sexual differences in species recognition of avian songs. *Nature* 332:152–4.

Slater, Peter (1983). The Buzby Phenomenon: thrushes and telephones. *Animal Behaviour* 31:308.

West, Meredith J. and Andrew P. King (1988). Female visual displays affect the development of male song in the cowbird. *Nature* 334:244–246.

West, Meredith J. and Andrew P. King (1990). Mozart's Starling. *American Scientist* 78:106–114.

Yasukawa, Ken (1981). Song repertoires in the red-winged blackbird: a test of the Beau Geste hypothesis. *Animal Behaviour* 29:114–125.

Chapter 6   A BIRD'S EYE VIEW

Andersson, Malte (1982). Female choice selects for extreme length in a widowbird. *Nature* 299:818–820.

Beehler, Bruce M. (1989). The Birds of Paradise. *Scientific American* 12/89, pp67–73.

Borgia, Gerald and Mauvis A. Gore (1986). Feather stealing in the satin bowerbird: male competition and quality of display. *Animal Behaviour* 34:727–738.

Diamond, Jared M. (1986). Bowerbirds and poker chips. *Proceedings of the National Academy of Sciences, USA* 83:3042.

Diamond, Jared M. (1982). Evolution of bowerbirds' bowers: animal origins of the aesthetic sense. *Nature* 297:99–102.

Foster, Mercedes (1984). Jewel bird jamboree. *Natural History* 7/84, pp55–59.

Greig-Smith, Peter (1986). Avian ideal homes. *New Scientist*, 2 January, pp29–31.

Hill, Geoffrey E. (1991). Plumage coloration is a sexually selected indicator of male quality. *Nature* 350:337–339.

Mohler, Anders Pape (1989). Viability costs of male tail ornaments in a swallow. *Nature* 339:132–134.

Pomiankowski, Andrew (1990). How to find top male. *Nature* 347:616.

Pruett-Jones, Melinda and Stephen Pruett-Jones (1983). The bowerbird's labor of love. *Natural History* 9/83, pp49–54.

Ridley, Matt (1981). How the peacock got its tail. *New Scientist* 13 August, pp398–401.

Sloane, Sarah (1991). The shrike's display advertising. *Natural History* 6/91, pp32–38.

Snoew, David and Paul Shwartz (1981). Wire-tailed manakins use tails as tactile organ. *Report of the British Museum*, (*Natural History*) 1978–80, p.39.

Solomon, Sue, Monical Minnegal and Peter Dwyer (1986). Great bowerbird make an archaeologist's life a 'hazard'. *Journal of Archaeological Science* 13:307.

Wolkomir, Richard and Joyce Wolkomir (1989). Looking for Mr Right. *National Wildlife* 27:44–51.

Chapter 7   BRINGING UP BABY

Akney, C.D. and C.D. MacInnes (1978). Nutrient reserves and reproductive performance of female lesser snow geese. *Auk* 95:459–471.

Baldridge, R. and F. Gehlback (1987). Airlifted snakes keep house for owls. *New Scientist*, 23 April, pp27.

Bertram, Brian (1979). Ostrich eggs. *Nature* 279:233.

Bloch, N. (1988). A room with a narrow view. *Earthwatch* 7:16–21.

Bond, Gill et al. (1988). Hatching methods. *Biological Reviews* 63:395.

Brooke, M.L. and N.B. Davies (1987). Recent changes in host usage by cuckoos *Cuculus canoris* in Britain. *Journal of Animal Ecology* 56:873–883.

Brooke, M.L. and N.B. Davies (1988). Egg mimicry by cuckoos *Cuculus canoris* in relation to discrimination by hosts. *Nature* 335:630–632.

Brosset, A. (1978). Social organization and nest building in the forest weaver birds of the genus *Malimbus*. *Ibis*: 120:27–37.

Brown, Charles R. (1984). Laying eggs in a neighbour's nest: benefit and cost of colonial nesting in swallows. *Science* 224:518–519.

Brown, Charles R. and Mary Bomberger Brown. Swallow nest parasites. *Science News* 133:22.

Brown, J.L. and E.R. Brown (1984). Parental facilitation: parent offspring relations in communally breeding birds. *Behavioural Ecology and Sociobiology* 14:203–209.

Campbell, B. and E. Lock (eds) (1985). *A Dictionary of Birds*. T. & A.D. Poyser.

Charnov, E.L. and J.R. Krebs (1974). On clutch size and fitness. *Ibis* 116:217–219.

Clark, L. and R.J. Mason (1987). Olfactory discrimination of plant volatiles by the European starling. *Animal Behaviour* 35:227–235.

Coates, B.J. (1985). *The Birds of Papua New Guinea*, vol. I Dove. Alderley, Australia.

Collias, N. (1977). What's so special about weaverbirds? *New Scientist* 12 May, pp338–339.

Crook, J.H. (1960). Nest form and construction in certain West African weaverbirds. *Ibis* 102:1–25.

Crook, J.R. and W.M. Shields (1987). Non-parental nest attendance in the barn swallow: helping or harassment? *Animal Behaviour* 35:991–1001.

Davies, N.B. and M. Brooke (1989). An experimental study of co-evolution between the cuckoo and its hosts, I. Host egg discrimination. *Journal of Animal Ecology* 58:207–224.

Davies, N.B. and M. Brooke (1991). Co-evolution of the cuckoo and its hosts. *Scientific American* 1/91, pp66–73.

Diamond, Jared M. (1983). The reproductive biology of mound-building birds. *Nature* 301:288–289.

Emlen, Stephen T. and Peter H. Wrege (1988). White-fronted bee-eater helpers. *Behavioural Ecology and Sociobiology*.

Fry, C.H., S. Keith and E.K. Urban (1988). *The Birds of Africa*, vol. II. Academic Press.

Ginn, P.J., W.G. McIlleron and P. le S. Milstein (1989). *The Complete Book of Southern African Birds*. Struick Winchester, Cape Town.

Gustafsson, Lars and Tomas Part (1990). Collared flycatchers aging. *Nature* 20 September.

Hall, K.R.L. (1958). Observations on the nesting sites and nesting behaviour of the Kittlitz's sandplover. *Ostrich* 29:113–125.

Harvey, P.H. and L. Partridge (1988). Of cuckoo clocks and cowbirds. *Nature* 335:586–587.

Heinsohn, R.G. (1991). Kidnapping and reciprocity in cooperatively breeding white-winged choughs. *Animal Behaviour* 41:1097–1100.

Hogstedt, G. (1980). Evolution of clutch size in birds: adaptive variation in relation to territory quality. *Science* 210: 1148–1150.

Howell, Thomas R. (1984). Treasure of the Egyptian plover. *Natural History* 9/84, pp61–67.

Hurxthal, Lewis M. (1986). Our gang, ostrich style. *Natural History* 12/86, pp34–40.

Jeni, D. (1979). Female chauvinist birds. *New Scientist* 14 June, pp896–899.

Kemp, A.C. (1976). A study of the ecology, behaviour and systemics of *Tockus* hornbills. *Transvaal Museum Memoir* 20.

Kooyman, G. (1990). Emperors of the Antarctic. *Equinox* Nov/Dec, pp36–47.

Lessels, C.M. (1986). Brood size in Canada geese: a manipulation experiment. *Journal of Animal Ecology* 55:669–689.

McFarland, D. (ed) (1981). *The Oxford Companion to Animal Behaviour*. Oxford.

McFarland, D. (1985). *Animal Behaviour*. Longman, Harlow.
Marchant, S. and P.J. Higgins (1990). *Handbook of Australian, New Zealand and Antarctic Birds*. OUP, Melbourne.

Martin, K. and F. Cooke (1987). Bi-parental care in willow ptarmigan: a luxury? *Animal Behaviour* 35:369–379.

Mock, Douglas W. (1984). Siblicidal aggression and resource monopolization in birds. *Science* 225:731-733.

Moller, A.P. (1985). Mixed reproductive strategy and mate guarding in a semi-colonial passerine, the swallow. *Behavioural Ecology and Sociobiology* 17:401-408.

Moller, A.P. (1988). Paternity and paternal care in the swallow. *Animal Behaviour* 36:996–1005.

Nur, N. (1984a). The consequences of brood size for breeding blue tits, I. Adult survival, weight change and the cost of reproduction. *Journal of Animal Ecology* 53:479–496.

Nur, N. (1984b). The consequences of brood size for breeding blue tits, II. Nestling weight, offspring survival and optimal brood size. *Journal of Animal Ecology* 53:497–517.

O'Connor, R.J. (1978). Brood reduction in birds: selection for fratricide, infanticide and suicide? *Animal Behaviour* 26:79–96.

Perrins, C.M. and A.L.A. Middleton (1981). *The Encyclopedia of Birds*. George Allen and Unwin, Oxford.

Perrins, C.M. and D. Moss (1975). Reproductive rates in the great tit. *Journal of Animal Ecology* 44:696–706.

Rowe, Matthew, Richard Coss and Donald Owings (1986). Burrowing owl imitates rattlesnake hiss. *Ethology* 72:53.

Ruyer, Heinz-Ulrich (1980). Kingfisher helpers. *Behavioural Ecology and Sociobiology* 6:219.

Sasvari, L. (1986). Reproductive effort of widowed birds. *Journal of Animal Ecology* 55:553–564.

Sibley, G.C. and J.E. Ahlquist (1973). The relationships of the hoatzin. *Auk* 90:1–13.

Skutch, A.F. (1957). The incubation of birds. *Ibis* 99:69–93.

Skutch, A.F. (1976). *Parent birds and their young*. Austin.

Smith, N.G. (1980). Some evolutionary, ecological and behavioural correlates of communal nesting by birds with bees or wasps. *Proceedings of the XVII International Ornithological Congress* pp1199–1205.

Sorenson, M.D. (1991). The functional significance of parasitic egg laying and typical nesting in redhead ducks: an analysis of individual behaviour. *Animal Behaviour* 42:771–796.

Thompson, K.R. and R.W. Furness (1991). The influence of rainfall and nest quality on the population dynamics of the Manx shearwater on Rhum. *Journal of Zoology*.

Veiga, Jose P. (1990). Infanticide by male and female house sparrows. *Animal Behaviour* 39:496–502.

White, F.N. and J.L. Kinney (1974). Avian incubation. *Science* 186:107–115.

Wolf, L., E.D. Ketterson and V. Nolan Jnr (1990). Behavioural response of female dark-eyed juncos to the experimental removal of their mates: implications for the evolution of male parental care. *Animal Behaviour* 39:125–134.

Woolfenden, G.E. (1975). Florida scrub jay helpers at the nest. *Auk* 92:1–15.

Woolfenden, G.E. and J.W. Fitzpatrick (1978). The inheritance of territory in group breeding birds. *Bioscience* 28:104–108.

Wanless, S. and M.P. Harris (1986). Time spent at the colony by male and female guillemots and razorbills. *Bird Study* 33:168–176.

Chapter 8 HUNTERS, GATHERERS AND PIRATES

Bednarz, James C. (1990). The hunters of Los Medanos: Harris hawks. *Natural History* 10/90 pp56–62.

Boswall, Jeffrey. *Tool-Using by Birds and Related Behaviour*.

Birkhead, Tim (1986). Guillemots and sand eels. *British Ecological Society Bulletin* 17:15.

Cole, Susan, F. Reed Hainsworth, Alan C. Kamil, Terre Mercier, and Larry L. Wolf (1982). Spacial learning as an adaptation in hummingbirds. *Science* 217:655–657.

Dekker, Dick (1990). Hit and myths: the hunting technique of the peregrine. *Nature Canada* summer, pp29–33.

Diamond, Jared M., William H. Karasov, Duong Phan, and F. Lynn Carpenter (1986). Digestive physiology is a determinant of foraging bout frequency in hummingbirds. *Nature* 320:62.

Grajal, Alejandro, Stuart Strahl, Rodrigo Parra, Maria Gloria Dominguez and Alfredo Neher (1989). Foregut fermentation in the hoatzin, a neotropical leaf-eating bird. *Science* 245:1236–1238.

Grajal, Alejandro and Stuart Strahl (1991). A Bird with the Guts to Eat Leaves. *Natural History* 8/91, pp48–55.

Goss-Custard, John D. (1987). Hard times at mussel beach. *Natural History* 3/87, pp64–70.

Hayward, Patricia H. and Gregory D. Hayward (1989). Lone ranger of the Rockies. *Natural History* 11/89. pp79–84.

Herd, Robert and Terry Dawson (1984). Emus and fibre diet. *Physiological Zoology* 57:70.

Higuchi, Hiroyoshi. Green-backed heron tool making. *Ibis* 128:285.

Houston, David (1989). Dung eating in vultures. *Journal of Zoology* 216:603.

Johnson, W. Carter and Curtis S. Adkisson (1986). Airlifting the oaks. *Natural History* 10/86, pp41–46.

Jones, Carl (1979). Food washing in birds. A letter in *Wildlife* pp533.

Knudsen, Eric I. and Phylis F. Knudsen (1985). Vision guides the adjustment of auditory localization in young barn owls. *Science* 230:545–548.

Krebs, John R. (1991). The case of the curious bill. *Nature* 349:465.

Lawrence, E. Simon (1985). Evidence for search image in blackbirds *Turdus merula*: short-term learning. *Animal Behaviour* 33:929–937.

Norberg, R.A. (1970). Hunting technique of Tengmalm's owl. *Ornis Scand.* 1:51–64.

Ohmart, Robert D. (1989). The roadrunner. *Natural History* 9/89, pp34–40.

Parfitt, Dan (1984). Sunflowers and birds. *Canadian Journal of Plant Science* 64:37.

Richardson, P.R.K., P.J. Mundy, and I. Plug (1986). Vulture chicks and calcium deficiency. *Journal of Zoology* 210:23.

Schluter, Dolph, Trevor D. Price and Peter R. Grant (1985). Ecological character displacement in Darwin's finches. *Science* 227:1056–1059.

Shettleworth, Sara J. Memory in food-hoarding birds. *Scientific American*.

Smith, Thomas Bates (1987). Bill-size polymorphism and intraspecific niche utilisation in an African finch. *Nature* 329:717–719.

Smith, Thomas Bates (1991). A double-billed dilemma. *Natural History* 1/91, pp14–20.

Snow, Barbara K. and D.W. Snow (1984). Long-term defence of fruit by mistle thrushes *Turdus viscivorus*. *Ibis* 126:39–49.

Strahl, Stuart D. (1984). A bird stranger than fiction: the hoatzin. *Animal Kingdom* Oct/Nov, pp15–19.

Sutherland, William J. (1987). Why do animals specialize? *Nature* 325:483–484.

Tatner, Paul (1983). The diet of urban magpies. *Ibis* 125:90–107.

Temeles, Ethan J. (1991). Interspecific territoriality of northern harriers: the role of kleptoparasitism. *Animal Behaviour* 40:361–366.

Wall, Stephen Vander and Russel P. Balda (1983). Remembrance of seeds stashed. *Natural History* 9/83, pp61–64.

Wenzel, Bernice M. (1974). The olfactory sense of the kiwi. *National Geographic Society Research Reports* 1967 Projects, pp293–300.

Ydenberg, R.C. (1984). The conflict between feeding and territorial defence in the great tit. *Behavioural Ecology and Sociobiology* 15:103–108.

Chapter 9   LIVING WITH PEOPLE

Allen, M. (1980). *Falconry in Arabia*. Orbis.

Beebe, F.L. (1976). *Hawks, Falcons and Falconry*. Hancock House, Canada.

Brough, T. (1968). Recent developments in bird scaring on airfields. *The Problems of Birds as Pests*, pp29–39. Academic Press.

Coniff, R. (1991). Why catfish farmers want to throttle the crow of the sea. *Smithsonian* 7/91, pp44–55.

Crooke, J.H. and P. Ward (1968). The quelea problem in Africa. *The Problems of Birds as Pests*, pp199–211. Academic Press.

Day, David (1981). *The Doomsday Book of Animals*, Ebury Press.

BIBLIOGRAPHY

Ford, E. (1982). *Birds of Prey*. B.T. Batsford.

Graham Jnr F. (1971). Bye bye blackbirds. *Audubon* 9/71, pp29–35.

Halliday, Tim (1978). *Vanishing Birds*, Sidgwick & Jackson.

Isack, H.A. and H.-U. Reyer (1989). Honeyguides and honey gatherers: interspecific communication in a symbiotic relationship. *Science* 243:1343–1346.

Mountfort, Guy (1988). *Rare Birds of the World*, Collins/ICBP.

Nicholson, E.M. (1951). *Birds and Men*. Collins.

Pettingill Jnr O.S. (1983). Winter of the bobolink. *Audubon* 1/83, pp102–108.

Raup, David. M. (1991). *Extinction: bad genes or bad luck?* W.W. Norton & Co.

Southern J.P. et al (1990). Magpies, jackdaws and infection of milk in South Wales. *The Lancet* 336:1425–1427.

Stables, E.R. and N.D. New (1968). Birds and aircraft. *The Problems of Birds as Pests* pp2–17. Academic Press.

Thearle, R.J.P. (1968). Urban bird problems. *The Problems of Birds as Pests*, pp181–199. Academic Press.

Wright, E.N. (1968). Modification of habitat as a means of bird control. *The Problems of Birds as Pests*, pp97–106. Academic Press.

APPENDIX 1: SPECIES CHECKLIST

(E) Extinct

albatross, black-browed, *Diomedea melanophris*
albatross, black-footed, *Diomedea nigripes*
albatross, Laysan, *Diomedea immutabilis*
albatross, wandering, *Domedea exulans*
anhinga, *Anhinga anhinga*
antbird, ocellated, *Phaenostictus mcleannani*
antbird, spotted, *Hylophylax naevioides*
antshrike, bluish-slate, *Thamnomanes schistogynus*
auk, great, *Alca (Pinguinus) impennis* (E)
auk, little, *Alle alle*
auklet, rhinocerus, *Cerorhinca monocerata*
avocet, *Recurvirostra avosetta*

bee-eater, carmine, *Merops nubicus*
bee-eater, rosy, *Merops malimbicus*
bee-eater, white-fronted, *Merops bullockoides*
bell minor, *Manorina melanophrys*
bird of paradise, blue, *Paradisaea rudolphi*
bird of paradise, Count Raggi's, *Paradisaea raggiana*
bird of paradise, Macgregor's, *Macgregoria pulchra*
bishop, red, *Euplectes orix*
bittern, Eurasian, *Botaurus stellaris*
blackbird, common, *Turdus merula*
blackbird, red-winged, *Agelaius phoeniceus*
blackcap, *Sylvia atricapilla*
bluebird, eastern, *Sialia sialis*
bobolink, *Dolichonyx oryzivorus*

booby, brown, *Sula leucogaster*

booby, masked (blue-faced), *Sula dactylatra*

bowerbird, Archbald's, *Archboldia papuensis*

bowerbird, flamed, *Sericulus aureus*

bowerbird, Macgregor's gardener, *Amblyornis macgregoriae*

bowerbird, Newton's golden, *Prionodura newtoniana*

bowerbird, great grey, *Chlamydera nuchalis*

bowerbird, regent, *Sericulus chrysocephalus*

bowerbird, satin, *Ptilonorhynchus violaceus*

bowerbird, spotted, *Chlamydera maculata*

bowerbird, Vogelkop gardener, *Amblyornis inortatus*

brambling, *Fringilla montifringilla*

brush turkey, *Alectura lathami*

bullfinch, *Pyrrhula pyrrhula*

bunting, corn, *Emberiza calandra*

bunting, indigo, *Passerina cyanea*

bunting, Lapland, *Calcarius lapponicus*

bunting, reed, *Emberiza schoeniclus*

buzzard, black-breasted, *Hamirostra melanosternum*

buzzard, common, *Buteo buteo*

buzzard, honey, *Pernis apivorus*

buzzard, rough-legged, *Buteo lagopus*

canary (wild serin), *Serinus canarias*

canvasback, *Aythya valisineria*

capercaillie, *Tetrao urogallus*

caracara, *Polyborus plancus*

cardinal, red-capped, *Paroaria gularis*

cassawary, double-wattled, *Casuarius casuarius*

canastero, cordillera, *Thripophaga modesta*

catbird, tooth-billed, *Scenopoeetes dentirostris*

chachalaca, plain, *Ortalis vetula*

chaffinch, *Fringilla coelebs*

chickadee, black-capped, *Parus atricapillus*

chickadee, Carolina, *Parus carolinensis*

chiffchaff, *Phylloscopus collybitus*

chough, white-winged, *Corcorax melanorhampos*

cinclodes, grey-flanked, *Cinclodes oustaleti*

cisticola, boran, *Cisticola bodessa*

cockatoo, palm, *Probosciger aterrimus*

cock-of-the-rock, Guianan, *Rupicola rupicola*

condor, Andean, *Vultur gryphus*

condor, Californian, *Gymnogyps californianus*

coot, common, *Fulica atra*

corella, long-billed, *Cacatua tenuirostris*

cormorant, blue-eyed (shag), *Phalacrocorax atriceps*

cormorant, common, *Phalacrocorax carbo*

cormorant, flightless, *Nannoopterum harrisi*

cormorant, Steller's spectacled, *Phalacrocorax perspicillatus* (E)

corncrake, *Crex crex*

courser, cream-coloured, *Cursorius cursor*

courser, Temminck's, *Cursorius temminkii*

cowbird, bay-winged, *Molothrus badius*

cowbird, brown-headed, *Molothrus ater*

cowbird, common, *Molothrus bonariensis*

cowbird, giant, *Scaphidura oryzivora*

crane, sandhill, *Grus canadensis*

crane, whooping, *Grus americana*

crossbill, red, *Loxia curvirostra*

crow, carrion, *Corvus corone*

cuckoo, European, *Cuculus canorus*

curlew, *Numenius arquata*

curlew, eskimo, *Numenius borealis* (E)

desert lark, bar-tailed, *Ammomanes cincturus*

dikkop, water, *Burhinus vermiculatus*

dipper, *Cinclus cinclus*

diver, black-throated, *Gavia artica*

diver, great northern diver, *Gavia immer*

dodo, *Raphus cucullatus* (E)

dove, barbary, *Streptopelia decaocto*

dove, mourning, *Zenaida macroura*
dove, rock, *Columba livia*
dowitcher, long-billed, *Limnodromus scolopaceus*
drongo, fork-tailed, *Dicrurus adsimilis*
duck, black-headed, *Heteronetta atricapilla*
duck, blue (mountain duck), *Hymenolaimus malacorhynchos*
duck, eider, *Somateria mollissima*
duck, Falkland steamer, *Tachyeres brachypterus*
duck, harlequin, *Histrionicus histrionicus*
duck, long-tailed duck, *Clangula hyemalis*
duck, Magellanic steamer, *Tachyeres pteneres*
duck, pink-headed, *Rhodonessa caryophyllacea* (E)
duck, ruddy, *Oxyyura jamaicensis*
duck, torrent, *Merganetta armata*
duck, tufted, *Aythya fuligula*
duck, wood, *Aix sponsa*
dunlin, *Calidris alpina*
dunnock, *Prunella modularis*
eagle, African fish, *Haliaeetus vocifer*
eagle, American bald, *Haliaeetus leucocephalus*
eagle, crowned, *Stephanoaetus coronatus*
eagle, golden, *Aquila chrysaetos*
eagle, imperial, *Aquila heliaca*
eagle, Steller's sea, *Haliaeetus pelagicus*
eagle, tawny (steppe), *Aquila rapax*
eagle, Verreaux's, *Aquila verreauxii*
eagle, white-tailed sea, *Haliaeetus albicilla*
eagle owl, *Bulbo bulbo*
eagle owl, Verreaux's (milky), *Bulbo lacteus*
eider, *Somateria mollissima*
elephant bird, *Aepyornis maximus* (E)
emerald, fork-tailed, *Chlorostilbon canivetii*
emu, *Dromaius novaehollandiae*
euphonia, thick-billed, *Euphonia laniirostris*

falcon, Eleonora's, *Falco eleonorae*
fieldfare, *Turdus pilaris*
finch, Gouldian, *Chloebia gouldiae*
finch, house, *Carpodacus mexicanus*
finch, woodpecker, *Camarhynchus pallidus*
finch, zebra, *Amandava subflava*
finfoot, *Heliornis fulica*
firewood gatherer, *Anumbius annumbi*
flamingo, greater, *Phoenicopterus ruber*
flamingo, lesser, *Phoeniconaias minor*
flowerpecker, mistletoe, *Dicaeum hirundinaceum*
flycatcher, collared, *Ficendula albicollis*
flycatcher, grey (East Africa), *Bradornis microrhynchus*
flycatcher, grey (Mexico), *Empidonex wrightii*
flycatcher, Lord Howe Island, *Gerygone igata insularis* (E)
fliycatcher, pied, *Ficendula hypoleuca*
flycatcher, spotted, *Muscicapa striata*
flycatcher-shrike, bar-winged, *Hemipus picatus*
frigate bird, great, *Fregata minor*
frigate bird, magnificent, *Fregata magnificens*
frogmouth, giant (large), *Batrachostoma auritus*
fulmar, *Fulmarus glacialis*
galah, *Eolophus roseicapillus*
gallinule, blue (azure), *Gallinula flavirostris*
gannet, northern, *Morus bassanus*
giant moa, *Diornis maximus* (E)
goldcrest, *Regulus regulus*
goldfinch, *Carduelis carduelis*
goldfinch, American, *Carduelis tristis*
goose, African pygmy, *Nettapus auritus*
goose, bar-headed, *Anser indicus*
goose, barnacle, *Branta leucopsis*
goose, brent (Brant), *Branta bernicla*
goose, Canada, *Brenta canadensis*
goose, lesser snow, *Anser caerulescens*
goose, Ross's, *Anser rossi*
goose, white-fronted, *Anser albifrons*
goshawk, northern, *Accipiter gentilis*
grackle, great-tailed, *Quiscalus*

mexicanus
grebe, black-necked (eared), *Podiceps nigricollis*
grebe, great crested, *Podiceps cristatus*
grebe, Rolland's, *Rollandia rolland*
grebe, silver, *Podiceps occidentalis*
grebe, western, *Aechmophorus occidentalis*
greenfinch, *Carduelis chloris*
greenshank, *Tringa nebularia*
grosbeak, black-headed, *Pheucticus melanocephalus*
grosbeak, pine, *Pinicola enucleator*
ground, finch, cactus, *Geospiza scandens*
ground finch, medium, *Geospiza fortis*
ground finch, sharp-beaked (vampire), *Geospiza difficilis*
ground finch, small, *Geospiza fuliginosa*
grouse, blue (dusky), *Dendragapus obscurus*
grouse, red, *Lagopus lagopus*
grouse, ruffed, *Bonasa umbellus*
grouse, sage, *Centrocercus urophasianus*
grouse, willow, *Lagopus lagopus*
guillemot, common, *Uria aalge*
guinea fowl, helmeted, *Numida meleagris*
gull, black-headed, *Larus ripibundus*
gull, brown-hooded, *Larus maculipennis*
gull, common, *Larus canus*
gull, glaucous, *Larus hyperboreus*
gull, grey, *Larus modestus*
gull, herring, *Larus argentatus*
gull, laughing, *Larus atricilla*
gull, lesser black-backed, *Larus fuscus*
gull, ring-billed, *Larus delawarensis*
gull, western, *Larus occidentalis*
hammerkop (hammerheaded stork), *Scopus umbretta*
harrier, hen, *Circus cyaneus*
harrier, Montagu's, *Circus pygargus*
Hawaiian 0–0, *Moho nobilis* (E)
hawk, bat, *Machaerhamphus alcinus*
hawk, Cooper's, *Accipeter cooperii*

hawk, Galapagos, *Buteo galapagoensis*
hawk, Harris, *Parabuteo unicinctus*
hawk, red-tailed, *Buteo jamaicensis*
hawk, sharp-shinned, *Accipiter striatus*
hawk eagle, black-and-white, *Spizastur melanoleucus*
hawk eagle, ornate, *Spizaetus ornatus*
heath hen, *Tympanuchus cupido* (E)
heron, black, *Egretta ardesiaca*
heron, Bonin night, *Nycticorax caledonicus crassirostris* (E)
heron, goliath, *Ardea goliath*
heron, great blue, *Ardea herodias*
heron, green, *Butorides striatus*
heron, grey, *Ardea cinerea*
hillstar, *Oreotrochilus spp.*
hoatzin, *Opisthocomus hoazin*
hobby, European, *Falco subbuteo*
honeyeater, white-fronted, *Phylidonyris albifrons*
honeyguide, black-throated, *Indicator indicator*
honeyguide, orange-rumped (Indian), *Indicator xanthonotus*
hoopoe, *Upupa epops*
hornbill, crowned, *Tockus alboterminatus*
hornbill, red-billed dwarf, *Tockus camurus*
hornbill, Indian great, *Bueceros bicornis*
hornbill, ground, *Bucorvis spp.*
hornbill, silvery-cheeked, *Bycanistes brevis*
hornbill, trumpeter, *Bycanistes bucinator*
hummingbird, Anna's, *Calypte anna*
hummingbird, bee, *Calypte helenae*
hummingbird, broad-tailed, *Selasphorus playcercus*
hummingbird, ruby-throated, *Archilochus colubris*
hummingbird, rufous, *Selasphorus rufus*
hummingbird, rufous-tailed, *Amazilia tzacati*
hummingbird, vervain, *Mellisuga minima*

ibis, sacred, *Threskiornis arethiopicus*
indigo bird, *Visua spp.*
jacamar, rufous-tailed, *Galbula ruficauda*
jacana, northern, *Jacana spinosa*
jacana pheasant-tailed, *Hydrophasianus chirurgus*
jackdaw, *Corvus monedula*
jay, *Garrulus glandarius*
jay, blue, *Cyanocitta cristata*
jay, pinon, *Gymnorhincus cyanocephala*
jay, scrub, *Aphelocoma coerulescens*
jay, Steller's, *Cyanocitta stelleri*
junco, dark-eyed, *Junco hyemalis*
junco, grey-headed, *Junco caniceps*
junco, yellow-eyed *Junco phaeonotus*
kagu, *Rhynochetos jubatus*
kakapo, *Strigops habroptilus*
kestrel, common, *Falco tinnunculus*
kestrel, Dickinson's, *Falco dickinsoni*
kestrel, lesser, *Falco naumanni*
kingfisher, African pygmy, *Ispidina picta*
kingfisher, common, *Alcedo atthis*
kingfisher, greater pied, *Ceryle lugubris*
kingfisher, lesser pied, *Ceryle rudis*
kinglet, golden-crowned, *Regulus satrapa*
kite, black, *Milvus migrans*
kite, Everglade, *Rostrhamus sociablis*
kite, red, *Milvus milvus*
kittiwake, *Rissa tridactyla*
kiwi, brown, *Apteryx australis*
knot, *Calidris canutus*
knot, red, *Caladris canutus rufus*
lammergeier (bearded vulture), *Gypaetus barbatus*
lancebill, *Doryfera spp.*
lapwing, *Vanellus vanellus*
lark, bar-tailed desert, *Ammomanes cincturus*
linnet, *Acanthis cannabina*
lovebird, rosy-faced, *Agapornis pullaria*
lyrebird, superb, *Menura superba*
macaw, Cuban red, *Ara tricolor* (E)
macaw, red-and-green, *Ara chloroptera*
magpie, *Pica pica*

mallard, *Anas platyrhynchos*
mallee, fowl, *Leipoa ocellata*
manikin, white-bearded, *Manacus manacus*
manikin, wire-tailed, *Pipra filicauda*
manucode, trumpeter, *Phonygammus keraudrenii*
martin, house, *Delichon urbica*
martin, sand (bank swallow), *Riparia riparia*
meadowlark, western, *Strunella neglecta*
merganser, Auckland Island, *Mergus australis* (E)
merganser, red-breasted, *Mergus serrator*
merlin, *Falco columbarius*
metaltail, *Metallura spp.*
miner, bell, *Manorina melanophrys*
moa, giant, *Diornis maximus* (E)
mockingbird, northern *Mimus polyglottus*
mockingbird, hood, *Nesomimus trifasciatus macdonaldi*
moorhen, *Gallinula chloropus*
munia, red, *Amandava amandava*
murrelet, Kittlitz's, *Brachyramphus brevirostris*
murrelet, marbled, *Brachyramphus marmoratus*
mynah, hill (southern grackle), *Gracula religiosa*
night heron, Bonin, *Nycticorax caledonicus crassirostris* (E)
nightingale, *Erithcacus megarhynchos*
nightjar, European, *Caprimulgus europaeus*
nightjar, pennant-winged, *Semeiophorus vexillarius*
nutcracker, Clark's, *Nucifraga columbiana*
nuthatch, European, *Sitta europaea*
nuthatch, brown-headed, *Sitta pusilla*
oilbird, *Steatornis caripensis*
oriole, black-headed, *Icterus graduacauda*
osprey, *Pandion haliaetus*
ostrich, *Struthio camelus*

ovenbird, *Seiurus aurocapillus*
owl, barn, *Tyto alba*
owl, Blakiston's fish, *Ketupa blakistoni*
owl, burrowing, *Speotyto (Athene) cunicularia*
owl, elf, *Micrathene whitneyi*
owl, great horned, *Bubo virginianus*
owl, little, *Athene noctua*
owl, long-eared, *Asio otus*
owl, Pel's fishing, *Scotopelia peli*
owl, Scops, *Otus scops*
owl, short-eared, *Asio flammeus*
owl, snowy, *Nyctea scandiaca*
owl, tawny, *Stix aluco*
oxpecker, red-billed, *Buphagus erythrorhynchos*
oxpecker, yellow-billed, *Buphagus africanus*
oystercatcher, *Haematopus ostralegus*
parakeet, Carolina, *Conuropsis carolinensis* (E)
parakeet, orange-fronted, *Cyanoramphus malherbi*
parakeet, Seychelles, *Psittacula wardi* (E)
parrot, Rodriguez, *Necropsittacus rodericanus* (E)
parrot, rosella, *Platycercus spp.*
partridge, grey, *Perdix perdix*
partridge, red-legged, *Alectoris rufa*
peafowl, common, *Pavo cristatus*
pelican, American white, *Pelecanus erythrorhynchus*
pelican, brown, *Pelecanus occidentalis*
pelican, eastern white, *Pelecanus onocrotalus*
pelican, white, *Pelecanus roseus*
penguin, Adelie, *Pygoscelis adeliae*
penguin, emperor, *Aptenodytes forsteri*
penguin, gentoo, *Pygoscelis papua*
penguin, Humboldt's, *Spheniscus humboldti*
penguin, little, *Eudyptula minor*
penguin, macaroni, *Eudyptus chrysolophus*
penguin, Magellanic, *Speniscus magellanicus*
penguin, Snares Island, *Eudyptes robustus*
peregrine, *Falco peregrinus*
phalarope, grey, *Phalaropus fulicarius*
phalarope, red-necked, *Phalaropus lobatus*
phalarope, Wilson's, *Phalaropus tricolor*
pheasant, ring-necked, *Phasianus colchicus*
pheasant, great argus, *Argusianus argus*
pigeon, long-tailed passenger, *Ectopistes migratorius* (E)
pigeon, wood, *Columba palumbas*
pintail, *Anas acuta*
pipit, meadow, *Anthus pratensis*
pipit, red-throated, *Anthus cervinus*
pipit, tree, *Anthus trivialis*
plains wanderer, *Pedionomus torquatus*
plover, American golden, *Pluvialis dominica*
plover, crab, *Dromas ardeola*
plover, Egyptian, *Pluvianus aegyptius*
plover, golden, *Pluvialis apricaria*
plover, ringed, *Charadrius hiaticula*
plover, semipalmated, *Charadrius semipalmatus*
pochard, European, *Aythya ferina*
poor-will, common, *Phalaenoptilus nuttallii*
potoo, common, *Nyctibius griseus*
ptarmigan, rock, *Lagopus mutus*
puffin, Atlantic, *Fratercula artica*
quail, common, *Coturnix coturnix*
quail, bobwhite, *Colinus virginianus*
quail, New Zealand, *Coturnix novaezelandiae* (E)
quelea, red-billed, *Quelea quelea*
rail, Aldabra white-throated, *Canirallus cuvieri aldabranus*
rail, Laysan, *Porzana palmeri* (E)
rail, Lord Howe wood, *Raffus (Tricholimnas) sylvestris*
rail, Mauritian red, *Aphanapteryx bonasia* (E)
rail, San Cristobal mountain, *Gallinula sylvestris*
rail, Wake Island, *Gallirallus wakensis*
raven, *Corvus corvax*

razorbill, *Alca torda*
redhead, *Athya americana*
redpoll, *Acanthis flammea*
redshank, *Tringa totanus*
redshank, spotted, *Tringa erythropus*
redstart, American, *Setophaga ruticilla*
redstart, black, *Phoenicurus ochruros*
redstart, common, *Phoenicurus phoenicurus*
redstart, white-capped water, *Phoenicurus leucocephalus*
redwing, *Turdus iliacus*
rhea, greater, *Rhea americana*
riflebird, *Ptioris spp.*
ring ousel, *Turdus torquatus*
roadrunner, greater, *Geococcyx californina*
robin, American, *Turdus migratorius*
robin, European, *Erithacus rubecula*
robin, red-capped, *Petroica goodenovii*
robin-chat, Cape, *Cossypha caffra*
roller, blue-bellied, *Coracias cyanogaster*
rook, *Corvus frugilegus*
rosy finch, *Leucosticte arctoa*
ruff, *Philomachus pugnax*
rushbird, wren-like, *Phleocryptes melanops*
sanderling, *Calidris alba*
sandpiper, Baird's, *Calidris bairdii*
sandpiper, pectoral, *Calidris melanotos*
sandpiper, semipalmated, Calidris pusilla
sandpiper, spotted, *Actitis macularia*
sandpiper, stilt, *Micropalama himantopus*
sandpiper, western, *Calidris mauri*
sandpiper, white-rumped, *Calidris fuscicollis*
scaup, greater, *Aythya marila*
scaup, lesser, *Aythya affinis*
scoter, velvet, *Melanitta fusca*
scrubbird, *Atrichornis spp.*
scrub hen, common, *Megapodius freycinet*
secretary bird, *Sagittarius serpentarius*
seed-cracker, black-bellied, *Pyrenestes ostrinus*

serpent eagle, Madagascar, *Eutriorchis astur* (E)
shag, *Phalacrocorax aristotelis*
shearwater, great, *Puffinus gravis*
shearwater, Manx, *Puffinis puffinus*
shearwater, short-tailed, *Puffinus tenuirostris*
shelduck, common, *Tadorna tadorna*
Shrike, boubou (brubru), *Nilaus afer*
shrike, red-backed, *Lanius collurio*
shrike tanager, white-winged, *Lanio versicolor*
siskin, *Carduelis spinus*
sitella, orange-winged (varied) *Daphoenositta (Neositta) chrysoptera*
skimmer, black, *Rynchops niger*
skua, arctic, *Stercorarius parasiticus*
skua, great, *Catharacta skua*
skylark, *Alauda arvensis*
smew, *Mergus albellus*
snipe, common, *Gallinago gallinago*
solitaire, Rodriguez, *Pezohaps solitarius* (E)
sparrow, chipping, *Spizella passerina*
sparrow, dusky seaside, *Ammodramus maritimus* (E)
sparrow, Harris', *Zonotrichia querula*
sparrow, house, *Passer domesticus*
sparrow, Java, *Padda oryzivora*
sparrow, rufous-collared, *Zonotrichia capensis*
sparrow, savannah, *Passerculus sandwichensis*
sparrow, song, *Melospiza melodia*
sparrow, swamp, *Melospiza georgiana*
sparrow, white-crowned, *Zonotrichia leucophrys*
sparrow, white-throated, *Zonotrichia albicollis*
sparrowhawk, European, *Accipiter nisus*
spinetail, rufous-breasted, *Synallaxis erythrothorax*
sterling, common, *Sturnus vulgaris*
starling, superb, *Spreo superbus*
starling, white mascarene, *Necropsar leguati* (E)
steamer duck, Falkland Islands

flightless, *Tachyeres brachypterus*
steamer duck, flightless, *Tachyeres pteneres*
stint, Temminck's, *Calidris temminckii*
stitchbird, *Notiomystis cincta*
stonechat, *Saxicola torquata*
stork, maribou, *Leptoptilos crumeniferus*
stork, white, *Ciconia ciconia*
streamcreeper, sharp-tailed, *Lochmias nematura*
swallow, bank (sand martin), *Riparia riparia*
swallow, barn, *Hirundo rustica*
swallow, American cliff, *Petrochelidon pyrrhonota*
swallow, tree, *Tachycineta bicolor*
swallow, white-backed, *Cheramoeca leucosterna*
swan, Bewick's, *Cygnus columbianus bewickii*
swan, mute, *Cygnus olor*
swan, trumpeter, *Cygnus cygnus buccinator*
swan, whistling, *Cygnus columianus*
swan, whooper, *Cygnus cygnus*
swift, cayenne (swallow-tailed), *Panyptila cayennensis*
swift, common, *Apus apus*
swift, white-collared, *Streptoprocne zonaris*
swift, white-throated, *Aeronautes saxatilis*
swiftlet, uniform, *Collocalia vanikorensis*
swiftlet, white-rumped, *Collocalia spodiopygia*
takahe, *Notornis mantelli*
tattler, wandering, *Heteroscelus incanus*
teal, cinnamon, *Anas cyanoptera*
tern, arctic, *Sterna paradisaea*
tern, fairy, *Sterna nereis*
tern, sandwich, *Thalasseus sandvicensis*
thornbird, rufous-throated, *Phacellodomus rufifrons*
thrasher, brown, *Toxostoma rufum*
thrush, clay-coloured, *Turdus clayi*
thrush, Japanese grey, *Turdus cardis*

thrush, mistle, *Turdus viscivorus*
thrush, song, *Turdus philomelos*
thrush, wood, *Hylocichla mustelina*
tit, bearded, *Panurus biamicus*
tit, blue, *Parus caeruleus*
tit, coal, *Parus alter*
tit, great, *Parus major*
tit, marsh, *Parus palustris*
tit, penduline, *Remiz penduline*
tit, varied, *Parus varius*
towhee, rufous-sided, *Pipilo erythrophthalmus*
trogon, violaceous, *Trogon violaceus*
tui (parson bird), *Prosthemadura novaeseelandiae*
turkey, common, *Meleagris galloparo*
turnstone (ruddy), *Arenaria interpres*
twite, *Acantha flavirostris*
vireo, red-eyed, *Vireo olivaceus*
vulture, bearded, *Gypaetus barbatus*
vulture, black, *Coragyps atratus*
vulture, Cape, *Gyps coprotheres*
vulture, Egyptian, *Neophron percnopterus*
vulture, griffon, *Gyps fulvus*
vulture, turkey, *Cathartes aura*
wagtail, pied, *Motacilla alba*
warbler, aquatic, *Acrocephalus paludicola*
warbler, arctic, *Phylloscopus borealis*
warbler, blackpoll, *Dendroica striata*
warbler, Cetti's, *Cettia cetti*
warbler, chestnut-sided, *Dendroica pensylvanica*
warbler, garden, *Sylvia borin*
warbler, grasshopper, *Locustella naevia*
warbler, great reed, *Acrocephalus arundinaceus*
warbler, hooded, *Wilsonia citrina*
warbler, marsh, *Acrocephalus palutris*
warbler, moustached, *Acrocephalus melanopogon*
warble, myrtle (yellow-rumped), *Dendroica coronata*
warbler, reed, *Acrocephalus scirpaceus*
warbler, Savi's, *Locustella luscinioides*
warbler, sedge, *Acrocephalus schoenobaenus*

warbler, willow, *Phylloscopus trochilus*
warbler, wood, *Phylloscopus sibilatrix*
warbler, yellow, *Chloropeta natalensis*
warbler, yellow, *Dendroica petechia*
warbler, yellow-rumped, *Dendroica coronata*
water dikkop, *Burhinus vermiculatus*
wattle-eye, *Platysteira spp.*
waxbill, common, *Uraeginthus granatina*
waxwing, Bohemian, *Bombycilla garrulus*
weaver, Cassin's (black-throated malimbe), *Malimbe cassini*
weaver, sociable, *Philetairus socius*
weaver, village, *Ploceus cucullatus*
weaver, white-billed buffalo, *Bubalornis albirostris*
weaver, white-headed buffalo, *Dinemellia dinemelli*
weaver, white-browed sparrow, *Plocepasser mahali*
weka, *Gallirallus australis*
wheatear, common, *Oenanthe oenanthe*
whimbrel, *Numenius phaeopus*
whip-poor-whill, *Caprimulgus vociferous*
whiteface, banded, *Aphelocephala nigricincta*
whitethroat, *Sylvia communis*

whinchat, *Saxicola rubetra*
whydah, Jackson's, *Euplectes jacksoni*
whydah, long-tailed, *Euplectes progne*
woodcock, *Scolopax rusticola*
woodcock, American, *Scolopax minor*
woodpecker, acorn, *Melanerpes formicivorus*
woodpecker, American ivory-billed, *Campephilus principalis* (E)
woodpecker, black, *Drycopus martius*
woodpecker, gila, *Melanerpes uropygialis*
woodpecker, great spotted, *Picoides major*
woodpecker, lesser spotted, *Picoides minor*
wood thrush, *Hylocishla mustelina*
wren, Bewick's, *Thryomanes bewickii*
wren, Carolina, *Thryothorus ludovicianus*
wren, common (winter), *Troglodytes troglodytes*
wren, house, *Trogiodytes aedon*
wren, long-billed marsh, *Cistothorus palustris*
wren, Stephen Island, *Xenicus (Traversia) lyalli* (E)
wryneck, *Jynx torquilla*
yellowhammer, *Emberiza citrinella*

SPECIES INDEX

SPECIES INDEX

woodhen, 52
woodpecker, 25, 162, 163, 280, 352, 378
woodpecker, acorn, 162, 378
woodpecker, black, 162
woodpecker, gila, 281
woodpecker, great spotted, 85, 162, 414
woodpecker, ivory-billed, 425
woodpecker, lesser spotted, 162
wood thrush, 175
worm, 15, 70, 71, 116, 365
wren, 41, 43, 77, 109, 156, 172, 206,
    276, 312
wren, Bewick's, 205, 206

wren, Carolina, 184, 185, 194, 206
wren, fairy, 172
wren, house, 206
wren, long-billed marsh, 191, 192, 206,
    207
wren, Stephen Island, 53
wren, winter, 76, 206
wryneck, 121, 259

yellowhammer, 84, 172, 221, 413

zebra, 263